A NOVEL BY KONSTANTINE SIMONOV

DAYS
AND
NIGHTS

TRANSLATED FROM THE RUSSIAN BY JOSEPH BARNES

SIMON AND SCHUSTER, NEW YORK

DECORATIONS ON THE CHAPTER OPENING PAGES
WERE DONE BY ALEXANDER DOBKIN

To those who died for Stalingrad

List of Principal Characters

Matveyev, Member of the Military Council
of the group of armies defending Stalingrad

Colonel Alexander Ivanovich Protsenko (later General),
in command of the 693rd Rifle Division
one of the units of this defending force

Lieutenant Colonel Philip Philipovich Babchenko,
in command of a regiment in this division

Colonel Sergei Vassilievich Remizov,
successor to Babchenko in command of this regiment

Captain Alexei Ivanovich Saburov (nickname: Alyosha),
commanding the 2nd Battalion of the regiment

Lieutenant Maslennikov (nicknames: Misha, Mishenka),
chief of staff to Saburov

Vanin, Senior Political Instructor
commissar of Saburov's battalion

Petya
Saburov's orderly

Konyukov
soldier in Saburov's battalion

Ivan Alexeievich Vassiliev
soldier in Saburov's battalion

Anya Klimenko
nurse and hospital assistant

DAYS AND NIGHTS

... there were those troubled times
When Russia, young,
Straining its strength,
Was growing under Peter.
More than one sudden, bloody lesson
Came at the hands of a foreign foe.
But in the long ordeal,
Surviving all the blows of fate,
Russia grew strong.
Thus a heavy sledge, which smashes glass,
Can also forge a sword.

–from *Poltava* by
Alexander Pushkin

AN exhausted woman sat leaning against the clay wall of the shed and in a quiet, tired voice told how Stalingrad had burned.

It was dry and dusty. A little breeze blew yellow puffs of dust along the ground. The woman's legs were bare and burned, and while she spoke she raked the dust with one hand onto her inflamed foot, as if trying to dull the pain. Captain Saburov looked at his own heavy, dusty boots, and automatically moved away from the woman. He was a very big man and seemed, in spite of his broad shoulders, almost too tall; his enormous, hunched figure and his plain, dour face made him look, in some subtle way, like Gorki when he was young.

He stood listening quietly to the woman, looking over her head at his troops unloading from their train directly onto the steppe beyond the last houses at the edge of the town.

At the far end of the steppe, the white band of a salt-water lake shone in the sun. The entire scene looked to him like the very edge of the world. Here, in September, they had reached the last railroad station east of the Volga, the nearest to Stalingrad. From here to the bank of the Volga they would have to go on foot. The little town was called Eltonskaya, after the name

1

of the salt lake. Saburov remembered from his school days the words Eltonskaya and Baskunchak. Once upon a time they had been only names in a school geography. Now here he was; this was Eltonskaya: small, low houses, dust, a provincial railroad town.*

The woman talked on and on about her misfortunes. Although her words were the same old words, they suddenly gave Saburov a sinking of the heart. Formerly they had retreated from town to town, from Kharkov to Valuiki, from Valuiki to Rossosh, from Rossosh to Boguchar, and in just this same way the women had cried, and he had listened to them with a mixed feeling of shame and weariness. But here was the naked steppe east of the Volga, the edge of the world. And in the words of this woman there was not a tone of reproach, but one of despair. There was no longer anywhere to retreat to in this steppe. For many versts behind them there were no towns, no rivers, nothing.

"Where have they driven us?" he whispered to himself. And all the limitless grief of the days gone by, when he had looked out over this steppe from the platform of a freight car, was compressed into these words.

At this moment his feelings were bitter, but he remembered the frightening distance between where he was now, and the frontier where the war had started—and he thought not about how he had come here, but about how he could go back. And in this unhappy thought there was that special, Russian stub-

---

* The German summer offensive in 1942 began on June 10 and drove back the Red Army slowly but steadily eastward from Kharkov. General Field Marshal Von Bock was then commanding the German forces in the south of Russia, and by the middle of August they had passed Voronezh and reached the Don River. Marshal Timoshenko fought delaying actions, but pulled out the bulk of his armies for re-equipment and regrouping east of the Volga. Many officers, like Captain Saburov in this story, then returned to the front with units made up partly of veterans and partly of new troops from Siberia. This unit was thus moving west towards the Volga and Stalingrad, where the Russians hoped to check the great German drive through the south of Russia.

bornness which since the beginning of the war had kept him and his comrades from ever admitting the possibility that there might be no going back.

But they could not go on like this. Here, in Eltonskaya, he suddenly felt that they had reached the line beyond which there could be no more retreating.

He looked at the soldiers hurriedly climbing down from the railroad cars, and he wanted somehow to push as quickly as he could through this dust to the Volga. He wanted to cross the river and to feel, suddenly and finally, that there would be no recrossing of it, and that his personal fate would be decided on the other bank, together with the fate of the city. If the Germans took the city, then that would mean he would certainly die. If he could keep them from taking it, then maybe he would live.

The woman, sitting at his feet, kept on talking about Stalingrad. One by one she named the streets that had been destroyed and burned. Their names, strange to Saburov, were filled for her with some special meaning. She knew where and when the houses had been built which were now burned, where and when the trees had been planted which were now cut for barricades in the streets. She mourned them all, as if she were talking not about a great city, but about her own home, where all the things belonging to her personally had come to utter ruin.

About her own home she said nothing. Listening to her, Captain Saburov thought how seldom, all through the war, he had met people who mourned their own lost property. The longer the war lasted, the less people even remembered their abandoned homes, and the more often and obstinately they remembered the cities they had left. Wiping her tears with the end of her kerchief, the woman looked long and questioningly at all who were listening to her, then said thoughtfully and with conviction:

"How much money! How much work!"

"What work?" asked someone, not understanding immediately what she meant.

"Building it all up again," the woman said simply.

Saburov asked the woman about herself. She said her two sons had gone to the front long ago; one of them was already killed. Her husband and her daughter had probably stayed in Stalingrad. When the bombing and the fires started she had been alone, and since then she had heard nothing of them.

"Are you going to Stalingrad?" she asked.

"Yes," said Saburov. He saw no military secret in this. Why else, except to go to Stalingrad, would a Red Army battalion be getting off a train at this moment in this God-forgotten town of Eltonskaya?

"Our name is Klimenko. My husband is Ivan Vassilievich Klimenko, and my daughter is Anya. Maybe you will meet them somewhere," the woman said with a vague sort of hope in her voice.

"It could be." Saburov gave the answer he always gave. Then he thought that it might actually happen, that sometime he might really meet them, by one of those strange accidents which happen so improbably but so often during a war.

The battalion was finishing its unloading. Captain Saburov said good-by to the woman, and after drinking a dipper of water from a pail placed in the street for the soldiers, he walked over to the railroad tracks.

The soldiers sat on the rails. They had taken off their boots and the cloth wrapped around their feet.* Some of the men who had kept part of the ration given them in the morning were eating bread and dry sausage. Through the battalion there had spread a soldiers' rumor, as true as usual, that after unloading they would begin to march, so all of them were

---

* Strips of coarse linen cloth, called "portyanki," are worn by Russian soldiers around their feet instead of socks. They are given credit by many Russians for the relatively low incidence in the Red Army of both trench foot and frostbite.

4

hurrying to finish whatever they had not done. Some ate, others mended their torn tunics, still others smoked.

Saburov walked along the railroad line. The train in which the commander of the regiment, Babchenko, was traveling should arrive at any minute, and until then one question would have to remain unanswered: Should Saburov's battalion begin its march to Stalingrad without waiting for the other battalions, or should the entire regiment start together the next morning, after sleeping here?

Captain Saburov walked along the tracks and looked at the men with whom he would go up to the front line the day after tomorrow. Many of them he knew well by face and by name. These were "the men of Voronezh," as he called those who had been with him in the fighting near Voronezh. Each of them was a man to be cherished, because you could command them without explaining all the little details.

They knew, for example, when the black drops which were bombs falling from an airplane were dropping straight on them, so that they had to lie down, and when the bombs were falling farther away, so that you could quietly watch them fall. They knew that when you are under mortar fire it is no more dangerous to move forward than to stay where you are. They knew that tanks most often kill soldiers who are running away from them, and that German automatic rifle fire from two-hundred meters away is always intended more to frighten than to kill.

Soldiers like this made up one-third of his battalion. The rest were going to see war for the first time. By one of the railroad cars, standing guard over equipment which had not yet been unloaded, stood a private who caught Saburov's attention from a distance by his Guardsman's bearing and his thick red moustaches standing out like spears from his face. When Saburov walked up to him he stood smartly to attention, and with straight, unmoving eyes looked in the captain's face.

5

The way he stood, the way he was dressed, the way he held his rifle, all betrayed a soldier with many years of service. At the same time Saburov, who could place almost all those who had been with him near Voronezh before the reorganization of the division, did not remember this soldier.

"What's your name?" he asked.

"Konyukov," the soldier answered, still looking straight into the captain's eyes.

"Have you been in action?"

"Yes."

"Where?"

"At Przemsyl."

"Well, well. That means you retreated all the way from Przemsyl."

"Not at all. We went forward there."

Saburov looked at him in surprise. "When? Last year?"

"Not at all. In 1916."

"So."

Saburov looked at Konyukov attentively. He had a serious face, even solemn.

"In this war, have you been in the army long?" asked Saburov.

"No. This is my first month."

Saburov looked again with satisfaction at Konyukov's strong face, and walked on farther.

By the last car he met his chief of staff, Lieutenant Maslennikov, supervising the unloading. Maslennikov reported to him that in five minutes the unloading would be finished, and looking at his square wrist watch asked:

"Comrade Captain, may I check my watch with yours?"

Saburov silently took his watch out of his pocket. It was fastened to its strap with a safety pin. Maslennikov's watch was five minutes slow. Distrustfully he looked at Saburov's old, silver watch with its cracked crystal.

6

Saburov smiled. "Never mind," he said, "change yours. In the first place, it was my father's watch, made by Buré. In the second place, you'd better get used to the fact that in war the correct time is always that of your commanding officer."

Maslennikov looked again at both watches, carefully changed his own and, saluting, asked if he might go. He had been in charge of the trip on the train, and now this unloading was the closest he had come to a front line assignment. Here, in Eltonskaya, it seemed to him he could almost smell the nearness of the front. He was excited with his first taste of war. Everything assigned to him today by Saburov he had carried out with special accuracy and exactness.

"Yes, yes, go right ahead," said Saburov after a moment's silence.

Looking at this red-cheeked, boyish face, so full of life, Saburov wondered anxiously what it would look like after a week, when the dirty, exhausting, merciless life in trenches would have stamped itself for the first time on Maslennikov.

A small engine, puffing, pulled up on a siding with the long awaited second train.

The commander of the regiment, Lieutenant Colonel Babchenko, jumped down from the step of the car while it was still moving. He was always in a hurry. He twisted his leg as he jumped, swore, and turned toward Saburov, who was hurrying toward him.

"How is the unloading going?" he asked in a surly voice, looking away from Saburov.

"It is finished."

Babchenko looked around him. The unloading obviously was finished. But his sullen look and severe tone, which Babchenko considered necessary in all conversation with subordinates, demanded that he make some kind of observation in order to support his own prestige.

"What are you doing now?" he asked abruptly.

7

"I am waiting for your orders."

"It would be better to feed the men than just to let them wait."

"If we are going to move forward at once, I had decided to feed the men at the first stop for rest. But if we are going to spend the night here, I had decided to give them a hot meal here, in an hour," Saburov answered slowly, dragging his words a little, as was his custom, and with the quiet logic which particularly irritated the eternally hurrying Babchenko.

The lieutenant colonel was silent.

"Do you want them to eat now?" asked Saburov.

"No, let them eat at the first break. Get started, without waiting for the others. Order your battalion to form ranks."

Saburov called Maslennikov and ordered him to line the men up. Babchenko kept a sullen silence. He was used to doing everything himself, and just because of this he was always up to his neck in detail, always hurrying, and often not accomplishing what he set out to do. As a matter of fact the commander of a battalion is not himself required to form his men in ranks for a march. But the fact that Saburov had turned the task over to another, and stood quietly beside him, the commander of the regiment doing nothing, irritated Babchenko.

He liked to have his subordinates sweat and run. But he never achieved this with the quiet Saburov. Turning around, he began to watch the column forming ranks. Saburov stayed by his side. He knew that the commander of the regiment did not like him, but he had become accustomed to this and he paid no attention to it.

For a minute they both stood silent. Suddenly Babchenko said, still without turning towards Saburov, but in quite a different tone, with unexpected anger and venom in his voice:

"Just look what they are doing to our people, the swine."

Beside them, marching with difficulty along the tracks, filed

8

a long line of refugees from Stalingrad, tattered, exhausted, many of them wearing bandages which were gray with dust.

Both men automatically looked in the direction in which the regiment was about to march. There lay the same low steppe as here, except that the dust, hanging over the little hills, looked like faraway puffs of battle smoke.

"The assembly point will be in Rybachi," said Babchenko. "Proceed by forced march and send messengers back to me." He was speaking again with his former sullen expression on his face. He turned away and went back to his railroad car.

Saburov went out on the road. The regiment had already formed, but it was standing at ease waiting for the order to march. In the ranks the men talked quietly to each other. Walking past Company Two Saburov again saw the red-moustached Konyukov, who was saying something in a lively manner, gesturing vigorously with his hands. Saburov walked closer.

"You want to know why it's better for us to attack than to go backwards?" Konyukov was saying. "Why, it's better because when we attack, with the east behind us, in the daytime, when it's hot, the sun is nice and warm on our backs, and in the evening, when it gets cold, we have it in our faces. Everything works by schedule."

"And do the bullets go by schedule, too?" someone asked with a smile.

Saburov walked past Konyukov to the head of the column. "Battalion, march!"

The column moved. Saburov strode ahead. The dust in the distance hanging over the steppe still looked to him like smoke but then, he thought, maybe the steppe in front of him was really burning.

TWO

WENTY days before, on a stifling August day, bombers of the Richthofen squadron had hung from early morning suspended in the sky over Stalingrad. It was hard to say how many there actually were and how many times they bombed, flew away, and came back again, but observers counted 2,000 airplanes over the city during the day.

The city was burning. It burned that night, all the following day, and all the following night. And although on the first day of the fire the fighting was still sixty kilometers from the city, at the crossings of the Don River, it was with that fire that the great battle of Stalingrad began, because both Germans and Russians—they in front, we behind—from that moment watched the glow of Stalingrad. All the fighting thoughts of both the warring sides, from that day on, were pulled toward the burning city as if by a magnet.

On the third day, when the fire started to die down, you began to smell in Stalingrad that special heavy odor of ashes which from then on never left the city through all the months of siege. The smells of hot iron, charcoal, and burned brick mixed themselves into a single, heavy, caustic stench. Cinders and ash settled quickly on the ground, but as soon as even the lightest breeze came off the Volga, this black dust began to roll in puffs along the burned-out streets, and then it seemed that the town was smoking again.

The Germans continued their bombardment of Stalingrad, now here, now there, starting new fires which no one bothered about any longer. Usually they burned themselves out relatively quickly because after consuming a few new houses, the flames soon came to a street already gutted and, finding nothing more to feed on, went out. But the city was so enormous that somewhere, just the same, something was always burning, and after a few days everyone became used to this unending fire as if it were an essential part of the night landscape.

Ten days after the start of the fire, the Germans came so close that their artillery and mortar shells began to explode not only on the edges, but in the center of the city. On the twenty-first day there came that minute when it might have seemed, to a man believing only in military theory, that to defend the city further was useless and even impossible. To the north of Stalingrad the Germans had already reached the Volga, to the south they were approaching it. The city, spread out over a length of sixty-five kilometers, was nowhere more than five kilometers wide, and along almost its entire length the Germans had already occupied the city's western districts.

Cannon fire, which began at seven every morning, did not stop until dusk. An uninitiated man happening into army headquarters might have thought that everything was in fine shape, and that in any case the defenders still had great strength. Looking at the staff map of the city, where the disposition of the regiments was shown, he would have seen a relatively small sector on the map thickly written over with the numbers of the divisions and brigades defending the city. He would have heard the orders given by telephone to the commanders of these divisions and brigades, and he might have assumed that it was necessary only to carry out these orders

11

accurately for success to be assured beyond any doubt. In order really to understand what was going on, this uninitiated observer would have had to go to the divisions themselves, which were marked on the map in such precise little red semicircles.

Having retreated from far beyond the Don, tired out after two months of heavy fighting, any one of these divisions, in its number of men, was at best no better than a regiment. At staff headquarters, in the artillery regiments, and in the medical corps there were still enough people, but in the rifle regiments and battalions men were counted one by one. In recent days everyone who was not absolutely essential had been taken from headquarters and rear units. Ambulance men, orderlies, telephone operators, cooks, and chemical warfare specialists were all transferred to the regiment commanders and, because there was no other choice, became infantrymen. Although the chief of staff of the army, looking at his map, knew very well that not one of his divisions was any longer a division, nor even a regiment, still the size of the sectors which they occupied demanded that each should carry out the military tasks which fall on the shoulders of a division. Although they knew that this burden was almost beyond human strength, still every officer from the highest to the lowest assigned these tasks to his subordinates because there was nothing else to do.

Before the war the commander of the army would probably have laughed if someone had told him the day would come when the entire mobile reserve which he could move around would consist of three hundred men. But today was that day. Three hundred machine gunners loaded in twenty trucks—this was all he could throw quickly from one end of the city to the other in the critical moment of any break-through.

On the large, flat top of Mamai Kurgan,* about one kilo-

---

* The Mamai Kurgan is a bluff on the west side of the Volga at Stalingrad, next to the business center of the city. It was once used by Tartar chieftains as a burial ground; later it became the city's principal park. On September 14 the Germans seized it, but were driven back by Major General Alexander

meter from the front line, the staff of the army was located in dugouts and trenches. The Germans had halted their attack, either postponing it until nightfall, or just deciding to take a rest. The situation in general, and especially this strange silence, made it clear that by morning there was certain to be a heavy attack.

"You should eat," said an adjutant, forcing his way with difficulty into the small dugout in the ground where the chief of staff of the Stalingrad army and the member of the military council of the army sat over their map beside a lamp.*

Both looked at each other, then at the map, then again at each other. If the adjutant had not reminded them that it was necessary to eat they might have sat over the map another hour. They alone knew how dangerous the position really was. And although everything had been done which should have been done and could be done, and the commander himself had gone out to the divisions to check the execution of his orders, still it was hard for them to tear themselves away from the map. They wanted so badly, if only by some miracle, to find some new and unsuspected possibility on this piece of ruled paper.

"All right, if we should eat, let's eat," said the member of the military council, Matveyev, a man with a happy disposi-

---

Rodimtsev in one of the most heroic charges of the entire Russian war. Dugouts cut deep into the bluff served as command posts for Lieutenant General Vassily Chuikov's 62nd Army, which held most of the bluff throughout the siege of Stalingrad. It is called "Hill 102" on military maps, because it rises 102 meters above the Volga.

* In the larger units of the Red Army, above the division level, authority has been traditionally vested in a "military council," usually made up of three men. One of these is always the commanding general; the second is usually his chief of staff; the third is always referred to in Russian as "member of the military council." In the past this third position has always been filled with exceptionally trusted members of the Communist party. His relation to the commanding general paralleled that of a political commissar to the commanding officer of a smaller Red Army unit. During this war, the system of dual control has tended to disappear in the Red Army, and these "members of military councils" have become, in effect, deputy commanding officers concentrating on political and strategic rather than on tactical problems.

13

tion, cheerful, who loved to eat on those occasions when, in the tumult of staff work, he could remember about eating at all.

Both walked out into the open air. It was just beginning to get dark. Below, to the right of where they stood, salvos of mortar shells flashed against the lead-colored sky. The Germans were preparing for the night, shooting into the sky the first white rockets designed to mark out, as was their custom, their own front line.

Across Mamai Kurgan ran the so-called Green Belt, at one time the pride of Stalingrad. In 1930, the Komsomols * of Stalingrad had planted it, and during the next decade they had ringed their dusty, stifling city with an entire belt of gardens, parks, and boulevards. The top of Mamai Kurgan was also planted with thin, ten-year-old linden trees, standing in neat rows like men on a chessboard.

Matveyev looked around him. This warm autumn evening was so pleasant, everything had become so unexpectedly still, and the last summer fragrance from the linden leaves now beginning to turn yellow smelled so fresh, that it seemed to him stupid on such an evening to sit in the only building there—a half-destroyed hut where the dining room had been set up.

"Look," he said to the adjutant, "tell them to bring a table out here so we can eat under the linden trees."

From the kitchen they brought a rickety table, spread a tablecloth, and brought up two stools.

"Well, General, let's sit down," said Matveyev to the chief of staff. "It's a long time since we sat together in a garden under the lindens, and it will probably be a long time before we do it again." He looked down at the burned-out city.

The adjutant brought tea in glasses.

"Remember, General," said Matveyev, "how nice it was at Sokolniki in the labyrinth? They had made sort of small rooms

* Komsomols are members of the Young Communist League, the chief youth organization of the Communist party in Russia.

out of the clipped lilac bushes, and in each one there was a little table and some benches. And they brought you a samovar . . . More and more, people used to go there with their families."

"Yes, and there were mosquitoes, too," said the general, who was a man not predisposed to poetic feelings. "There aren't any here."

"No, but here there isn't any samovar, either," said Matveyev.

"That's why there aren't any mosquitoes," the general answered stubbornly. "But the labyrinth was—you're quite right —a good labyrinth. It was really hard to find your way out."

Matveyev looked down at the city spread out beneath him and laughed quietly. "Labyrinth . . ." Below him there met and parted and crossed and tangled an endless maze of streets along which, together with the fate of many human beings, there would now be decided one great question—the fate of the army.

Through the half-darkness the adjutant hurried up to their table.

"They have come from the other shore, from Bobrov," he said in a voice which showed that he had been running.

"Where are they?" Matveyev asked abruptly.

"With me," the adjutant said. Then he called out: "Comrade Major."

By his side there rose a tall figure which was hard to distinguish in the darkness.

"Did he meet them?" asked Matveyev.

"Yes," answered the major. "Colonel Bobrov ordered me to report to you that he met them and that the crossing of the river is about to start."

"Wonderful," Matveyev said as he stood up, moving back the bench and sighing with deep relief. For the last few hours what had been profoundly worrying him, and the chief of staff, and everyone around them, had now been decided.

15

"The commander hasn't yet returned?" he asked the adjutant.

"No."

"Send at once to find out the division where he is, and report to him that Bobrov has met them."

THREE

COLONEL Bobrov had left in the morning to meet and to hurry up the division in which Saburov commanded a battalion. Bobrov met the battalion at noon. It had not yet crossed the Middle Akhtuba, a stream thirty kilometers from the Volga. The first man he spoke to happened to be Saburov, who was walking at the head of his battalion. Having asked Saburov the number of the division, and having learned that his commander was following some distance behind, the colonel quickly stepped back into his automobile. Its motor was still running.

"Comrade Captain," he said to Saburov, looking into his face with tired, quiet eyes, "I don't need to explain to you why your battalion should be at the crossing by six o'clock." Without another word he slammed the door and nodded to the chauffeur.

By six o'clock in the evening Bobrov, on his way back, found Saburov already at the bank of the river. As always after an exhausting march, the battalion had come up to the Volga with broken ranks, sprawled out, but a half hour after the first soldier had seen the river, Saburov succeeded in collecting them all along the ravines and slopes of the hilly bank where they waited for further orders.

17

When Saburov had placed his battalion along the bank, ready for the crossing, he sat down to rest on a log lying half in the water. Colonel Bobrov sat down with him, opened a handsome cigarette case, and offered him a "Northern Palmyra," which he had secured from God-knows-where. They began to smoke.

"Well, how is it there?" Saburov asked. He nodded in the direction of the west bank.

"Hard," said the colonel. "Hard." For a third time, in a whisper, he repeated: "Hard," as if there were nothing to add to this all-inclusive word. And if the first "hard" meant simply difficult, then the second "hard" meant very difficult, and the third "hard," whispered, meant terribly difficult, unutterably hard.

Saburov looked across at the west bank of the Volga in silence. There it was—high and steep, like all the western banks of all the rivers in Russia. The eternal bad luck, which Saburov himself had experienced in this war, was that all the western banks of Russian rivers were steep, all the eastern banks sloping, and all the Russian cities stood without exception on the western banks: Kiev, Smolensk, Dnepropetrovsk, Moghilev, Rostov, every town he could think of. And all of them were hard to defend because they were up close to the rivers; and all of them would be hard to take back, because they would all lie beyond their rivers.

It had begun to get dark, but he could easily see how German bomber planes were still circling, diving, and pulling out again in the sky over the city, and how in a thick layer, looking like little feathery clouds, antiaircraft bursts covered the sky. In the southern part of the city a great grain elevator was burning. Even from where he was, Saburov could see how the flames heaved up over it. In its enormous stone chimney, obviously, there was a terrific draft. And into the waterless steppe beyond the Volga toward Eltonskaya were walking thousands

18

of hungry refugees. The whole picture gave Saburov at this moment no eternally true or general feelings about the uselessness and monstrosity of war. Instead it filled him with a simple and clear hatred for the Germans.

The evening was cool, but after the scorching sun of the steppe and after the dusty march, Saburov somehow could not feel refreshed. He wanted badly to drink. He took a helmet from one of his soldiers and let himself down the slope to the Volga itself, his feet sinking in the soft sand along the shore. The first time he ladled the helmet full of water, cold and clean, and drank it thirstily. When he filled it the second time, already half satisfied, and raised the helmet to his lips, suddenly the most simple and at the same time bitter thought came to him. This was Volga water, he was drinking water from the Volga, and at the same time he was at war. These two ideas—the war and the Volga—were both obvious ideas, but somehow they did not go together. From his childhood, from school, all his life, the Volga had been for him something deeply and incredibly Russian, and now that he stood on the bank of the Volga and drank water from it, the fact that there were Germans on the other bank seemed to him improbable and mad.

Bobrov looked at him, and as if answering his unspoken thought said, pensively: "Yes, Captain, the Volga . . ." He waved his arm toward the river and added: "Look, there comes our cutter with its barge." He looked a second time, carefully, professionally, and said: "You can manage one company and two guns . . ."

Fifteen minutes later the little steamer, pulling a barge behind it, came up to the bank. Saburov and Bobrov went to the wooden jetty which had been hastily nailed together, where the loading was to take place. Past the soldiers crowding onto the dock, wounded were being carried from the barge. Some of them groaned but most were silent. A young nurse moved

19

from stretcher to stretcher. Following the severely wounded from the barge walked a dozen men who still could walk.

"How few slightly wounded!" Saburov said to Bobrov.

"Few?" Bobrov answered, and he laughed. "Just as many as everywhere, but they don't bring them all across the river."

"Why?" asked Saburov.

"How can I tell you? They stay because it's tough there, and then there is anger, too. And a kind of hardness. No, I guess that's not the reason, either. Maybe it's the kind of thing you can't explain. Go over yourself; on your third day you'll understand why the slightly wounded don't come back."

The soldiers of Company One began to board the barge. Meanwhile an unexpected complication developed. It seemed that a large number of people had collected on the bank who wanted to cross at once, and on this particular barge going back to Stalingrad. One was returning from a hospital, another was carrying a keg of vodka from a quartermaster depot and demanded that he and his vodka should both be taken. A third, a big, burly fellow, was holding an enormous box close to his chest. He came up to Saburov and said that these were percussion caps for mines, and that they would cut his head off if he didn't deliver them, and deliver them today. Finally, there were people who had collected since morning on the eastern shore for different reasons of their own and now wanted to be back in Stalingrad as quickly as possible.

No amount of talking had any effect. By their tone and by the expression on their faces no one would have thought that there on the far bank where they were hurrying so was a besieged city, and that in its streets shells were exploding literally every minute.

Saburov quietly decided to take the man with the percussion caps and the orderly with the vodka, and to turn away the others, telling them they could come on the next barge.

Last of all came up the nurse who had just crossed from

Stalingrad. She had been helping the wounded as they were unloaded from the barge. She said there were still wounded on the other bank and that with this barge she would have to bring them here. Saburov could not refuse her, and when the company had embarked she crossed the narrow gangway after the others, first onto the barge and then onto the little steamer.

The ferry captain was an elderly man, dressed in a blue jacket and an old Soviet Mercantile Fleet cap with a broken visor. He shouted some kind of order to the deck cabin and the steamer pushed off from the bank.

Saburov sat on the poop, swinging his legs over the edge and holding on to the handrail. He took off his coat and laid it by his side. It was pleasant to feel the wind from the river blow under his tunic. He unbuttoned his tunic and held it away from his chest until it puffed out like a sail.

"You'll catch cold, Comrade Captain," said the nurse who was standing beside him.

Saburov smiled. It seemed funny to him that in the fifteenth month of the war, crossing the Volga to Stalingrad, he would suddenly catch cold and get the grippe. He did not answer.

"You won't notice that you're catching cold," the girl repeated. "It's cold here on the river in the evenings. Every day I cross the river and I've caught such a cold that I haven't any voice left."

In fact in her thin, young girl's voice there could be heard a kind of hoarseness.

"Do you cross every day?" asked Saburov looking at her. "How many times?"

"Depending on how many wounded there are, that's how many times I make a crossing. You see, here things aren't the way they used to be—taking wounded first to the regiment, then to a first-aid point, then to a hospital. Now we take them straight from the front line and move them across the Volga right away."

She said this so quietly that Saburov, without meaning to, asked one of the empty and idle questions which he usually didn't like to ask: "Aren't you frightened to cross the river so many times?"

"Frightened?" said the girl. "When you're bringing wounded over, it's not so frightening, but when I go back there alone, then I get frightened. When you're alone, it's always more frightening, isn't it?"

"True," said Saburov, and he thought to himself that he also was always less afraid when he was with his battalion than in those rare moments when he was left alone.

The girl sat down beside him and swung her legs over the water. She tapped him on the shoulder confidentially, and said in a whisper:

"Do you know what's really frightening? No . . . you don't know. You're already pretty old, you wouldn't know . . . I get frightened that suddenly I'll be killed and there won't be anything left. There won't be anything of what I've always dreamed about."

"What won't there be?"

"There won't be anything at all . . . Do you know how old I am? I'm eighteen . . . I haven't seen anything yet, anything at all . . . I've dreamed how I would study, but I haven't studied . . . I've dreamed how I would go to Moscow and everywhere, everywhere . . . and I haven't been anywhere at all. I've dreamed . . ." she grew still, then in a whisper continued: "I've dreamed how I'd fall in love, how I'd get married . . . and there hasn't been any of that . . . so I sometimes get frightened, terribly frightened, that suddenly none of this will happen after all. I shall die and there won't be anything, anything."

"But if you had gone to school and traveled where you wanted to and had been married, do you think it wouldn't be frightening to you?" asked Saburov.

"No," she said with conviction. "For example, you, I know, are not as frightened as I am. How old are you?"

"How old do you think?"

"Well, maybe thirty-five or forty. Yes?"

"Yes." Saburov smiled and then he thought a little bitterly how useless it would be to say that he wasn't forty or even thirty-five, and that he also had not studied everything that he wanted to, and had not been everywhere he would have liked to go, and had not fallen in love as he would like to fall in love.

"So you see," she continued, "for that reason you oughtn't to be frightened. But for me it is frightening."

This was said with such sorrow and at the same time such self-control that Saburov immediately wanted to pat her on the head as if she were a child, and to say some stupid but good words about how everything would come out all right, and how nothing would happen to her. But the sight of the burning city kept him from saying the words, and instead he simply patted her on the head and quickly took his hand away, not wanting her to think that he had misunderstood her frankness.

"Our doctor died today," the girl said. "I was taking him across the river when he died . . . He was always such an angry man, he swore at everybody. When he operated, he always swore, and he yelled at us. Do you know, the more the wounded groaned and the worse their pain was, the more he swore. But when he began to die himself, and I was taking him across the river—they had wounded him in the stomach and it hurt him terribly—he just lay there and didn't swear. In fact, he didn't say anything; there was nothing to say. And then I understood that in actual fact he was probably a very good man. He swore because he couldn't watch people suffer, but when it came his turn to be hurt he just shut up and said nothing, right up until he died, nothing at all . . . Only when I cried, he suddenly smiled. What do you think, why did he do that?"

23

"I don't know," said Saburov. "Maybe he was glad that you were still alive and well in all this war, and so he smiled. But maybe it wasn't that. I don't know."

"I don't know either," the girl said. "It was just that I felt awfully sorry for him and strange: he was so big, so healthy always . . . It always seemed to me that all of us, and I, too, could be killed but that he would get it last of all, or perhaps never . . . Then suddenly it turns out just the other way."

The little steamer was puffing towards the Stalingrad shore, only two or three hundred meters away by now. At just that moment a shell fell into the water in front of them with a whine. Saburov started with surprise. The girl never moved.

"They're firing," she said. "And here I was riding along and talking with you and I was thinking: why don't they fire?"

Saburov did not answer. He was listening, and even before the second shell fell he knew it would pass over them. The shell, in fact, fell about two hundred meters behind the steamer. The Germans had taken the steamer in what is called an artillery fork, one shell in front and one behind. Saburov knew that now they would divide the fork in half. Then this distance they would divide again in half, and make their corrections. Beyond this, as always in war, it would be simply luck.

Saburov stood up, took several steps to the stern of the boat, made a megaphone with his hands, and yelled at the barge: "Maslennikov, tell your men to take off their coats and put them down beside them."

The Red Army men standing with him on the little steamer understood that the captain's order referred to them, too, and they hurriedly unbuttoned their greatcoats, took them off, and placed them at their feet.

The German artillery, just as Saburov had foreseen, divided their fork so exactly that the third shell plunged into the water right next to the steamer.

"Frame," the girl said.

24

Saburov looked up and saw directly over his head, not very high, the twin fuselage of a German Focke-Wulf artillery spotter, which was always called a "frame" at the front because of the strange shape of its tail. Now the accurate shooting of the German artillery could be understood.

The steamer had no chance to maneuver because of its barge. There was nothing to do but wait out the five minutes still separating them from the bank. Saburov looked at the girl and noticed with surprise that she apparently did not have the feeling people usually have in minutes of danger: she did not want to touch anyone, nor be at someone's side. She stood calmly five steps away from Saburov on the deck where he had left her, and waited quietly, looking straight at the water rushing past beneath her feet. Saburov went up to her.

"If something happens, can you swim to the shore?"

"I don't know how to swim," she said.

"Not at all?"

"Not at all."

"Then stand nearer to me," Saburov said. "Look, see the life belt hanging there."

He pointed with his hand where he had seen a life belt hanging, and at just that second a shell hit the steamer. It landed, apparently, in the engine room or in the boilers, because suddenly everything surged and roared around him, and someone flying through the air knocked Saburov off his feet. Then he was himself thrown upwards and away from the deck, and he fell into the water. Almost at once, striking out with both arms, he pulled himself to the surface. That part of the steamer on which the stack still remained keeled over about twenty meters from Saburov, and with its stack dipping up water like an enormous glass, disappeared below the surface of the river.

All around men were floundering in the water. Saburov realized he had done well to tell the soldiers to take off their coats. His own boots, heavily weighted with water, kept pulling down his legs, and at first he decided to kick them off. But the barge which was drifting toward him was so close that he was reluctant, soldier-fashion, to lose his boots, and decided that he could swim with them.

These thoughts poured through his head all at once. A moment later he saw the girl, several meters away from him and trying unsuccessfully to catch hold of a fragment of the boat floating in the water. Saburov made several quick strokes toward her, and when the girl came up to the surface again he grabbed her by her tunic. Luckily, the barge was drifting almost straight onto them. Using all his strength, he moved his free arm to shove himself in its path.

A half minute later he had grabbed a soldier's hand reached out to him from the barge. Holding on the side, he pulled the girl after him, and when he saw that strong arms were already dragging her onto the barge he pulled himself up quickly.

"Thank God, Comrade Captain," said Maslennikov, standing beside him. He was without his boots and without his tunic; unsure whether Saburov could make it or not, he had been ready to dive into the water.

"Wait," said Saburov, and turned back towards the river.

One after another the soldiers swam to the barge. Last of all they pulled out the captain of the tug. He climbed onto the barge, swearing a blue streak. By some fluke, the cap of the Soviet Mercantile Fleet with its broken visor was still on his head, but pulled down still farther over his forehead.

Cutting diagonally across the course of the barge another cutter hurried, puffing, from the bank. "Get ready to make fast," someone yelled from it in a thunderous, Volga bass voice.

A minute later the little sack of sand on its thin rope whistled through the air and fell on the barge. The soldiers began to pull in the hawser. Far behind the barge a few more shells fell into the water, and then everything was quiet. The high bank was too close now and it kept the Germans from shooting.

"Count the men," Saburov said to Maslennikov. "Yes, and get dressed. What's the matter, are you going to stand there barefoot?"

Maslennikov looked in confusion at his bare feet and hurriedly pulled on his boots. One of the soldiers threw his overcoat around Saburov's shoulders.

"Give a coat to the girl," Saburov said. "Where is she?"

She was sitting there, several steps away from him, with someone's coat already thrown around her shoulders. Just as if she had forgotten that she was wet to the skin, she was wringing out her long hair, twisting it on her fists. Saburov wanted to go over to her, but just at that moment Maslennikov came up to him.

"Well?"

"Eight men missing," Maslennikov said in a whisper. There was a kind of hurt look on his face. They had not even crossed the river, there had been no fighting, and already eight men were missing.

The barge was tied fast to the dock. Now there could be heard not only artillery explosions but the crackling of machine-guns. Saburov, who did not yet know the real state of things in the city, was surprised by this. Machine-guns must have been firing not more than two or three kilometers from where he was.

The excited men hurried to get ashore as quickly as they could. Saburov let them pass him. The girl went among the first, and by the time Saburov remembered about her, she was no longer either on the barge or on the dock. He and Maslennikov were the last to leave. They found the Stalingrad bank of the river hard and full of clay. They felt the ground under their feet and it was ordinary soil, like everywhere else, the earth on which Stalingrad stood.

FOUR

BY night a storm had broken. At ten o'clock when Captain Saburov had accounted for his last company, the scene around him seemed to him like some fantastic painting. The Volga clamored behind them; with the night as background, columns of flame rose against the entire horizon; somewhere above, reflected on the black sky, purple lights were dancing. Frequent lightning, picking pieces of the shore out of the darkness, illuminated the weird remains of houses fallen in on themselves, roofs torn open to the sky, enormous gasoline tanks crumpled up like paper bags squeezed in a fist. The rain fell, slanting, heavy, beating against his face. On the shore, in the strange darkness, it was difficult to make his way among the ruins and the debris. People found each other by touch and by voice. All around the rain roared and splattered.

Saburov sent off from the last barge his field kitchens and his trucks with stores. There could be no thought of preparing a hot meal in this darkness and chaos. The sergeants gathered around the provisions trucks, where they were given dry rations. Groping their way in the darkness, they distributed them among the soldiers.

28

The machine-gun firing which Saburov had heard at sunset had almost ceased; only occasionally an unexpected burst of fire would clatter and then stop. From somewhere far away, both to the right and to the left, the rolling of cannon fire could be heard mixing with the roar of thunder.

Saburov knew the greatest danger would begin at dawn, but still he wished it would grow light more quickly. Then, at any rate, he could find out where he was and see what was going on around them, and where they should go. At midnight, when Saburov had finally succeeded in placing his men along the ruined streets lying closest to the river bank, and when the soldiers, mortally tired, had somehow gone to sleep—some of them in the open under the rain—a messenger came up from Babchenko and ordered Saburov to go to the division commander.

Staff headquarters of the division were located near the shore, only ten minutes away. For the time being they were in a cellar by the side of a completed building. It was a deep burrow, encircled by concrete supports like columns buried in the ground. Here it was possible to light a light and the whole cellar was illuminated by a "Bat" storm lantern suspended from a pillar, and by electric flashlights which flashed on and off whenever it was necessary to write something or to look at a map. Even the lantern made Saburov blink after the complete darkness outside. He could not distinguish faces but he understood from the rumble of voices that there were many people in the cellar.

"Saburov," he heard Babchenko say.

"Well, that's fine, now we're all here," said another voice which sounded familiar to Saburov.

Saburov looked around and saw that Colonel Protsenko, commander of the division, was standing next to Babchenko. Saburov had known him well for a long time, but he had not seen him for almost a month and a half, since the colonel had been severely wounded near Voronezh and sent to the hospital. The colonel took a step out of the darkness towards the lantern, and clapping Saburov on the shoulder, asked:

"Well, Alexei Ivanovich. You're still alive?"

"Still alive," said Saburov.

"Alive," Protsenko said. "Well, and I'm alive, too." Turning to someone, hard to distinguish in the darkness, he added: "We're old friends, Comrade General; we were together in front of Moscow . . ."

Suddenly shifting from a caressing, friendly tone of voice to one which was strictly official, he asked again whether all the officers had assembled, and then he began to explain the night's assignment. It was necessary that night to relieve the remnants of a division bearing the brunt of the heaviest German attack. Babchenko's regiment was to drive the Germans back from the outskirts of a factory settlement where they had that day come closest of all to the Volga, and where Saburov had obviously heard the machine-gun firing during the evening. This would have to be done by a night attack.

Precisely and in great detail, as was his custom, Protsenko explained the task, pointing with his pencil on a map. Then, dismissing the officers of two regiments which would be required during the night simply to move up to their positions, he turned to Babchenko.

"Do you understand, Phillip Philipovich, what you are to do?"

"We'll do it," said Babchenko.

"To each battalion I'll give an officer who knows the city and the layout. Comrade Officers!" he called.

Out of the darkness came three men: two first lieutenants and a captain.

"You are now under the command of the lieutenant colonel. The situation is tough," Protsenko turned and looked hard at Babchenko. "Very tough . . . it's night fighting, in a city you don't know. Here, there can be no precise directions. The more men you use, the more confusion there will be, and the more losses. Surprise and determination, but not numbers . . . you understand, Comrade Babchenko?" Protsenko asked sternly as if he anticipated some decisions by Babchenko of which he would not approve. "Tonight you will send up only one battalion, and the two others should be ready by dawn for support and for beating back the counterattack. The attack itself you will entrust to Saburov."

Turning to Saburov, Protsenko continued: "You must understand, too, that at night it's not numbers, but surprise. Just as it was at Voronezh . . . Do you remember Voronezh?"

"Yes."

"Do you remember it well?"

"Yes."

"Well then, that's all. Fight the way you did at Voronezh, and even better. That's all the good advice there is."

Protsenko turned to a man standing in the rear who had been quietly listening to the conversation. Saburov saw he was dressed in a black leather coat, glistening with rain, with a general's green shoulder straps. Evidently he had given Protsenko his instructions earlier and was now simply listening to see how the colonel made his dispositions.

"Have you any commands, Comrade General?" Protsenko asked. "May I release the officers?"

"In just a minute," the general said as he came closer to the light.

Now Saburov could see him quite clearly. He was of medium height, with a leonine head, gray, heavy eyes looking upwards from under bushy eyebrows, and a strong chin. There was something stubborn in his eyes and in the way he bent his head. From the expression on his face, it seemed he was going to say something morose and sour, but his voice when he spoke was clear and low.

"Have you seen street fighting before?" he asked Saburov.

"Yes."

"Put your sappers in front, the tommy gunners in front along with your best sharpshooters, do you understand?"

"I understand."

"And go first yourself. In situations like this here in Stalingrad, that's our custom."

"And in our division, it is also our custom," Saburov said with a sharpness he did not expect to hear in his own voice, just as if the conversation were with a civilian and not with the commander of an army. Saburov forgot even to add the words: "Comrade General." The general's face showed nothing. It was impossible to guess whether the answer had pleased him or displeased him.

"May I dismiss the officers?" Protsenko asked again.

"Yes, let them go," said the general.

Walking out, Saburov felt the general's eyes following him, and he heard a final phrase, spoken loudly by Protsenko, in answer to some question of the general:

"Don't worry; he'll make it . . ."

Walking into the darkness with Babchenko, Saburov asked him when, if ever, he would finally give him a replacement for his commissar, who had caught typhus and had been taken from the battalion on its way to Stalingrad.*

"What do you mean, do you want me to beget one for you?"

---

* Political commissars were first appointed in the Red Army in 1917 to check on the loyalty and revolutionary zeal of officers, and to organize political education inside the army. They became an integral feature of all Red Army units. In the spring of 1940, the whole system of political commissars was abolished, presumably because of political mistakes made in the first Finnish campaign. When the German war began, political commissars were reintroduced, although in October, 1942, just when the events described in this book were taking place, their title was changed to "political instructors." Many former political commissars had become commanding officers by the time of the Stalingrad siege, and the principle of undivided command was firmly established. But the word "commissar" was still used in ordinary conversation, and the "political instructor" in any Red Army unit became, in effect, an assistant chief of staff in charge of political work inside that unit.

Babchenko answered roughly. "The political instructor of your first company is holding down the job now, isn't he?"

"He's holding it down," Saburov answered, packing into those few words all the bitterness he felt on the subject. But Babchenko gave no sign that he understood the meaning of his tone of voice.

"Well, once he's holding it down, let him go on doing it."

They walked on a little way in silence. Saburov did not like Babchenko, but he respected him for his personal bravery, and he was, after all, the commander of his regiment with whom, in an hour's time, he would be going into action. Saburov was not actually afraid, but a stronger feeling than usual gripped him before this night attack, and he would have liked to hear something encouraging from Babchenko at this moment.

"What do you think, Comrade Lieutenant Colonel, will everything go all right?"

"I don't think, and I advise you not to. We have our orders. What more do we want? Thinking—we'll do that tomorrow when we've carried them out." He said this gruffly, as was his custom. He never understood what was going on inside any of his subordinates. Suddenly Saburov felt that he did not want to ask him anything more.

When Saburov returned to where his battalion was quartered, it turned out that his orderly had already set up something like a command post in the middle of a ruined house. You had to get there on all fours, but once there it was relatively dry, and a lamp was burning. The orderly was an enterprising tommy gunner called Petya by everybody in the battalion, in spite of the fact that he was over thirty.*

Saburov summoned Maslennikov, the political instructor Parfenov, who was substituting for the missing commissar, and the officers of all three companies in his battalion: Gordi-

---

* Petya is the diminutive, in Russian, of Pyotr (Peter), and is usually used only for small boys of that name.

enko, a lanky, whiskered man who looked like Chapaev; the little Vinokurov, and Potapov, a short, placid, heavy-set Siberian recently sent up from the reserves. Saburov gave each officer half an hour to choose from his company fifty men who were good with automatic rifles and who were sharpshooters.

"In front of us," he explained, spreading out a map of the city, "is this square. On that side are the houses already taken by the Germans—three big apartment houses, each one covering half a block. We've got to take back these houses tonight." He underlined the meaning of these last words by pausing after each one, as if he were writing down a period.

He divided his forces into three groups: the left-hand house, on the left of the square, would be taken by Gordienko and his group; the house on the right would be taken by Parfenov; he himself would attack directly across the square. The officers listened to him silently.

Saburov turned to Maslennikov. "You will stay in reserve. When you have reached our present front line, you stop, station all those who are not going with us, and wait for dawn. You've got to place the men so that at dawn, just as soon as we have driven out the Germans, you will be as close to us as possible and can come and help us. Understand, Maslennikov?"

"I understand," Maslennikov answered. There was a little chagrin in his voice. He was unhappy to be left in the reserve on his first big action.

In the half hour left before the attack, Saburov visited all three companies which were rummaging around in the dark. Calling to mind one after another those who had fought with him near Voronezh, he picked them out so that in this first attack, a night attack at that, as many veterans as possible would be taking part. Even if he should lose a lot of men during the night, he would lose even more, he thought, if he did not succeed in capturing the buildings before morning and had to do it in the daytime.

When Saburov was walking through Company Two, he suddenly remembered the soldier with whom he had talked in El-tonskaya. It occurred to him that this quiet, middle-aged, moustached fellow had probably been a pretty skillful hunter at some time in his life. He might do well at night fighting.

"Konyukov," he called.

"Here," a soldier said in his ear, looming up from the ground in front of him.

"Include this man," Saburov said to Potapov. "He should go along, too . . ."

A half hour later, the companies began to move slowly through the rain along the burned-out streets still filled with the acrid smell of smoke. In front went the assault troops especially picked out by Saburov. A small, black-haired lieutenant named Zhuk, who had been attached to Saburov's battalion, led them through the back yards of buildings on the street which for this night constituted the front line. Beyond was a broad square, and on its opposite side, cut out from it like peninsulas, stood the three large buildings now occupied by the Germans, barely visible as big shadows in the dark. On the near side of the square stood the remnants of the regiment which had retreated here during the daytime.

The commander of the regiment had been killed, also its commissar. The regiment was now led by a captain, commander of one of its battalions, and the first lieutenant who was guiding Saburov turned out to have been temporary chief of staff of the regiment. His original assignment was now completed. But after whispering at one side to the commander of his own regiment, he returned to Saburov and said that he knew the houses which they had to seize, and that if Saburov did not object he would go along. Saburov did not object; on the contrary, he was glad, although also a little surprised, at this decision of the first lieutenant. As if he sensed the surprise, Zhuk said:

"Of course, I'll guide you. Once we managed to retreat, I ought to know how to get back . . ."

Saburov pointed out the positions from which all three of the attacking groups should start. For himself he took the center of the square. He had more men, therefore it was up to him to move straight across, right through the open square, on which the only cover was a round fountain, now no more than a shadow, but clearly marked on the map.

Before the start Saburov once more called Gordienko and Parfenov to him. Taking out of his pocket a cigarette case in which there were four precious cigarettes, he left one to be smoked after the business was finished and quietly handed each of his companions a cigarette, taking a third himself. They squatted on their heels and lit their cigarettes under cover of the skirts of their overcoats. Then, shielding the light and smoking through their fists, all three stood up again.

What could he say to them? That they should go forward—they knew this. That they should not be afraid of death—they would still be afraid, just exactly as he would himself. That the taking of these three houses was urgent, very urgent—but if it had not been urgent, would anyone have been sending people out through this hellish darkness to the unknown and death? Of course, it was urgent and necessary. Instead of any of these words, with a quick impulse he quietly drew the tall Gordienko and the thin, short Parfenov to him by the shoulders, squeezed them both in his long, muscular arms, and just as quietly released them. When they had disappeared back into the dark, he found himself thinking not about himself but about them, and whether he would see them again. Whether they would ever see him again or not did not occur to him.

A minute later he moved forward with his own unit. Fifty or sixty steps he took along the square in silence, in his excitement holding his breath as if the Germans might hear him breathe. Then suddenly from the German side clattered a burst of rifle fire. First, tracer bullets flew obliquely across the square, and then, one after the other, two small white rockets exploded and for a few seconds lit up a section of the square with the black shadow of the fountain in front of him and men to his right and left. At this unexpected flash every one hit the hard, paved ground. Saburov got up again and lunged forward. Behind him, answering the German shots, could be heard the Russian mortars, and in long bursts our Maxims began to fire. Over their heads, from both directions, so many tracer bullets could be seen that the wild idea came suddenly to Saburov —some of them must be colliding in the air.

From this point on, both time and life were measured only in meters . . .

Time after time Saburov stood up, raised his men, ran several steps, and again fell flat on his face on the paving. Soon the German mortars began to fire. Their shells burst first in front and then behind, plowing up the paving. The rain had stopped, then it began to pour again, and the rumble of the thunder mixed with the explosions of the shells.

One shell went off very near. Saburov threw himself forward, falling, hurting himself painfully, and when he lifted himself up a second later, he clutched something standing in front of him. In a flash of lightning he saw that he was holding on to the fountain, clutching in his hand a little stone statue of a child. The head and half the torso of the child had been carried away by a shell, and Saburov was holding on to it by its stone leg.

This large round fountain, serving temporarily as cover, now proved to be an unexpected obstacle. No matter how frightening it was to stay here, it seemed even more terrifying to go on across the hundred meters which still separated the attackers from the wall of the apartment house itself. None of the men wanted to leave this shelter. They lay along the base of the fountain and for a short time could not make up their minds to move farther. Several times Saburov moved forward beyond the fountain, dragging his men with him, and then returning for others. Machine-gun fire kept them pressed more and more tightly to the ground. So far, there had been almost no losses.

"Listen to that noise!" said a voice near Saburov the next time they flattened themselves on the ground. "Listen to that noise!" the voice repeated. Saburov recognized Konyukov.

"Is this worse than it was in the other German war?" he asked, turning his face, but still not lifting his head from the ground.

"No," Konyukov said. "No, it isn't. But will there be any barbed wire?"

"There shouldn't be."

"Well, it's all right, then. In that war, they sometimes strung as many as twelve rows of wire. You cut it and cut it, but there was always more to cut," Konyukov said in the quiet voice of a man just getting ready to start a long story. At that moment a shell exploded and they both hugged the ground.

"Come on," Saburov yelled when a German machine-gun, firing blind, had swung its fire somewhere to the left of them. Again they ran forward several steps.

It went on like this for perhaps five minutes. Saburov, with mixed feelings of fright and satisfaction, realized that he had done as he had hoped to do and had taken the blow on himself, so that Gordienko and Parfenov, probably during the same time, had managed to sneak up unnoticed through the ravines and back courtyards to the houses on both sides of the square. Everything would have been fine if only there had not been the frightening, uninterrupted curtain of white, yellow, and green tracer bullets over them.

On the last fifty meters, he did not have to pull anyone along with him. After having waited through one more burst of machine-gun fire, they all dashed forward at once to the wall of the courtyard which could now be seen in front of them, a safe harbor. Whatever was there—Germans, demons, devils—it would be better, happier, and less frightening than this naked square across which they had been dragging themselves. They were all unaccountably seized and thrown forward by the desire—which grows greater as the end approaches for any man going forward in attack—to seize something with a bayonet, to reach out a hand and feel a German.

When Saburov came up to the wall of the house, he saw that the first-floor window was very high. His orderly, Petya, came up and hoisted him on his shoulder. Saburov clutched the window sill with one hand and with all his strength threw a heavy antitank grenade through the window. Then he fell back down to the street.

Inside could be heard a heavy explosion. Petya again lifted Saburov, who sat astride the sill and reached down his hand to Petya. The latter climbed up, reached down his hand to someone else, and together all three men slipped through the window into the house. As insurance, copying a trick he had learned at the beginning of the war from the Germans, Saburov fired a burst with his tommy gun fanwise from his stomach, without looking. Someone right on top of them screamed. Deep in the room groans could be heard.

Feeling his way, groping, Saburov crossed the room, kicked the door open, and walked out into a corridor. The corridor was blind, without windows, and at its two ends, to the left and to the right, were burning small carbide lamps which had not been put out by the Germans. Suddenly several men tumbled out of a door placed far down toward one end of the corridor. Saburov realized, or felt instinctively, that they were Germans. Bending over, he fired another round along the corridor through the crack in the door. Several of the running men fell. One of them, stumbling and waving his arms, ran as far as Saburov and fell flat on the ground at his feet. Another, dodging from wall to wall, jumped past Saburov and collided beyond him with a figure which cried out in a savage voice, in Russian: "Ha! I got him." Saburov heard a loud racket behind him. He yelled, "Come on, Petya," and ran forward along the corridor.

In the next half hour it was difficult to know what was happening. Saburov's soldiers and the Germans bumped into each other, fired point-blank with their automatic rifles, wrestled, fired again, threw grenades. From the running and the confusion, from the way the Germans scrambled from the upper floor downstairs and from downstairs back again, it was clear that they were badly scared, and that what the soldiers lying on the square had dreamed of had actually come to pass— they had caught the Germans with their bayonets and with their hands.

Gradually the fighting shifted to the inside courtyard, and then subsided. The Germans were either killed, or had hidden themselves, or had run away. Their mortars, placed on the next street, began to fire on the house, which made it clear that the house was now ours.

It began slowly to grow light. Saburov sent messengers to Gordienko and Parfenov. From the way the Germans fired and from the place they were firing, it seemed clear that the two houses to the left and to the right had also been taken.

At last, when it had become entirely light, First Lieutenant Zhuk appeared. He was limping. Behind him walked three Red Army soldiers and five Germans with their hands tied behind their backs.

"Here they are . . . What do you think? They were in the boiler room—they were getting into the boiler," Zhuk said with that sincere surprise at the slyness and cunning of a German which no Russian ever quite loses. "What do you know, they were actually getting into the boiler," he repeated, ob-

40

viously pleased that in spite of this he had routed out these cunning Germans after all.

Saburov was pleased, both that Zhuk was still alive and that he had captured these Germans, but his own legs suddenly folded up with fatigue. He sat on the nearest chair and almost indifferently said, wiping the sweat from his forehead:

"Well, you don't mean it, in the boiler . . ."

"In the boiler," Zhuk repeated triumphantly, for the third time. "What do you order me to do with them?"

"Are you going back to the regiment, to your own head-quarters?" asked Saburov.

"Yes."

"Take some riflemen and escort them back; then turn them over."

"Take them back—all right," Zhuk said happily, "but riflemen I don't need; these won't run away from me."

"Will you be sure and get them there?" he asked.

"Sure, I'll get them there . . ." Zhuk answered. "Do you now know more or less the entire layout here?"

"More or less," Saburov said.

"Well, then I'll be going," said Zhuk, "but I won't say good-by. I'll be coming back to visit you."

"Glad to have you," Saburov smiled. "I'm going to find myself an apartment here."

"Fine, look for one, I wish you luck." Zhuk had already turned around, but as he went out he added: "Only I advise you to pick one on the ground floor; on the first floor it's likely to be draughty. As soon as the Germans see you set yourself up on the first floor, they'll knock the walls out along with the windows, you can be sure of that."

Saburov picked himself a place for a temporary command post in one of the basement rooms which was, nevertheless, quite light and big. When he sat down for a second and tried

41

to figure out what he should do next, in came Konyukov leading behind him a red-haired, middle-aged German prisoner.

"I caught him, Comrade Captain," Konyukov said. "I caught him. Look, I caught him and I give him to you . . ."

Konyukov had the look of a conqueror on his face. Just like Zhuk, he had tied the prisoner's arms behind his back, but at the same time he kept clapping him on the shoulder in a friendly way. This German was his booty. And Konyukov treated him as if he were his property, as he would treat anything else he owned. Saburov noticed that the prisoner was a sergeant-major, by his insignia, and he asked him some questions in halting German. The German answered in a hoarse, choked voice.

"What does he say? What does he say?" Konyukov asked, interrupting the German two or three times.

"He's saying everything he should say," Saburov answered.

"He's hoarse . . . Listen, he's lost his voice all of a sudden," Konyukov observed with surprise. He was still panting himself from the fighting. "That's because I strangled him a little. Now he'll be without a voice for a couple of weeks, maybe a whole month," he added, giving the German an appraising look.

"How far did you get in the old army?" Saburov asked him.

"Sergeant," Konyukov said.

"Well, he's a sergeant, too," Saburov said.

"Well, imagine that," Konyukov muttered in disappointment, "and I thought he was a colonel."

"Why a colonel?"

"Look how many trimmings he's got . . . I thought he . . . well, I thought he might be a colonel so I'd better treat him carefully, but now look, damn it, if I'd known I would have gone right on squeezing him . . ."

Gradually, a kind of order was restored in the area which had been won. The prisoners, eleven men in all, were taken into a storeroom in the cellar. From Gordienko in the neighboring house a telephone line had been laid. Maslennikov, according to the couriers, should soon arrive with the remaining units of the battalion.

Machine gunners and tommy gunners took up their posts in the basement windows, after barricading them with stones, furniture, and whatever lay at hand. Beyond the stone wall, where Saburov indicated, the mortar gunners were hurriedly digging themselves trenches. There could be no thought of setting up a field kitchen here before the following night, so Saburov ordered the soldiers to take food from their emergency rations. An observer, perched high on the wall of the house just under the burned-out roof, reported the movements of the Germans along the nearest streets.

Gordienko reported by telephone that everything was in order in his section, that he had taken four prisoners, and that he was digging in, waiting for further commands. Saburov told him that the only command was to dig in as fast as he could.

When, finally, the telephone line was clear from Parfenov, Saburov picked up the receiver.

"Lieutenant Grigoriev at the phone," said a thin, young voice.

"Where's Parfenov?"

"He cannot come to the phone."

"Why can't he?"

"He is wounded."

Saburov hung up the phone. At this moment Maslennikov appeared, panting but happy.

"Look what I got, while I was coming," he said with enthusiasm, showing the edge of his trousers where there was a bullet hole. Saburov smiled.

"If that will always make you happy, then it's a safe bet you're going to be cheerful around here. As far as I can see, you'll have a lot of chances to mend your uniform here in Stalingrad. Well, did you bring up the men?"

"I brought them."

"Without losses, I hope?"

"Three wounded."

"Well, that's nothing . . . As for me, my friend, I've got twenty-one killed," he said quietly. "Stay here a minute, I'll be right back."

Taking Petya with him, Saburov went down the corridor to the right, squeezed through a breach in the wall, and taking cover behind a few puny saplings, ran over to the neighboring house. The Germans, apparently, did not notice them at first, and only a few random bullets whistled over his head.

He found Parfenov in a room where Lieutenant Grigoriev was sitting at the telephone. Parfenov lay on the floor. Under his head there had been placed two knapsacks, his own and someone else's. He was bleeding badly. A big shell fragment had torn his stomach, and when Saburov came in Parfenov only looked at him with an understanding and sorry expression on his face, and said nothing.

Saburov felt sorry for Parfenov, as one always feels especially sorry for people who fall in their first fighting. As far as Saburov knew, Parfenov had been a political worker in the army on the western front from the begininng of the war. He was a short, thin man with a simple face, kind, brown eyes, and not the slightest knowledge of how to arrange things, give commands, shout, order anyone around. Now he was behaving so bravely and quietly, so simply, not complaining, not saying a word, just dying, that Saburov felt an urge to come closer to him and to say something as nice as possible. He looked at the terrifying open wound, which had not yet been bandaged, and he thought that if Parfenov did not have the strength to lift his head from his improvised pillow to look at his own wound, it would be all for the best. Saburov leaned over towards him, squatting on his heels, and looked closely into his face. Then he straightened the wounded man's moist and tangled hair, and said:

"Well, how's it going, how do you feel, Parfenich?"

Parfenov, it was clear, was afraid to talk, because then he would have to unclench his teeth, and once he opened them he would yell out with pain. So he did not answer, but only opened and closed his eyes again, as if to say:

"It's nothing."

Saburov saw that he was dying. He half thought and half imagined with complete clarity how this little man had run, probably in front of all the others, just a little while before, without crying and without saying a word. Not probably, but beyond any doubt, he had been running at the Germans, without even stooping. He probably had not wanted to crouch, since he was so short anyway.

"It'll be all right, Parfenich, it'll be all right." Saburov repeated the stupid but friendly words, and bending over still lower, kissed Parfenov on his closely pressed lips.

FIVE

AT dawn, after a two-hour silence, there began a battle which was not to stop for four days and nights. It began with bombing, during which Saburov was slightly wounded for the fifth time since the war began. The bombing was long and merciless. Together with Junkers-88's, Junkers-87's bombed the position of the battalion; these were the dive-bombers with screaming bombs about which so much was said during the German conquest of France. In actual fact, there were no screaming bombs. It was simply that special appliances had been attached to the wings of the plane which gave out a terrifying sound when the planes were diving. This was no very ingenious invention, but simply an adaptation of the noisemakers often attached to children's kites. Neither Saburov, who had already gone through bombardment by screaming airplanes, nor the majority of the soldiers who were hearing this noise for the first time, were very frightened by these machines.

"Let them howl," they said, lifting their heads from the ground and looking upwards, "let them howl . . ."

To Saburov's surprise Konyukov, who had fought so well during the night, quite simply turned coward during the

46

bombardment and lay flat on the ground as if he were killed, without raising his head.

"Konyukov," shouted Saburov, coming up to him. "Konyukov."

Konyukov lifted his head warily, saw the captain, and then suddenly jumped up, grabbed him by the shoulder, and pulled him down.

"Lie down," he cried in an unnatural voice.

Saburov wrenched the hand loose from his shoulder with difficulty and sat down beside him.

"What do you mean—lie down?"

"Lie down," Konyukov said again, trying to drag him to the ground.

Saburov realized that only ingrained discipline and the soldier's habit of guarding his superior officer could make the frightened Konyukov jump up from the ground and try to force him to lie down by his side.

"Does it scare you?" Saburov asked quietly and understandingly, and Konyukov answered, just as simply and frankly:

"Ah, this is frightening. This is real bad luck . . ."

"Are you going to lie here like this all the time?"

"As you order, Comrade Captain."

"Well, all right then, my order is . . . go on and lie down, get used to it. Only why lose all the time? When they bomb, lie down; when they fly away, stand up again."

"It's really frightening, Comrade Captain. Don't think I won't take it, but it is frightening, it scares me stiff."

This very frankness convinced Saburov that Konyukov could actually take it, and grow used to it. Four years of the first war against the Germans, with all its fighting, all its climbing over twelve rows of barbed wire, all that had been one thing, but this bombing which he was experiencing for the

47

first time in his life was something quite different. He would just have to get used to it.

Before noon, Babchenko called him on the telephone.

"I can't come to you," he said, "I'm going over to another sector. Probably the boss will be coming along to you, so watch out . . ." and he hung up the phone.

The boss in the division was Protsenko. "Watch out" meant that Saburov should try his best not to let the boss go to the most dangerous places where he would want to go.

Protsenko soon walked in with his adjutant and a tommy gunner. After Saburov had reported to him, he asked, as was his custom: "How's your health, Alexei Ivanovich?" and held out his left hand. After his wound, his right hand would not work, and he kept moving his fingers while he talked, trying to restore circulation and to make up for the massage treatments prescribed for him by the doctors.

"Good, good," he said, walking around and looking appraisingly at the ceiling. "Fritz"—he always said Fritz with a marked Ukrainian accent—"would need five hundred kilograms; he'll have to waste at least that much if he really doesn't like you. And if he doesn't want to waste the five hundred, then you'll be all right."

He wandered with Saburov around the machine-gun emplacements, then walked with him up to the stone wall behind which the mortar squads had settled down in trenches they had dug for themselves. He looked critically at the shallow, carelessly dug ditches, and talking off into the distance as if he did not notice the mortar gunners who were there, he said:

"What wonderful people Russians are! What do you think, Alexei Ivanovich, who is killing us in this war? You'll say to me: it's the Germans. And I'll agree with you: it's the Germans. Out of every three men we lose, two are killed by Germans, but the third is killed by laziness."

He turned to the soldiers and suddenly asked the sergeant

48

standing near him: "Do you know about the African bird, the ostrich?"

"Yes."

"Why are you like an ostrich, do you know? You don't know? Because you also try to hide yourself by hiding your head, but you leave your buttocks out in the open and think that you're hidden. Lie down!" Protsenko suddenly shouted out in a rough voice.

"What's that?" the sergeant asked, not understanding.

"Lie down. Look—a shell. Lie down in your trench while you're still alive."

The sergeant threw himself in one jump into his little trench, and as Protsenko had predicted, he could not find room in it.

"So, you see," Protsenko said, "your head, it's true, is all right, but they could have shot your rump off. It's as good as shot off now. Stand up," he shouted again, roughly.

The sergeant stood up, smiling in an embarrassed way.

"Give your orders," Protsenko said to Saburov, and turning around, walked on farther. Saburov hung back, ordered the men to dig the trenches deeper, and then ran to catch up with Protsenko.

At the stone wall were lying two machine gunners. They had tried to get a maximum of cover behind the wall, and as it turned out, had placed themselves so close behind it that the muzzle of their machine-gun pointed almost straight at the sky. Protsenko came up to them, lay down by the machine-gun, checked its sights, and then stood up, brushing the brick dust from his knees.

"You a hunter?" he asked an elderly, pock-marked sergeant who was in charge of the gun.

"Yes, once in a while, Comrade Colonel," the sergeant answered, fully in a mood for a cordial little talk with a superior officer.

49

"Yes, I see you're a hunter," said Protsenko. "You're all set to shoot a duck, with your machine-gun pointed straight up like that . . . You've done it well, you'll get them in full flight. But it's too bad that the Germans walk mostly along the ground; except for that, I've got to admit you've set yourself up wonderfully."

He turned and walked on with the same unhurried manner. The soldier in charge of the gun looked after him in confusion and then turned angrily on the soldier with him.

"Didn't I tell you where the muzzle was pointing, into the sky? Why did you set the machine-gun that way?"

"Yes, but you did it, too," the other tried to justify himself. "I did just what you . . ."

"Never mind what I said. It's your job, as my assistant, to pick out the spot with me."

Saburov did not hear the end of their dispute. Protsenko had walked on, moving the fingers of his wounded hand as if he were beating time to a tune in his head. Without turning around to Saburov, he talked into the distance, which was one of the signs that he was in an ugly mood.

"A divisional commander has to make it clear how a machine-gun should be pointed, into the sky or into the ground. That's a fine thing. It's for that they taught me at the General Staff Academy, I suppose. And when will you ever learn to blush?" He suddenly yelled at Saburov, turning quickly on him. "How can I teach you to blush?"

Saburov remained silent. The colonel was right, and even if regulations had permitted it, there was nothing for him to say.

"When divisional commanders don't have to check up on how machine-guns are pointed, and when you learn how to blush, then we'll win the war. Until then, we haven't a chance— you might as well know it."

They had only just managed to return to the basement

command post when the Germans began with artillery and bombing to prepare for an attack.

"In general, you've dug yourself in here all right, you've dug yourself in so that you can hang on," Protsenko said, cocking his head sidewise as he listened to the explosions.

"You'll hang on all right, but you've got to teach the men . . . Day and night you've got to teach them. Because, if you don't train a soldier today, then tomorrow he'll get himself killed. And not simply killed. Getting killed, after all—that's what war is for, but to be killed stupidly and cheaply, that's what's sad. Where's your observation post?"

"On the fourth floor, under the roof."

"Well, climb up there, and see what's happening. Meanwhile, tell them to give me something to eat."

As he went out, Saburov whispered to Petya to feed the colonel. He climbed up to the fourth floor. From there, through a wide, three-sectioned, French window leading onto a burned-out balcony, he could see almost everything going on in front of them. Along the neighboring street, from house to house, from fence to fence, Germans were running. Shells were throwing up pillars of dirt in front of the apartment house itself. Some of them were falling with a rumble against the walls of the building, and then the whole house shivered, as if an enormous wave had rocked it.

Saburov noticed that the heavier part of the German fire was directed against the house on the right where Maslennikov had replaced Parfenov in command. Saburov ran down the staircase to the basement and telephoned first Maslennikov and then Gordienko, warning them of the German preparations for an attack. Both answered that they had spotted the same thing and were ready for a fight.

Protsenko, who did not like to mix into the arrangements of his subordinates except in cases of extreme necessity, sat in the cellar and quietly ate a hard rye biscuit with a piece of dry

51

sausage on it. When the German attack finally began, before the racket made by the mortars had stopped, Protsenko went up to the observation post with Saburov, despite the latter's protests. They stood there together about an hour.

Saburov was nervous. He wanted to get Protsenko somewhere down below. When a heavy shell passed through the wall and exploded in the next room, showering little pieces of brick and plaster through a breach in the wall, he grabbed the colonel by the arm and tried to drag him below almost by force. But Protsenko freed his arm, looked at Saburov, and instead of the reprimand to be expected from a superior officer in such a situation, said only: "How long have we fought together? Two years? Too long, anyway, for you to pull me by the arm . . ." and considering the subject closed, he took off his cap and began carefully to brush the plaster dust from it with his fingers.

When the Germans had fallen back after a first unsuccessful attack, and Saburov and Protsenko had begun to descend from the observation post, a delayed shell hit the staircase itself on the floor below them. An entire section of the stairs was completely blown out by the explosion, and they had to get down by hanging onto the beams and the remains of the balustrade.

"Now do you see why you oughtn't to hurry your commanding officer?" Protsenko said. "If we had hurried, you'd have had me right under that one. What did Babchenko tell you: 'the boss is coming, take care of him . . .' "—suddenly he imitated Babchenko's voice in a funny way—"and yet you would have had me directly under a shell that time. You see what happens . . ."

Protsenko left during an hour of relative lull between the first and second German attacks.

"All right, take care of yourself," he said to Saburov as he left. He added confidentially: "You know, when I've learned how to fight really well, then I'm going to stop coming to the battalions. Let the regimental commanders come, and I'll go only to the regimental headquarters . . . But I'll look in on you from time to time just for old times' sake. Those who fought together at Voronezh are just like people who've been to a christening together. I'll come to see you like an old gossip."

He turned around and walked away, limping a little as always, and strumming with his fingers on the air.

Before evening the Germans attacked again but were driven off. When it began to get dark, Petya brought Saburov a pan of boiled potatoes.

"Where did you get these?" Saburov asked in surprise.

"Here, right around the corner," Petya said.

"But where exactly?"

"Right here, not far away," Petya repeated evasively.

Saburov, who was hungry and had no time for explanations anyway, began to fill his face with potatoes. Petya stood beside him in the pose of an anxious mother.

"Where did you really get them?" Saburov asked with his mouth full of potatoes.

On Petya's face could be seen an inner conflict. On the one hand, he had to answer the question; on the other hand, he wanted to keep secret from the captain his newly-discovered base of supplies. Saburov looked at his stony face and smiled.

Petya was distinguished by courage, thoughtfulness, and a happy disposition—the three chief qualities to be desired in an orderly. Before the war he had worked as supply agent in a Moscow factory. He had fallen in love with this work during the first Five-Year-Plan. To secure, God-knows-how and God-knows-where, something no one else could get, had a special charm for him. He could get plywood boards from Yalta, grapes from Kostroma, building lumber from Kara-Kum. He accomplished the impossible, and it delighted him. He looked for nothing for himself and never profited personally, but to get materials needed by the factory where he worked, he was ready for anything, from bribery to housebreaking. His competitors hated him; his chiefs bowed before him. In the war, when he became Saburov's orderly, he showed great bravery in the face of the enemy, but an even more incredible bravery in the face of all manner of difficulties with army supplies. When there was nothing to eat in the battalion, Saburov would send Petya out to look for food and he would always find something. When there was nothing to smoke, Petya would find tobacco. When there was nothing to drink, Petya could always come up with at least a little keg of vodka so quickly that Saburov sometimes suspected him of holding a secret emergency reserve. Petya had only one failing: although he never did anything really illegal, he still loved to conceal his triumphs under a smoke screen of secrecy. He was always bitterly disappointed when Saburov or anyone else cross-examined him about his methods.

"Come on, where did you get them?" Saburov repeated. Petya, realizing that he could not get out of it, decided to confess.

"Here," he said, "there's a little house in the courtyard, and under the little house there's a cellar, and in that cellar there's a woman . . ."

"What kind of a woman?" Saburov raised his eyebrows.

"A Stalingrad woman. She used to live in the little house. Her husband was killed. So she went down in the cellar with her three children and has been sitting there. She's got everything—potatoes, carrots, all kinds of vegetables, so as not to die from hunger. She's even got a goat in the cellar with her, only she says the goat has stopped giving milk on account of the darkness. I say to her: My commanding officer has a great respect for potatoes. Without a word, she boils a kettle of them and says: Whenever you need them, just ask for them, and she even gives me some lard. You didn't notice, by the way, but you

54

are eating potatoes with lard on them," Petya added with reproach in his voice.

Surprised that in the middle of these ruins there should suddenly be a woman with children, Saburov stood up quickly, put on his cap, and said to Petya: "Take me to her. Where is she?"

They walked down several corridors and ran, crouching low, across an open place to the house in the courtyard. There, between its shattered walls, Saburov saw something like a door propped up with stones and boards. They descended several steps, and entered a fairly large cellar, apparently enlarged during the fighting. A little stove was burning on a barrel in the corner, covered with boards. Near it a woman, who was not old but had a face worn old by suffering, sat on her heels and rocked a baby. Two little girls who looked as if they were eight and ten years old crouched next to her and looked at the two soldiers with big eyes filled with curiosity.

"How do you do?"

"How do you do," the woman answered.

"Why have you stayed here?" Saburov asked.

"Where else could I go?"

"But the Germans were here."

"We covered up everything on top so they couldn't see anything," the woman said quietly.

"You covered up everything . . . you might have been suffocated."

"It would have been all the same, once the Germans were here."

"It's too late today," Saburov said, "but tomorrow I'll think of some way to send you out of here."

"I'm not going, thanks."

"What do you mean, not going?"

"Just not going," she repeated stubbornly. "Where should I go?"

"To the other side, across the Volga."

"I'm not going. With them?" the woman pointed to the children. "Alone I would have gone, but with them I won't go. I'd get through all right alone, but they would die, they'd die across the Volga. They would die," the woman repeated.

"And here?"

"I don't know. I've brought everything we had down here. Maybe it will last for a month, maybe for two months, and by then, maybe, you'll drive the Germans out. But if we left here, they would die, I'm sure of it."

"Well, but if a bomb or a shell lands here, all of a sudden—have you thought about that?" Saburov asked. He was no longer trying to convince her, but he was still unable to accept the idea that here, right next to his soldiers, a woman was continuing to live with three children.

"What of it?" the woman said quietly. "If it falls, then it will get us all together, me and them—it will finish us all at once."

Saburov did not know what to say to her. There followed a long silence.

"If you want something cooked, I'll cook it. I've got lots of potatoes. Let him tell me when you need something." She pointed to Petya. "I can cook cabbage soup, too, only without any meat. Or I could kill the goat," she added after a pause. "If I kill him, then there'd be soup with meat."

She saw in Saburov's eyes that he had understood, and that he would no longer insist on her going. Her talking now about her cooking was not to persuade him to leave her there, but simply part of the deep desire of all old Russian women to take care of soldiers far from their homes. Look, she seemed to be thinking, just look at these soldiers. (She made no distinction of rank, not understanding it.) Look at them, unwashed, their clothes unmended, hungry. Some day—God knows when —they will go back to their homes. She must cook for them,

56

while they were here, even if only cabbage soup. And once it's cabbage soup, then why not kill the goat? What good was the goat now, anyway? It was all the same, you couldn't milk her.

Saburov walked out into the open air. Looking at the ruins around him he thought again, just as he had before at Eltonskaya: "Where have they driven us?" In front of him, as far westward as the eye could see, were only Germans. He looked around at his shattered apartment house, battered and riddled with bullets and shell fragments. "Still, here we are," he thought. And he realized now that there was no place for him to go outside this building.

The night went by with uninterrupted firing. At dawn the Germans mounted their third attack. They did not succeed in advancing directly towards the building which Saburov was occupying, but to the right of him and to the left they broke through into the edges of the square. At nine o'clock in the morning, he heard over the telephone the rough, complaining voice of Babchenko:

"Well, how goes it, are you holding out?"

"Holding out."

"Keep it up, hang on tight. I'm coming over to see you right away."

These words were the last he heard on the telephone. A minute later the communication line was broken, and although he liked neither Babchenko himself nor his querulous voice, he kept remembering these phrases during the three succeeding days and nights when he had no line of communication with anyone. They helped him to believe that he was not all alone, that there would be again, sometime, a telephone, and Babchenko, and the division, and everything that these things together meant.

All his communications had been severed. Babchenko, naturally, did not come. The Germans occupied the whole square behind him and the buildings around it, and Saburov found himself with his entire battalion in the situation which is called in war, no matter what the particular circumstances, by the one word "encircled." He had to sit where he was, keep the Germans off, and wait either until his own side could cut a path through to him and help him, or until his own last shells and bullets should be exhausted, and they would have to die. Although at intervals he was inclined to think that the second was sure to happen and that his ammunition would run out before help could come, he tried to suggest the exact reverse to everyone around him, both officers and soldiers. Since each one of them knew only how many bullets were in his own belt and how many shells in his own reserve, they thought that he, the captain, probably still had plenty in reserve. He alone knew that there was no reserve and would be none. This made it harder for him than for the others.

He taught his men to shoot to kill, only at sure targets. He took bullets away from most of the soldiers, giving them only to the best marksmen. To the others he gave hand grenades to be used against any Germans who might break directly into the building. This happened only twice in these three days, and both times they succeeded in throwing the Germans out. Along the walls in the courtyard, directly in front of the broken windows of the apartment house, dead Germans lay as they had fallen. No one dragged them away. There was no time, nor strength, nor desire.

On the third day a shell breached the wall and exploded in the basement where Saburov had established himself. Curiously, no one was killed. Petya had gone out, and Saburov, who had been lying down on his cot for a minute, simply crashed down with the cot from the blast. When he stood up he noticed that the whole wall above his head looked as if it were covered with blood stains. It was the bricks showing through the white plaster in hundreds of places.

He had to move to an apartment on the first floor which had

escaped destruction by some miracle, and where Petya had urged him to move two days before. The fact that the apartment had survived at all gave Petya a superstitious notion that maybe no shell would ever fall in it.

On the fourth day, when everything was dancing and shuddering under an artillery barrage, the woman walked quietly into the room and placed an earthen pot on the table.

"I boiled you some cabbage soup. Try it," she said.

"Thank you."

"If you like it, I'll bring you some more."

Saburov looked at her and said nothing. All this was strange, almost incredible—the dugout with three children, the woman herself, boiling cabbage soup. At the same time there was something fantastically reassuring about it. It made him remember an antitank gunner, taking up his gun and placing his cigarette on the earthen shelf of a trench, instead of dropping it and crushing it under his boot, in order to finish smoking it later after he had taken care of an advancing tank. There was something of this coolness in the woman, in the way she walked in.

"Thanks, thanks," Saburov repeated. Seeing that she continued to stand there quietly, and guessing suddenly what she was waiting for, he pulled his spoon out of the top of his boot and began to eat.

"It's wonderful soup," he said, "good, tasty soup. It's wonderful. But you'd better go, they're going to start firing again right away."

At night, under cover of the darkness, Maslennikov got through to Saburov, and the latter could hardly recognize him—he was so unshaved and so suddenly, strangely grownup. Looking at Maslennikov, Saburov thought that he, too, must have changed during these days. He was terribly tired, not so much from the constant feeling of danger as from the responsibility which lay on his shoulders. He did not know what was happening to the north or to the south. Judging by the cannon fire, fighting must be going on in a circle all around him. Of only one thing was he certain, in a hard sort of way: these three apartment houses with their shattered windows, their wrecked apartments, he, his soldiers, dead and living, the woman with her three children in the cellar—all these taken together were Russia, and he, Saburov, was defending it. If he were killed or should surrender, then this spot would cease to be Russia and would become German territory, and this he could not even imagine to himself.

During the entire fourth and last night of the encirclement, a desperate cannon duel sounded to his left and to his right. Apparently both German and Russian shells were landing in the courtyard and directly on the building. By morning the Soviet shells seemed more numerous than the German. Saburov at first could not believe, then did believe, again could not believe, and only at dawn finally realized that his side was actually breaking through to him.

A little after dawn, a few sweating, dirty, angry tommy gunners broke through into the yard of the house on the left. They had been chasing Germans, and at first they thought that Germans were here, too. It was hard, at first almost impossible, to hold them and keep them from running down the long corridors and through the basement of the buildings in search of Germans.

One of the first men Saburov saw and embraced was Babchenko, the same unlikable, rude, and quarrelsome—the same tired, unshaved, nice, and long-awaited Babchenko—with his rifle slung around his neck, and his arms and knees smeared with mud and lime.

"I told you on the telephone that I'd be coming," Babchenko almost yelled at him, trying to cover up as quickly as possible the excitement which seemed to him unusual and unbecoming in any conversation between an officer and his subordinate.

60

Still smiling in an awkward way, Babchenko crossed the room twice, then discarded his rifle and sat down at the table, leaning on it and at last giving his face its usual bored and dissatisfied expression. In his old familiar tone, he asked:

"How many losses?"

"Fifty-three killed, one hundred and forty-five wounded," Saburov answered.

"You don't take care of your men," Babchenko said. "You don't take care of them. You take bad care of them. Never mind, you held out well. Tell them to give me some water."

Saburov turned to Petya and asked for water, but when he turned back again it was clear that the lieutenant colonel did not need it. Leaning over the table and resting his head on the clip of the automatic rifle which stuck out awkwardly from under his arms, he had fallen sound asleep. Probably he had not slept through all these days, any more than Saburov. This occurred to Saburov and suddenly, thinking back over everything that had happened in these four days, he felt fatigue flow over him with bone-crushing force. In order not to fall on the table, like Babchenko, he stood up, leaned against the wall, and with difficulty pulled out of his pocket his big watch. It said 9:15. Just four days and seven hours had gone by since he had jumped from Petya's shoulders through the broken window, after throwing a grenade through it, and had come into this room.

SIX

ON top of these four days of fighting, four more days went by with surprising swiftness. They were filled with the shriek of dive-bombers, the dull, thudding sound of shells, and the dry machine-gun crackle of German counter-attacks. Only on the ninth day was there something resembling stillness.

Saburov lay down soon after darkness fell, but the telephone woke him after three hours' sleep. Babchenko, who did not like his subordinates to sleep when he was awake, had ordered the soldier on watch to wake Saburov.

He stood up from the cot and walked to the telephone.

"Were you asleep?" Babchenko said into the telephone in a faraway voice.

"Yes."

"Sleeping. Is everything in order?"

"Everything is in order," Saburov said, feeling that with every second of this maddening conversation sleep was running away from him in little drops.

"Have you taken measures against a possible night attack?"

"They've been taken."

"Well then, go and sleep."

And Babchenko hung up the telephone.

From the way Saburov sighed, Maslennikov, who had also awakened and was sitting on the bed across from him, could imagine pretty clearly the content of the conversation, and could guess that the captain felt even angrier than usual.

"The lieutenant colonel?" Maslennikov asked.

Saburov silently nodded and tried again to lie down and fall asleep, but as often happens during days of particular tiredness, sleep would not return. After lying still for several minutes, Saburov swung his bare feet onto the floor, lit a cigarette, and for the first time looked carefully around the room in which his battalion headquarters had been located for several days.

Saburov was not a man to ask many questions. It always seemed to him awkward and unnecessary to ask people about something until they wanted to talk themselves. By nature untalkative, he was still full of interest in things. Things were quiet, like himself, and it always seemed to him that in things, as in himself, much was buried that was unsaid and interesting.

On the oilcloth covering the table there were two freshly burned rings: one bigger, obviously from a frying pan, and the other smaller, from a coffee pot. Probably the owner of the apartment had sent his family away in advance, and during the last days had lived here an unaccustomed bachelor's life. Blast had broken the glass doors of the sideboard, and it had nothing to say about who had lived here because everything had been stripped from it. But on the writing table were many traces of the life of an entire family. There were needles with unfinished knitting, a pile of technical magazines, several dog-eared volumes of Chekhov, some old, slobbered-over, third-grade readers, and one neat, new package of fourth-grade school books. One child's Russian-language notebook caught Saburov's eye. With the professional curiosity of a man who once upon a time had studied to be a teacher, he began to turn over its pages. On the first page began an essay: "How We

Went to the Mill." "Yesterday we went to the mill. We saw how they make flour . . ." In one of the words, a letter had been crossed out, written differently, again crossed out, and written the way it should have been. "At first they bring the grain to the elevator, then from the elevator a truck takes it to the mill, then . . ."

Closing the notebook, Saburov remembered how he had watched an enormous burning elevator from the far bank of the Volga; maybe it was the same one he was now reading about in this school child's notebook.

Maslennikov was sitting opposite him and swinging his legs. He also reached for the pile of notebooks and slowly leafed through them. Suddenly he began to talk about his childhood. In conversations with Saburov, from their first acquaintance, he had returned to this subject several times, and now Saburov felt that Maslennikov did not want so much to tell him about his childhood as to try to tempt him to talk about his own past.

Saburov was a quiet man, not out of moroseness or on principle; he talked little simply because he was nearly always busy with work and because he liked to be left alone with his thoughts; also because when he found himself with company, he always preferred to listen to others, believing in the depth of his heart that he himself had done little so far and achieved almost nothing, and that the story of his life would have no interest for anyone else. So it was now—he preferred to listen to Maslennikov quietly, sometimes thinking about what he was saying, sometimes surrendering to his own thoughts, and all the time examining attentively and at leisure the things lying on the table.

The second child in the apartment, apparently, had been quite young. On the table lay several sheets of paper torn from a notebook and scrawled over with red and blue pencil marks. In the scrawls could be made out drawings of a crooked house, burning Fascist tanks, a Fascist airplane falling with a black

64

rail of smoke behind it, and over everything a small Soviet fighter plane drawn with the red pencil. This had been, he thought, from time out of mind, every child's picture of war: our side did all the shooting and the Fascists were always destroyed. Bitter as it was for him to remember the mistakes of the past, Saburov reflected that before the war too many adults had had a picture of war not very different from this.

The war . . . Recently, whenever he recalled his former life, he unconsciously reduced it all to this common denominator, and divided everything that had happened to him before the war into good and bad—not in the abstract, but in relation to the war. Some civilian habits and inclinations hampered him now that he was fighting, others helped him. There were more of the latter, as there should have been. People who had begun their independent lives in the years of the first Five-Year-Plan, as he had, had gone through such a rough school for living, had learned such discipline and self-control, that war itself, except for its constant possibility of death, could hardly break them with its daily hardships.

Saburov was a man of his own generation. Like nearly all persons of his age, he had begun to work as a boy and had been shifted from construction site to construction site. Several times he began to study and each time, first mobilized by the Komsomols and later by the Communist party, he had failed to complete his courses and gone off to work again. When his compulsory military service came up, he served for two years in the army and left it as a second lieutenant. He had gone back to his profession of building foreman in the construction industry, and had begun again to spend his days and nights in the cofferdams and on the scaffoldings of the Magnitogorsk steel plant.

The years of the first Five-Year-Plan had attracted him, as they did many others, by their fever of construction. Scrambling the cards completely, these years had drawn him away

65

from the work about which he had dreamed from childhood. But, again like many others, in the end he found within himself strength enough to turn down the work he was used to, his pay-check, and his normal life, and to exchange all of these, even though he was no longer a young boy, for a student's desk, a cot in a dormitory, and a one-hundred-ruble stipend.

One year before the war he had matriculated in history at Moscow University. On June 21, 1941, with a brilliance which surprised all who knew him, he passed his first university examinations. On the morning of the following day he had heard Molotov's broadcast announcing the Fascist invasion. There had happened what everyone had been waiting for but what everyone, deep inside himself, did not really believe would ever happen. The war had started. It was the war which, in a year and three months, would lead Saburov—a man who had once wanted to become a history teacher, now a man who had broken out of encirclement three times, been decorated twice, and five times slightly wounded, here—to Stalingrad. It had led him to this room which might at any minute remind him of peace, were it not that on the back of the plush couch, decorated with home-made embroidery, an automatic rifle hung slantwise over the corner.

It was long after midnight. Absent-mindedly listening to Maslennikov's tales about his life, and dreamily recalling at the same time his own past, Saburov slowly rolled a cigarette, placed it neatly in a holder, and lit it. Maslennikov finally grew silent. He was sitting directly across from Saburov. So they sat quietly, for perhaps five, perhaps ten minutes. Then Maslennikov again began to speak, this time about love. At first he told about his schoolboy enthusiasms, with the seriousness of a little boy. Then he talked about love in general. He finished by asking Saburov suddenly:

"And you, have you been in love?"

"What do you mean, in love?"

66

"In love, haven't you really ever been in love?"

"Love?" Saburov grew thoughtful, inhaled deeply, and closed his eyes. Love. Was it really true that there had never been any in his life . . . ?

He could remember two or three women who had passed casually through his life, just as casually as he had passed through theirs. In these relations, probably, they had been quits; he could remember no special disappointment and he had hurt no one. Maybe this wasn't good—who could tell? Maybe, rather than anything else, it had just turned out like this—easy and quits—not because he had not wanted love, but because he had wanted it too much, and both those with whom he had tried it and also the way it had worked were so unlike love, as he imagined it to himself, that he had never tried to pretend it was the real thing. These were thoughts which he kept to himself, and when Maslennikov, after a long silence, repeated again: "Haven't you really ever been in love?" he said: "I don't know. I guess I haven't been . . ."

He stood up from the couch and walked back and forth across the room. "No, it can't be true that I won't ever fall in love," he thought. "More likely, I just haven't yet, but it can't be true that I won't sometime."

Suddenly he recalled the words of the girl on the little steamer, about how she feared death most of all because she hadn't been in love, and how he shouldn't be afraid because he was already grown up and probably had experienced everything.

"No, not everything," he thought. "Not everything. My God, how much there is to live through, and how little of life I have seen. How stupid and impossible life must be for anyone who even for a minute thinks that he has lived through everything!"

Again he crossed the room, and walking straight up to Maslennikov, placed his hand on his shoulder.

"Listen, Misha," he said, not trying so much to answer him as to answer his own thoughts. "Listen, Misha. You and I must not die. We mustn't get killed, under any circumstances."

"Why?"

"I don't know. I know simply that we mustn't."

A soldier walked into the room and said, simply: "They are attacking." Saburov sat down on the couch and almost in one movement put on the cloth he wore around his feet and drew on his boots. Then he fell with another routine movement into the sleeves of his overcoat.

"Well, we never got a chance to sleep," he said to Maslennikov, tightening up his leather belt.

Maslennikov felt in the captain's words a sad, wholesome irony about all that had just been recalled with such emotion and that meant so little now in the face of those few words suddenly flowing over the edges of their lives: "They are attacking."

This September night was cold and dark in Stalingrad. Everything had grown confused in these two weeks during which fighting had been going on in the city itself. The front shifted so fantastically from block to block, and from building to building, that the Germans were afraid to bomb at night for fear of hitting their own men. Only our little U-2 "jewelers," as they were called, could be ordered to destroy the left wing of a building while our own soldiers were occupying its right wing. They did their jeweler's work at night, and it was a local joke to say that they could stand at anchor all night long over the Germans and drop their little bombs one by one.*

Near the operetta theater, in the gallery of which two weeks ago our army headquarters had been located, were now the

* Originally a light observation plane, the U-2 was used by Russian pilots during the first years of the war for tactical bombing in support of ground troops.

68

eadquarters of German regiments. Half of Mamai Kurgan, here Matveyev had drunk his tea under the linden trees nine ays before, was also occupied by the Germans. Fighting was oing on in the railroad station, in the shops of the Red Octoer and the Stalingrad Tractor Factories, and in the buildings f the settlement built a long time ago by the French concesion "New France." In the city everything was crowded close ogether now. Distances came to be measured in hundreds of eters, and sometimes in tens of meters, and even the headuarters of German divisions, contrary to their usual custom, ere now located within a few kilometers of the front line, in he basement floors of buildings in the western sections of the ity. At night German staff cars tore through the empty, urned-out city streets which still smelled heavy and bitter ith the exhaust fumes of tanks.

In the center of the city and in its eastern districts, firing ent on without pause all night long. In the western districts, erman patrols stamped their feet loudly on the street corners, eeling both their triumph and an uneasy fear of this strange, isfigured, silent city.

At just about the same moment that Saburov and Maslenikov were rushing out of their quarters at word that an attack ad started, a tall man, about thirty years old, in the uniform f a Red Army sergeant, was sitting in a basement room two ilometers away on Vladimir Street. This was the headquarters f a German division. It was a big room, furnished with soft hairs assembled from every floor of the building. The staff fficer on duty was a German major, thin, tired, and in an evil ood from lack of sleep.

"Who is in command of your division?"

"Colonel Protsenko."

"Who's in command of your regiment?"

"Lieutenant Colonel Babchenko."

"Who's in command of your battalion?"

"Captain Saburov."

The German major looked through his square glasses at a piece of paper in front of him. "Everything you say is true, but in addition you allege . . ."

"I don't allege, it's really so."

"Your proof?"

"I assume you know that I am not supposed to carry any proof," the man said in a quiet voice. "I'm not allowed to." He was silent for a few seconds, then he added: "Camp No. 3, in Krakow, the special school. The leader of our group was Major Hanke. My number was thirty-four. If these details don't satisfy you . . ."

"For the time being, they are satisfactory," the major said. "How did you get that?" He pointed to the medal, "For Bravery," on the sergeant's chest.

"Because I didn't study for nothing."

"Your name is Vassiliev?"

"Yes."

"You're on a scouting trip right now?"

"Yes."

"How much time have you got?"

"Sunrise is at six. That means I have five hours, provided you give me a gun and somebody's documents, best of all an officer's, so I can go back and show that my trip was successful."

"Well, what kind of information have you brought?"

Vassiliev looked at his big, round wrist watch. "Since there's not much time," he said, "and since you'll make me repeat whatever I say to the colonel, why don't you let me report to him right away?"

The major looked at him over his glasses. "All right," he said, and he rose and went out.

Vassiliev sat where he was; behind him sat a German soldier with his rifle in his hands. Vassiliev said nothing, but he drummed his fingers on the top of the table. He knew what was coming. They would take him to the colonel, they would be suspicious of him at first, then he would prove he was what he said he was and they would believe him, listen to what he had to say, and give him some new assignment. They would fire at him when he left, for appearances, and he would probably be fired at when he got back, if someone took him for a German. And if he were not hit, he would get back to the quarters of that lanky simpleton, Saburov, and he would have three or four days of relative quiet until they sent him out on another scouting expedition. Then when he showed up here again, everything would be repeated all over, just as it had been seven or eight times already in this war. In a word, his profession did not guarantee him a quiet life. The hopes he had had a year before in the special school at Krakow had fulfilled themselves only in one respect: he was still alive. But it was like some crazy lottery in which, sooner or later, you were pretty sure to draw your own death. The only thought that comforted him was that he had known danger before at Dnepropetrovsk, at Rostov, at Voronezh, and now he was finding it at Stalingrad—it must be almost the end of the war.

He had only to hold on until the end, and the end could not be far off now. It would be good if he could manage tonight the secret meeting he had been thinking about for a long time, and which had made him volunteer for this scouting expedition before he absolutely had to. If this could be worked out, then everything would be fine, better than fine.

The major came back, sat on the chair opposite Vassiliev and said: "In two minutes, we'll go in."

"I have a request to make, Major," Vassiliev said. "I wish you would support it, with the colonel."

"What is it?"

"Six kilometers from here, in the village of Gorodisha, my father used to live. I haven't seen him for a long time. Maybe

71

he isn't there any longer, but maybe he is. It's only fifteen minutes in a car, fifteen there and fifteen back, and if I find him, half an hour with him."

"Who is your father?"

"He's the priest of the village church."

"I don't know," the major said, "I don't know. Ask the colonel, maybe he'll allow it."

The major was hurt that this Russian, obviously an experienced spy but still a Russian, had tricked him into letting him make his report straight to the colonel. Now it was clear that this saving of time was necessary only because he wanted to see his father. "Let's go," the major said drily.

Vassiliev stood up and walked to the door, followed by the heavy stamp of the German with the rifle.

An hour later a tall, fastidious lieutenant, adjutant to the colonel, was sitting next to the chauffeur in the front seat of a little Opel car, with Vassiliev and a soldier squeezed into the back seat. With its headlights dimmed but still shining, the car moved down the dark street. For several minutes they drove through the destroyed buildings on the western outskirts of the city, then they turned onto a paved highway, then onto a rutted, village road, and in twenty minutes they were driving down the long village street of Gorodisha. As often happens in places where heavy fighting has gone on, some of the houses were intact, and others were in ruins.

The automobile stopped at the skeleton of the church. Next to it stood a small, three-windowed, brick house, or rather all that was left of it. Part of the house had disappeared. The roof over this part hung down to the ground.

"Here?" the lieutenant asked.

"Here," Vassiliev answered with a little nervousness in his voice. He got out of the car, following the lieutenant. Yes, this was the house where he had been born and where he had grown up.

The German walked through a door in the part of the house which was still standing, and Vassiliev followed him. Soldiers were lying on the floor of the only room that was left. The lieutenant snapped on his flashlight, but the soldiers were so exhausted and sleeping so hard that no one moved. With the toe of his boot, the officer roused a corporal sleeping next to the door. The corporal leaped to his feet, saluted, and stood at attention, looking at the lieutenant with eyes still drowned in sleep. The lieutenant asked the corporal several questions; Vassiliev, who knew a little German, could guess their meaning.

"Your father isn't here," the lieutenant said to Vassiliev. "They just got here yesterday. They don't know who or what was here before them. There's no one in the house except our soldiers."

He asked the corporal another question and then turned again to Vassiliev. "He says there's only some old madman, living in the courtyard, or in the cellar. Maybe he's your father?"

Vassiliev shrugged his shoulders.

"Do you want to talk to him?" the German asked.

"Yes," Vassiliev said. He looked around the room again. Here used to be the table at which they ate, there the cupboard with his father's books, here the couch and the low armchair in which his father used to doze in the evenings. But not a single thing was left in the room. Soldiers had been coming and going, spending the night in the house, and only a pile of rubbish in a corner showed that this had once been a place where people lived.

The lieutenant sat on a bench, smoking a cigarette and leaning against the wall. "Go out with him," he said in German to the corporal, and he pointed to Vassiliev. "Show him the old man. Don't go away from them while they're talking. And don't stay long—five minutes, no longer."

He should have gone, instead of the corporal, because he

73

knew Russian, but he felt lazy. He wanted to smoke, and the wind was blowing hard outside. "No more than five minutes," he repeated. "Go on."

Vassiliev walked out behind the corporal. They walked around the house towards the end which had been demolished. The corporal turned on his flashlight several times at random, then stopped and stamped with his heel on a crackling sheet of metal. It looked as if it were tin lying on the ground, but when the corporal stamped on it, it rose in the air and the gray head of an old man appeared from under it.

"Come here," the corporal said.

The old man came out of his hole, rattling the tin sheet. Blinking and screwing up his teary old eyes, he stood full in the beam of the flashlight. Vassiliev looked at him with amazement. He recognized him as Timofei, the sexton of his father's church. It was Timofei, beyond any doubt; that was his long beard, and that was his deep-wrinkled face. But at the same time it was hard for Vassiliev to believe that this creature standing two steps away from him was really Timofei. The old man was all stooped over, as if someone had broken his spine with a stick; his face had become like a baked apple, his beard was matted like felt, his eyes were red and burning, and his tangled hair was standing straight up on his head.

"Timofei," Vassiliev said.

The old man said nothing.

"Timofei," Vassiliev repeated, and he walked up close to him.

The German, who was bored, looked at his watch, switched off his flashlight, and put his hands in his pockets. He began to walk around, without hurrying but making it clear by his even pace that he would not give them a minute extra for talking.

"Timofei," Vassiliev said a third time, and he put his hand on the old man's shoulder.

74

"Who would you be?" the old man asked.

"I'm the son of Father Alexei, Ivan Alexeievich," Vassiliev said. "What's the matter, have you forgotten me? Come on, wake up." He shook the old man by the shoulder, hard and almost angrily. "Where's my father? Where's my mother? Where are they?" He had now come so close to the old man that he could see every detail of his face, the deep wrinkles, the toothless gums, the eyes filled with tears.

At Vassiliev's last words, something stirred in the old man, and for the first time Vassiliev saw a human expression in his eyes.

"But who are you?" the old man asked in a low voice. "Who are you?" It was as if he had not heard what Vassiliev had just told him.

"I'm Ivan Alexeievich," Vassiliev repeated angrily. "Ivan Alexeievich, don't you remember? Where's my father?"

The old man leaned over to Vassiliev, breathing a smell of rotting teeth in his face, and whispered in his ear: "He passed away. And your mother passed away."

Then he turned his head towards the German, cocked it as if he were listening, and suddenly broke out in a crazy staccato laugh. Vassiliev shuddered. The old man continued to laugh until it turned to coughing. Trying to catch his breath, he clutched at his chest and he coughed for a long time. Then he leaned towards Vassiliev again and in the same almost inaudible whisper said into his ear: "They're killed."

He listened again to the footsteps of the German, and giggled a little.

"All my folks are killed," he added, still in a whisper. "I'm the only one left."

"Where's my father?" Vassiliev asked again, not having understood the old man's terrifying words.

The old man laughed again, listened in the German's direction, and noticed that the corporal had wandered fairly far from them. This time he clutched Vassiliev's shirt, pulled himself up to him and whispered, quickly: "They dropped a bomb on the house. They killed the old man. And they killed your old woman, too. And they killed all my people." The old man lifted his head and listened; the guard was still some distance away. "And what are you doing here?" he whispered.

But Vassiliev said nothing. At first, with the old man mixing his words with senseless laughter, he had not been able to believe what he had heard. But now, as he listened to this quiet, even whisper, he realized suddenly that the old man had not lost his mind but was pretending to have lost it when there were Germans around. So what he had just heard whispered in his ear must be serious and the truth.

"When did it happen?" Vassiliev asked.

"A week ago Sunday," the old man said, and again he began to giggle.

Vassiliev covered his face with his hands. For a second, he thought he was going to cry. But he did not cry. He rubbed his hands across his face, as if he were wiping away a bad dream. The old man whispered something more, but he was not listening. Of course, the Germans had bombed Gorodisha; he had known this before. He looked towards the house, two-thirds of which was now in ruins; he saw beams and bricks scattered around his feet, and suddenly he thought that his mother and father had probably not even been buried. They were lying somewhere here, under the ruins. He felt a quick pang of sorrow; instinctively he clenched his hands into fists. He had not seen them for six years, not since he had been sent away to the concentration camp, and he had long ago given up missing them or thinking of their faces. But now, when he suddenly imagined them lying here, under these ruins, he was filled with an overpowering desire to see them. For a moment he thought of refusing to go away from here; he would fling himself to the ground and start digging in the bricks with his bare hands.

"The sons of bitches," he whispered, and for the first time in a long while he thought of the Germans with hatred. "Ah, what swine!" For a moment he wanted to grab the corporal by the legs, lift him in the air and beat his head against the bricks. "Why did they do this?" he thought. "Why did they do all this?"

"What are you doing, Ivan Alexeievich, working for them?" the old man asked.

"Yes," Vassiliev answered absent-mindedly, thinking about his parents.

"For the Germans, yes?" the old man whispered.

"Yes, yes," Vassiliev answered, just as distractedly. "What do you mean, for them?" he added quickly, when he realized what he had said. "What do you mean, for them? I'm a prisoner, they captured me."

"You're a prisoner of war, then?" the old man said. He heard the German's steps, and began to laugh his crazy laugh again.

"A prisoner of war," Vassiliev said. "Yes, they captured me," he repeated. Now he could tell his standard falsehood in a normal tone of voice. "They take me around, drag me places, try to ask me all sorts of questions, where I came from, what I did."

The German had now come up close to them. Vassiliev thought again it would be nice to beat his head against the bricks, but this time not as something he might actually try to do, but quite simply, as something that would be pleasant. He stared through the dark at the ruins of the house and tried to compose his mind. "Well, they're killed," he said to himself. "After all, that's what war is. And in the final analysis, the Germans aren't to blame for it, but those who sent me to the concentration camp." And although these thoughts did not convince even him, everything he had been doing during the last year made it impossible for him to think in any other way.

He swore out loud, long and ugly oaths, and if you had asked him whom he was swearing at—those he was working for or those he was betraying—he might not have been able to answer. He was swearing at everything, at the sky and at the earth, at people, at this German pacing around them, at the old man, and most of all at his own hard and dirty life.

"It's time," the German said, flashing on his light and walking up to Vassiliev.

The old man was laughing again and more loudly. It was coming out of him now as an insane gurgle of laughter.

"Maybe he's not altogether mad," Vassiliev thought, "but he must be a little touched in the head."

"Well, all right then, good-by," he said, looking once more closely into the old man's face. The old man did not move. His face was dancing with laughter.

"Yes, he must be cracked," Vassiliev thought as he turned to follow the German. When they were ten paces away, the old man suddenly stopped laughing. He stood up, thrust his head forward, and for a long time quietly watched the two backs disappear into the darkness—the back of the German, and the broad, slightly round-shouldered back of the priest's son, Vassiliev.

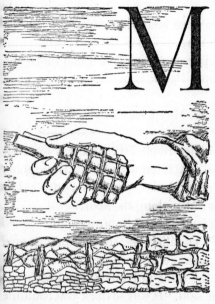

SEVEN

MORNING was already drawing near. Having returned to his headquarters after he had found out that the news of a German attack was for once a false alarm, Saburov did not lie down. It was five o'clock, the quietest hour of the day. Saburov walked over to the curtain which served as door into the corridor. He wanted to call Petya to fix him something to eat. Pulling the curtain aside, he stopped. Petya was sitting on the floor of the next room with the soldier on guard and two dispatch riders and they were talking.

"You ask me when the war will be over," Petya said in the kindly but patronizing tone of voice of a man with important knowledge which he usually used with other soldiers. "How should I tell you? I don't know when it will end. When we beat the Germans, then it will be over, but when we'll beat them—I don't know . . ."

"Ah, it's a long way we've got to drive them back . . ." a young messenger said, blowing out smoke in rings and looking at the ceiling. "A long way," he added. It sounded like an expression of full confidence that it would work out just that way, and it was obvious that he was bothered only by the distance to the frontier.

79

Not wanting the soldiers to know that he had overheard their conversation, Saburov quietly dropped the curtain, went back, sat at the table, and yelled loudly for Petya. He came to the door at once.

"How about dreaming up some kind of breakfast?"

"That I can do," said Petya, and soon beyond the curtain could be heard the rattle of pans and tin cans. Then there was the sound of heavy footsteps. Petya came back to the door again.

"The scouts have come back. May I let them in?"

"Let them come in."

Vassiliev walked into the boiler-room. His tunic was smeared with mud and brick dust and spattered with blood. Besides his own tommy-gun, hanging around his neck, he was dragging a German tommy-gun by its strap along the floor.

"It looks as if you'd been successful," Saburov said.

"Yes, I had good luck." Vassiliev leaned the tommy-gun against the wall, pulled a package of documents from inside his tunic, and put them on the table in front of Saburov.

"They're a little torn," he said. "It was so dark you couldn't see a thing, Comrade Captain."

"Where's Panasyuk?" Saburov asked.

"He's gone. The Germans killed him while we were crawling along."

"Where?"

"On the other side, between their trenches." Vassiliev edged the documents closer to Saburov. "But I killed one in exchange. Quietly, too," he added, and he pulled a flat bayonet halfway out of his boot top. It was spotted with blood.

"Sit down," Saburov said, "take it easy," and he picked up the documents.

Vassiliev sat down on the edge of the couch and began to look around the room. It was this room he had described today in detail to the Germans. By tomorrow, they would be taking

80

measures to leave no stone standing where this room now was. He looked at Saburov and thought with regret that the Germans would be unlikely to get him here. When the shells landed, he would probably be up in the front line.

Saburov was examining the documents. They were the papers of a Corporal Hans Shpinau—several letters and a few deckle-edged photographs. There was a little house, a woman with a baby, several soldiers on a spree, the little house again, the same woman, some other soldiers on a drinking bout. It seemed to Saburov that he had seen all these before, dozens and dozens of times.

"Yes, it checks," Saburov said to Maslennikov. "It's the 134th Infantry. We'll have to pass these on to the division where they can really take them apart. There may be something interesting in the letters."

"But about Panasyuk," he went on, looking up from the documents. "He was a good soldier. How did it happen to him, Vassiliev?"

"A tommy-gun," Vassiliev said, "in the back. It cut him down. It was after I had got the German."

"How far had you gone? Come over here and show me."

Vassiliev walked over to the table where Saburov was studying his map, on which the street occupied by the Germans moved at right angles from the red-pencil line which marked the front.

"Here," Vassiliev pointed with his finger. "We crawled through these ruins, and then across that ravine, and then behind their trenches, about there. I got the papers from a German there; he was standing guard. Then when we were crawling back, they killed Panasyuk."

"Yes, he had bad luck," Saburov said. "Well, all right, you can go. You did a good job."

"If you need something more, Comrade Captain, send me again," Vassiliev said.

"Good. I will. Go and rest."

"Shall I leave the gun here?" Vassiliev pointed to the German weapon leaning against the wall.

"That's fine. Leave it. Go and take it easy."

Vassiliev walked out. Saburov bent over the map and marked with little dots the route Vassiliev had followed.

"You know," he said to Maslennikov, "this means they're not setting any special guard there. Maybe we could play them a dirty trick. I'm sorry for Panasyuk, but everything else is fine. I thought it would be possible to crawl through there."

He stood up and walked back and forth across the cellar. Panasyuk's death could not have been helped, any more than a lot of others, yesterday and tomorrow, but Panasyuk was one of those who had fought with him near Voronezh. It was tough that he had to get it here, on his first scouting job.

"That Vassiliev had courage," Maslennikov said.

"Yes, it looks that way," Saburov answered casually. Somehow, he had not liked it when Vassiliev had pulled out his bayonet. But, he thought, that didn't matter. What mattered was that the reconnaissance had been a success, and that the Germans were obviously careless about setting guards even here, in spite of their reputation for painstaking vigilance.

"How about our wounded, have they all been taken back?" Saburov asked Maslennikov.

"There were only eighteen left last night," Maslennikov answered. "This bombing costs us plenty. If it's not splinters, it's stones; if it's not stones, then it's broken glass."

"Yes, it would be better in an open field," Saburov agreed.

He frowned, and on his face there came the evil look he had when he thought about something he had known a long time but still did not like to think about.

"You know, by the way, there was a defense line built around Stalingrad," he said.

"I know, someone told me . . ."

"About fifteen kilometers from the city they dug ditches, and trenches, and strong points, and covered them all over with concrete. Thousands of people, they say, worked day and night. But we never got a chance to fight in them."

"Why not?"

"If you only knew, Misha," Saburov said thoughtfully, "how many times in a year of war I've seen trenches and ditches dug for nothing. Millions of cubic meters of dirt have been dug up from the frontier all the way to here, and all for nothing. Why? Because we so often dig a line behind ourselves but then don't place soldiers in it in advance, or don't give them guns, or machine-guns—give them nothing to fight with. And the Germans, once they outflank us, get to these lines before we do. And there go the fortifications, time after time. Meanwhile we retreat to the town, stand with our backs to it, and dig new trenches—not in three months, but in three days, which is all we usually have, and we have to fight in them to the end, to the death. It's tough, and it's humiliating . . . Well, you say there were eighteen wounded left last night," he changed the subject. "How about finding out whether they've taken them out by now or not."

Maslennikov went out. Saburov picked up a knife and fiddled with the wick of the homemade kerosene lamp, a "Katyusha." The lamp was the case of a 76-mm. shell; its top had been flattened down, and a wick placed inside. A little above the middle a hole had been bored and stopped up with a cork; through it you could pour in kerosene or, when there wasn't any, gasoline with salt.

Having trimmed the wick, Saburov lazily stirred with his fork the pan full of hot canned meat which Petya had brought him. He did not really want to eat—why should he? Maybe, he thought, six o'clock in the morning was not exactly a good

83

time for dinner. The hours were all mixed up. He felt like going out into the open air. He had already thrown his coat over his shoulders when Maslennikov returned.

"They took them all out during the night. You know who came for the wounded?" Maslennikov said. "That same girl we pulled out of the water."

"Well," Saburov said.

"It seems it was she taking the wounded away all the time, but I didn't see her. I've brought her along. Let her sit down and rest here for a while," he added quietly.

"Let her rest, of course," Saburov said. He suddenly remembered that he was the host here and that among his many obligations was that of hospitality.

Maslennikov went to the corridor and shouted loudly: "Anya, Anya, where are you?"

The girl came in and stood shyly on the threshold. It seemed to Saburov that in these eight days she had grown even thinner.

"Sit down, sit down," Saburov said bustling about. He was trying to be hospitable, but he did everything clumsily. Instead of simply moving up the little stool, he picked it up and dropped it on the floor with such a crash that the girl started with surprise.

"How are you?" Saburov asked, addressing his question to no one in particular.

"All right," the girl said. She smiled and sat down. "And you?"

"I'm all right, too."

"What do you mean—all right? We're wonderful," Maslennikov interrupted cheerfully. "We're getting along fine. Look how it is here . . ." He waved his arm proudly as if everything around them really did represent a wonderful and comfortable life.

"It seems you've been taking out our wounded?" Saburov asked.

84

"The first day it wasn't I," the girl said, "but these last three days, I . . ."

"In all, you've taken one hundred and eight men?"

"Yes, including those on the first day. I myself only ninety."

"You didn't duck anyone crossing the river?"

"No." She smiled, remembering how she herself had been ducked. "No one . . . Only in the evening, once, they fired at us from an airplane while we were on a raft. They killed four men."

"Mine?"

"Yours."

"You disappeared so fast that time . . ."

"Yes, I forgot to thank you."

"For nothing."

"I know. Still, all the same, thank you."

"When are you going back?" Saburov asked.

"I have to wait until evening. I was late this time and it's already growing light."

"Yes, when it gets light you can't get back with wounded. Never mind, you can get a rest here."

"Yes, I'm going right away, to rest. My orderlies are already lying down outside. For two nights they haven't slept," the girl said, standing up.

"No, where are you going? Where are you going? You can rest here. The lieutenant and I are going out right away, so you lie down here and rest."

"But won't I be bothering you?"

From the way this was said, Saburov saw that she was tired beyond belief and that a cot on which she could lie down and cover herself with a blanket seemed to her at that moment almost a dream.

"No, not at all," he said.

"Fine, then, I'll get a rest," the girl said simply.

"Only you should eat first."

85

"Good, thank you."

"Petya," Saburov shouted. "Bring in something to eat."

"But look," said Petya, appearing at the door, "you've already got the frying pan, Comrade Captain."

"Ah, that's true . . ." Saburov moved the frying pan toward the girl.

"And you?"

"We'll eat, too."

Saburov took the cork out of a German flask lying on the table and poured drinks for himself and Maslennikov into shell-cases or, as they called them to each other, "land mines." Recently these had replaced cups and glasses more and more in officers' dugouts.

"Do you drink?" he asked.

"When I'm tired, I drink," she said. "But only half."

He poured her a drink and she drank it with them, quietly, without frowning, the way an obedient child drinks medicine.

"And can you sing, too?" Maslennikov asked, for no apparent reason.

"I used to sing a little, with a guitar."

"And the guitar, probably, hangs over your bed at home, and I'm sure it has a bow of ribbons on it," Maslennikov went on.

"It had a bow of ribbons," the girl said. "Only now it doesn't exist any more . . . You see, I come from here," she added.

These words "from here" had just one meaning for all three of them: once she was from here, that meant everything she had was destroyed, and there was nothing left.

"Well, have you stopped being frightened yet? You remember our conversation?"

"I'll never stop," she answered. "I already told you why I get frightened, so how can I stop? I won't stop . . . I didn't think I would meet you again," she added after a moment's silence.

"I did, though," Saburov said. "I was certain I would meet you again sometime."

"Why?"

"I've noticed, somehow, it just works out that way; in war you seldom meet people only once. Where did you live, far from here?"

"No, very near. If you go down that street to the right, then in the third block . . ."

"That means the Germans still have your home?"

"Yes."

"Anya, Anya. . . ." Saburov said, suddenly remembering something. "Do you know, Anya, I think maybe I've got a surprise for you. But maybe not, I don't know, maybe it won't surprise you."

He was not really certain, but somehow it seemed to him that if one coincidence had already taken place with this girl whom he had once pulled out of the water showing up now to take out his wounded, then why couldn't another coincidence happen?

"How are you going to surprise me?"

"Is your name Klimenko?" Saburov asked.

"Yes."

"Then for certain I'll surprise you, and even make you happy. I've seen your mother."

"Mother? Where?"

"On the other side of the river, at Eltonskaya," Saburov said. "And your father is somewhere here, in the city, isn't he?"

"Yes," Anya said.

"I saw your mother in Eltonskaya, nine days ago, the same day we crossed the Volga with you. Only then I didn't know your name. That was why I didn't mention it."

"How about her, how is she?" Anya asked eagerly.

"All right. She had come there on foot. She said the bombing had separated her from you."

87

"Yes, she was at home and I wasn't. How is she?"

"Very well," Saburov said. "She had walked all the way to Eltonskaya."

"Where did you see her? How can I find out where she is?"

"I don't know. I saw her in Eltonskaya, sitting next to one of the houses there. I think she had just got there the same day."

"Well, how did she look? How was she?" Anya asked. "Very tired?"

"A little . . ."

"What's most important, she was alive."

"That's exactly what she said to me about you: 'what's important is that she's alive.'" Saburov smiled.

"You're right; that's the main thing nowadays."

The girl put her arms on the table and lowered her head on them. She wanted to cross-examine Saburov about her mother but what could he add? He had seen her only for a couple of minutes.

"You lie down," Saburov said. "Lie down on my couch. I'm going out right away and won't be back until evening. I'll wake you up when you've got to go."

"I'll wake up myself," she said confidently. Then she walked over to the couch, sat down on it, and bounced up and down on the springs like a child. In surprise she said: "Oh, it's soft; for a long time I haven't slept on anything like this."

"There's something else we're going to fix up differently here," Maslennikov said. "I saw two leather armchairs outside in the ruins; they'll need a bit of cleaning, but then they'll make this place like a parlor car."

"You didn't see any guitars in your ruins?"

"No."

"Too bad . . . I would have played for you."

"Never mind. This isn't the last time you'll come to see us . . ."

"Probably not. Not the last time."

"So I'll find you a guitar. May I go over to Company One?" Maslennikov asked, trying to hold himself even straighter than usual in front of Saburov.

"Go ahead," Saburov said. "I'm going over there myself soon."

Maslennikov went out.

"What's he to you?" the girl asked.

"My chief of staff."

"Is he nice, too?"

"What do you mean—too?"

"I mean, like you," she said. "That is, not exactly like you. He's like me; that is, I don't mean that—not that he's nice, like me . . . But I . . ." She got all mixed up, grew confused, then smiled. "What I wanted to say was that he is like me, still quite young, while you're already grown-up. That's what I wanted to say."

"You've already written me down for an old man." Saburov shook his head.

"No, why an old man?" she said seriously. "It's just that I can see that you are grown-up, and we aren't yet. You, probably, have already lived through a great deal in your life, haven't you?"

"I don't know, maybe . . . I guess I have," Saburov agreed doubtfully.

"And I—I haven't. I've hardly got anything even to remember. Only sometimes I remember Stalingrad, what it was like. You were never here before?"

"No."

"It was very beautiful. I know Moscow was probably more beautiful, but it always seemed to me that Stalingrad couldn't be better. Maybe because I was born here. It's a shame," she said suddenly and with feeling, "it's a terrible pity . . . It's such a pity, you can't imagine. Mother didn't cry, did she, when you were talking with her?"

"No."

"You know, she's a funny sort. If something trifling goes wrong, if she breaks a plate, she cries. But when something really terrible happens, she doesn't cry, she just keeps quiet; she doesn't even say anything."

"What happened to your father?"

"I don't know. He didn't go across the river. He said to me: 'I'm not leaving Stalingrad,' and he didn't go. I know that. They've both been good to me. When I went home and said I was going into the army it was only three days after Misha— he was my oldest brother—had been killed. I thought they would object . . . I would have gone anyway, but still I was afraid I would have to have an argument about it. But on the contrary, they simply said: 'go,' and that was all. It's good, that they understand everything," she added with an unexpected directness which showed that she still had a child's conception of parents as people who seldom really understand anything, and who are surprising and comforting when they do understand.

"It's good that I saw you today," she went on. "Every time I took your wounded out, when they talked with each other, they kept repeating your name, and I didn't know that Saburov was you. And then I wanted to see you, to thank you. We were together on the little steamer and I told you all sorts of things. That day I was in a mood to tell everything, and then later it seemed to me that if I should suddenly see you again I'd want to tell you everything all over again."

"What, for instance?"

"I don't know what . . . everything in general . . . If you hadn't landed here, in Stalingrad, we would never have seen each other."

"Why not? Didn't you want to study?"

90

"Yes."

"Then that means you would have landed at the university n Moscow and I would have been a teacher there."

"Were you really a teacher before the war?"

"No, I was still studying, but I was going to teach."

"I wouldn't have thought it. It seemed to me you'd been in the army all your life."

This mistake was as pleasant to Saburov as it is to every man from the reserve list who is made an officer.

"Why did you think that?" he asked.

"I just thought so. You look so military, as if you'd always been in the army. You have a look . . ." covering her mouth with her hand, she yawned.

"Lie down," he said. "Go to sleep."

She stretched and lay down. Saburov took his overcoat from a nail in the wall and covered the girl with it.

"But what will you go out in?" she asked.

"In the daytime I always go without a coat."

"That's not true."

"Yes it is, I always tell the truth. Remember that in the future."

"All right," she said. "How old are you?"

"Twenty-nine."

"Is that the truth?"

"I already told you. I always tell the truth."

"Well, all right, I know," she looked at him untrustingly. "Of course, it's the truth, if you say so, but you don't look it. Maybe it is true that you're only twenty-nine, but somehow you seem much older . . ."

She closed her eyes, then opened them again.

"Do you know, I'm terribly tired. The last two days, everywhere I went, I kept thinking to myself how nice it would be to lie down and fall asleep."

"Go ahead and sleep."

"Right away . . . Have you got any children?"

"No."

"And haven't you got a wife?"

"No."

"Is that the truth?"

Saburov laughed. "We already agreed about that."

"All right, I believe you," she said. "But I asked because when you soldiers at the front joke with us—with girls, I mean —it's as if you had all agreed with each other—you always say you aren't married and then laugh . . . Look, you're laughing, too, just see . . ."

"I'm laughing, but it is the truth just the same."

"Then what are you laughing at?"

"You asked it in such a funny way."

"Why was it funny? I wanted to know, so I asked," she said in a voice already heavy with sleep, and she closed her eyes.

Saburov stood for a moment looking at her, then sat down at the table and fumbled in his pocket. His tobacco pouch had somehow disappeared. He looked in his field trunk. There, between a map and a notebook, to his surprise, he found the crumpled cigarette box from which he had taken three cigarettes—for himself, for Gordienko, and for the unlucky Parfenov—when they were getting ready that night to attack this house. One cigarette had been left "for afterwards," and since that moment he had forgotten about it. He looked at the box and without hesitating, as if something very special had just happened which gave him the right to smoke this last cigarette, he took it out and lit it.

Through the window it was growing light. It was the start of another day of backbreaking work, another day of siege, another of the days to which he had now grown accustomed. But on this particular day a new worry had been added to all he had already. It was a worry he did not want to admit even to himself but which he could already feel. It was anxiety about this girl, lying there in the corner, under his overcoat. He had a confused feeling that the girl had become somehow tied up with all he would have to think about, with the battle and death around him, with the fact that he was sitting here, besieged, in these very buildings, in Stalingrad, in the city where she had been born and had grown up. He looked at the girl, and it suddenly seemed to him that when evening came and she had to leave this room and recross the river, then he would miss her, more than he could imagine. He finished his cigarette and stood up.

"You going out without a coat?" Petya asked him as he walked out.

"It's too heavy and, besides, it's still warm today."

"Heavy or not, I'll carry it for you, when it gets really warm."

"Never mind, I don't need it. Let's get going."

EIGHT

THE DAY dragged on heavily. Most of the time Saburov was needed with Company Two on the left flank, where a broad street ran past the apartment house into the square. In the morning the usual bombardment began, this time more furious and more accurate than ever. Saburov was convinced that they would not get by today without a particularly strong attack.

By noon it was clear that he was right. After bombing the buildings three times, the Germans began a heavy mortar barrage and under its cover sent tanks along the street. Behind them, running from doorway to doorway along the walls, moved riflemen. As well as Saburov could count them, there were probably two companies engaged in the attack. The first attack was beaten back, but two hours later a second began. This time two tanks broke through and crashed their way into the courtyard of the apartment house. Before they were burned up, they had crushed several soldiers and an antitank gun with its entire crew. The first tank burned like a torch and no one got away from it. The second was knocked out, but only after it had stopped could it be set afire with bottles of gasoline. Two Germans squeezed out of it. They were shot down at once, even though it might have

94

been possible to capture them. Saburov did not hold back his men; in front of his eyes lay the antitank gun which had just been smashed, and the mutilated bodies of the crew who had stayed with it to the last.

At four o'clock the bombing began again and it continued until five. At six, after a long spell of mortar fire, the Germans attacked again. This time they came without tanks. At one place they succeeded in seizing a small building which had formerly housed a power transformer unit and the ruins of a wall.

Just before dark, in the twilight, Saburov assembled fifteen riflemen. He was convinced he could not leave things as they were until morning. They crawled up to the little building and after a long, confused, and noisy exchange of shots recaptured it. It cost him several killed and wounded. Although he did not notice it at first, because of the confusion and his own exhaustion, his sleeve was ripped to the shoulder and his arm seared by a bullet. In the middle of the day he had been hit by concusssion blast from a bomb exploding against a wall close to him, and as a result he had become half deaf. Through the rest of the day he did everything in a kind of depressed, dull spirit, moving almost automatically, tired to the bone. When the little power house had finally been recaptured, he sat down on the ground, worn out. He leaned against a fragment of wall, unscrewed the cap of a flask, and took several swallows. He felt cold, and for the first time that day realized that he was still without an overcoat. As if guessing his thoughts, Petya gave him someone else's coat, obviously taken from a dead soldier. It was too small for him, and at first he threw it over his shoulders, but Petya made him slip his arms through the sleeves.

Saburov and Maslennikov returned to their quarters only when it had become quite dark. The lamp was burning on the table. Saburov looked casually at the couch. The girl was still sleeping. "She must be really tired, but she'll have to be wakened," he thought, and suddenly he realized that throughout the entire day, from the minute he had first realized there would be a strong attack to the minute when he returned, he had not once thought about the girl.

Without taking off their coats, he and Maslennikov sat down at the table across from each other, and Saburov poured vodka into their homemade cups. They drank, and only stopped drinking because there was nothing to eat with it. Fumbling in the drawer of the table, Saburov took out an attractive American can of tinned meat. On all four sides, the can carried pictures of different colored dishes which could be prepared from its contents. Neatly soldered to the bottom was an opener. Breaking it off and threading through its eye the special little device on the can itself, Saburov began to take off the top.

"May I come in?"

"Yes, come in."

Into the room walked a short man with one bar on the shoulder of his uniform. He walked over to the table, limping, and leaning slightly on a homemade cane.

"Senior Political Instructor Vanin," he said, saluting a little carelessly. "I have been appointed your commissar."

"Glad to meet you," Saburov said, standing up and shaking hands with him. "Sit down."

Vanin shook hands with Maslennikov, too, and sat down on a squeaky stool. Betraying a civilian's habits, he took his hat off at once and placed it on the table, and then let out his leather belt one hole. Only after this, as if his uniform and belt had been making him uncomfortable, did he sit back and relax.

Saburov looked closely at this fellow who from now on was to be his chief assistant. Vanin had a heavy head of slightly wavy hair, with a few chestnut-colored locks drooping over his forehead. His eyes were bright blue, of a shade seldom found in men.

Saburov pulled the lamp over to him and carefully read Vanin's letter of recommendation. This was a carbon copy of a divisional order naming Vanin commissar for the 2nd Battalion of the 693rd Rifle Division.

It took hardly more than ten minutes to fill in Vanin officially on the situation in the battalion. Everything was covered without superfluous words: the circumstances of the siege; shells and mines running low; cartridges also low but not yet dangerously so; hot food distributed at night in thermos containers; vodka which they still had above their ration because every day soldiers were being killed or wounded and the sergeants, by old custom, never hurried to take their names off the vodka ration lists; uniforms which in eight days of creeping and lying in trenches had either disintegrated into rags or been rubbed threadbare and covered with mud—all these things were familiar to any man who had been at the front for even a few months.

Saburov leaned back on his stool against the wall, by force of habit, and began to roll a cigarette, showing in this way that the official part of the conversation was finished.

"Have you been in the city long?" he asked Vanin.

"I came over from the other side of the river only this morning. I'm straight from the hospital," Vanin said, underlining his last words with the tapping of his cane on the cement floor.

"Were you ever in Stalingrad before?"

"I was," Vanin smiled. "I was," he repeated with a strange expression on his face. He sighed. "I should say I was. Before the war I was secretary here of the Stalingrad Komsomols."

"Is that so?"

"Yes, three months ago, when I left here for the southern front, Stalingrad was thought of as a city deep in the rear, so far from the front that it would have been hard to imagine that we would be sitting here tonight in this building. You know, in front of this building there was a park, but now, I guess, there's little of it left . . ."

"Very little," Saburov agreed. "A few trees, and the posts for a volley ball net."

"Well, well, the volley ball posts," Vanin laughed. "You know, we never succeeded in making tennis courts. It wasn't long before the war that I got all the young fellows together on Sundays; we levelled off the dirt, rolled it with rollers—but now, probably, it's all dug into holes."

"Dug into holes," Saburov again agreed.

Vanin grew thoughtful. "The devil alone knows, I guess it's hard for everyone to be fighting here. It's terrible to have the Volga so close. But still and all, it must be somehow easier than it is for me. For me it's really terrible . . . You see, I know every corner here, literally every corner. I'm not saying this to make a speech. Twelve years ago we decided to build a green belt around the city, so that there would be less dust. Yes, we didn't think then that those three-year-old linden trees we were planting would be broken up in about ten years by war, or that the fifteen-year-old boys who helped to plant them would never live to thirty but would die along these streets. There was a lot, in general, we didn't think about in those days. I suppose you didn't either."

"Probably not."

Vanin stretched his arms and then looked searchingly at Saburov.

"Where is your home?"

"Recently, it's been wherever I was."

"And before that?"

"Before that in the Donets Basin."

"That means you've been homeless more than a year and have already succeeded—well—not in becoming resigned to it, but at least in becoming used to it. But I . . . Imagine for yourself, this morning I looked at the city from the other bank . . . No, you can't imagine it . . . Probably your division commander put me down as out of my head. I kept answering his questions like a machine: yes, no, yes, no, yes, no. You probably can't even understand what I'm talking about."

"Why not?" Saburov said. "It seems to me it isn't at all hard to understand you. Do you know, in the evenings when a breeze comes up and blows warmth and ashes in here, it sometimes seems to me that it's a wind blowing from the west, beginning right at the frontier, blowing from Chernigov, from Kiev, from Poltava . . . No, I understand what you mean completely, only with me, instead of sadness, I sometimes get a kind of bitter feeling . . ."

"At whom?"

"Against myself, against you, against other people. God only knows. Maybe we should have paid less attention to all your planting of green trees, and more attention to a few other things. Look at me—I served for two years in the army. When I went into the reserve, people said to me: 'what a waste! We could make a good soldier out of you.' But I left anyway . . . And mark you, if I hadn't believed myself then that there would be a war, maybe I would have been right. But I was convinced, really, that there would be a war, and that means I wasn't right, I should have stayed in the army."

"I know what you mean," Vanin said, "only it would have been impossible for us all to become soldiers; you'll agree with that."

"I'll agree, with one reservation. We have all become soldiers anyway, and a lot later than we should have . . . Well, what's the use of remembering all this; now our business is the business of being a soldier, regardless of what delusions we used to have, our own and other people's. Now there are just these three buildings, and that's all." Saburov punched his finger on the map lying in front of him. "How about it, we won't give up the buildings, will we?"

Vanin smiled. "I hope not. Do you know," he added confidentially, "what the commander of the regiment said to me when he sent me to you?"

"What?"

"'Go to Saburov. He fights not so badly, but he loves to argue and he's nearly always in some kind of mood.' 'What kind of mood?' I asked him. 'In general, some kind of mood,' he said and waved his hand as if that explained everything."

Saburov laughed. "Thank you for your frankness. I admit, I do get moods sometimes—sometimes one kind and sometimes another. In general, I often think, a man can't live without moods. Don't you agree?"

"Yes, I think so, too."

"You know, your volley ball court," Saburov said, suddenly changing the subject, "is almost untouched. It's got five or six shell holes from bombs, but you would only have to sprinkle a little dirt on it and roll it two or three times. The posts are still standing, with a piece of the net on one of them. The lieutenant here," Saburov pointed to Maslennikov sitting beside him, "was on the first team in Moscow. You've given me an idea about him today. I've been noticing how he's always asking permission to go over to Company Two; that's his favorite company. Now I understand what it's all about: the volley ball court is there and it must give him pleasant memories."

"The captain still refuses to take me seriously," Maslennikov said jokingly, but with a slight hint of hurt feelings. "He can't get over my being only twenty years old . . . No, I don't think about volley ball any more often than you do. I give you my word."

"No reason why you shouldn't. Twenty years—that's a good age, after all. Do you know, Misha, some day you'll be thirty, but I'll be forty, and when you're forty, I'll be fifty, so that you'll never catch up with me anyway, and the longer you live the clearer it'll be to you that being ten years younger is a lot better than being ten years older. You understand?" He threw his arm around Maslennikov's shoulders and hugged him.

"No, Commissar, you and I have a really remarkable chief of staff. He's good, he's been shot up, he's cool under fire, but, do you know, he thinks too much about how to dream up something special which will make him a real hero. Say a powder magazine, with a fuse in his hand—he'd like something of that sort. But except for that he's a good fighter. He's got a few good whiskers on his face and a diligent, steely look in his eye . . . I'm joking, Misha, I'm joking. Don't get sore. Instead, get up and put on some kind of record for us."

"Have you really got a gramophone?" Vanin asked.

"Of course. We even thought of moving a piano down from the third floor, but yesterday they shot it out from there ahead of us, and now there's nothing left but its strings."

Beyond the wall two close, heavy explosions went off one after the other.

"Maybe it doesn't make such sense to bring anything to this room," Saburov said after a pause. "It looks as if we might have to change our apartment soon. All day today, as if on purpose, they've been landing right around us."

Vanin and Maslennikov went over to the radiator on which the gramophone stood. Carelessly turning over the records, Vanin picked one up and said: "Let's try this one." Maslennikov wound up the gramophone.

> "Our comrade's off to distant lands,
> With following winds from home he flies,
> Blue in the haze are the town he knows,
> A home, a garden, a pair of loving eyes."

Vanin walked away from the table into the shadow and listened quietly, holding his head in his hands. When the record had finished, he wiped his eyes shamelessly and quietly.

"Put it on again, please," he said. The record was played through a second time.

"The girl is certainly sleeping soundly," Saburov said when the gramophone stopped. "Even the music didn't wake her. It's too bad, but she's got to get up."

He crossed the room and went up to the cot. What he had thought was the girl turned out to be nothing but his overcoat thrown flat on the bed.

"That's funny," he said in surprise. "Petya, where's the nurse?"

Petya, who knew everything, as orderlies do, said the girl had gone out two hours before.

"Where did she go? Across the river?"

"No, Comrade Captain, she's still here . . . Something has happened. This is how it was. Over there, in front, where the little garden was, there were groans coming from no man's land. It sounded as if someone were calling for help. Well, they came along to tell this to the soldier on duty, and it was just then that she woke up. Well, so they went out there—that is— they crawled off in that direction."

"Who went out?"

"Well, she went along . . ."

"She did! You ought to be ashamed to admit it. A whole battalion of soldiers, but when you hear some groans, the nurse has to go . . . And she's from another unit, too . . . What sort of guest appearance is this?"

"No, Comrade Captain, she didn't go alone; her own stretcher-bearer crawled out with her, and our Konyukov, too. He was on duty here and he went along."

"When was all this?"

"Just now—I mean, two hours ago," Petya said, looking at his watch.

"Call the guard," Saburov said, putting on his overcoat.

102

"Stay here, I'll be back right away," he added to Vanin and Maslennikov.

The night was cold and clouds covered half the sky, but a half-moon was shining and it was fairly light. Saburov shivered from the cool of the night. The soldier on duty ran up to him.

"Where did they crawl off to?"

The soldier pointed with his hand: "In that direction, Comrade Captain, between the fences, to the left, and along the ruins there."

"What have you heard?"

"You couldn't hear anything special, Comrade Captain. Thirty minutes ago, they dropped some shells just about there, but nothing else . . ."

For a second Saburov felt a desire to crawl forward himself and find out what was going on, but he quickly controlled it. This was not an occasion when he had the right to risk his life.

"As soon as anything is known, report it to me at once. I'll be waiting," he said to the soldier.

He did not have to wait. Out of the darkness, three figures appeared from the direction in which the ruins of the building sloped off to the ground like the side of a hill. Two were holding up the third, who was limping. Saburov walked up to meet them. Konyukov and the stretcher-bearer were holding Anya under her shoulders. Saburov could not see her face but he could tell she was in bad shape from the way she hung helplessly between the arms of Konyukov and the stretcher-bearer.

"Permit me to report," Konyukov said, continuing to support Anya with his left arm and saluting with his right.

"Later," Saburov said. "Take her into my room. Or no, lay her down here, in the guardhouse."

They called the guardhouse a small recess between a staircase and a wall. On its fourth side it was closed in by a curtain. In this recess there stood a table, a stool for a telephone operator, and an upholstered armchair which had been dragged out of someone's apartment for the soldier on duty. In the corner a mattress lay on the ground. The orderly and Konyukov placed Anya on it. Konyukov quickly folded up an overcoat and placed it under her head.

"Well, have you fixed her up?" Saburov asked, standing outside.

"Yes, Comrade Captain," Konyukov said, coming out of the room. "Permit me to report."

"Go on."

"We heard some groans. So she," Konyukov nodded in the direction of the girl, "says, 'I'll crawl out there, there must be someone wounded,' and she called her stretcher-bearers. Well, one of them is a little fellow; he looks half-dead, just a young boy. 'I'll go,' he says, but I see that he's not happy about it . . . So I tell him that I'll go instead."

"Well?"

"Permit me to report. We go along, all of us crawling, everything's quiet. We crawl along maybe one hundred and fifty yards, and there beyond the ruins we find him."

"Whom?"

"Look, let me show you . . ."

Konyukov dug into the pocket of his shirt and pulled out a package of documents. Saburov snapped his flashlight on for a moment. They were the documents of Sergeant Panasyuk.

"Where did you find him, closer to the Germans or closer to us?"

"Permit me to report. To be precise, right in the middle. It's clear he was crawling along, the poor fellow, and couldn't make it, so he started to call."

"Where is he?"

"We left him there. He's dead now."

"What do you mean, dead?"

"When we crawl up to him, he's still living, wounded, groan-

104

ing with all the voice that's in him. I say to him: 'Shut up, you, or they'll shoot you for your voice.' We quieted him but then the Germans, when they saw they didn't have a chance of getting us between the bricks with bullets, started throwing over some shells. They got him; they got him for good, and they got her in the leg, and she also got hit by the stones. At first she was so excited she wanted to drag him out, even though he's dead, but then she lost consciousness herself. We took his papers, but left him, and we dragged her out, and we brought her here. Permit me to report, Comrade Captain."

"Well, what else?"

"I'm sorry for the girl. After all, for God's sake, aren't there really enough men for this kind of work? All right, let her take care of the wounded back in the rear, in the hospital, but what's she here for? I was carrying her along, she's light as a feather, and I started to think: why do they let such a little girl go up under fire?"

Saburov answered nothing.

"Permit me to go," Konyukov said.

"You may go."   · ·

Saburov walked into the guardhouse. Anya was lying quietly on the mattress. She opened her eyes.

"Well, what's the matter with you?" Saburov asked. He wanted to reprove her for going out so foolishly, without asking anyone, but at the same time he knew it would do no good.

"Well, what's the matter with you?" he repeated more gently.

"They hit me," she said, "and then I got a rap on the head, a pretty heavy one . . . But the wound, it's nothing, I think, just a scratch."

"Have they bandaged you?" Saburov asked, and then he noticed a bandage showing white under her cap.

"Yes, they fixed me up," she said.

"How about your leg?"

"We also bandaged her leg," said the stretcher-bearer who was standing over her. "Would you like a drink, nurse?"

"No, thanks."

Saburov was wavering at this moment between two decisions: on the one hand, perhaps, it would be better not to touch her and to leave her here for two or three days, until she got better; on the other hand, several days ago a general order had gone out to the entire division not to leave any wounded in places where the slightly wounded could become severe cases by evening, and severely wounded could become dead men. Saburov decided he should treat the girl like any soldier and send her that same night across the river.

"You can't walk, can you?"

"At the moment, I'm afraid, I can't."

"That means we'll have to move you down to the shore with the other wounded, and right away, with top priority," Saburov said.

He expected her to say that she was not severely wounded and that she could just as well go with the last trip. But she understood from Saburov's face that he would send her with the first trip in any case, so she kept silent.

"If they hadn't wounded me," she said suddenly, "we would have got him out of there. But when they wounded me, the two of them couldn't manage alone . . . For he was killed," she said, as if trying to justify herself.

Saburov looked at her and realized that she was talking only to forget her pain, and that she was hurting all over, and ashamed at having been wounded so stupidly and unnecessarily. It seemed to him that she was also sad because he had talked to her so roughly. She's just a little girl, he thought, almost a child; she's hurt, and she's sorry for herself, and probably upset because he did not understand.

"Never mind," he said with unexpected softness in his voice. "Never mind." Moving up the armchair, he sat down next to her. "They'll take you across the river right away; you must get well quickly, and then you'll soon be taking the wounded out again."

She smiled. "You're talking now just the way we always talk to the wounded; 'never mind, old boy, you'll get better quickly, you'll be all right again.' "

"Well, why not, you are wounded now and so I talk to you just as I should."

"Do you know," she said, "I was just now thinking how really terrible it is, probably, for the wounded to be moved across the Volga when there's shooting. We move around and do everything, but they have to lie there and simply wait. Now it's the same with me, and so I was thinking of how frightening it probably is for them . . ."

"Are you frightened, too?"

"No, for some reason I'm not a bit frightened now, for the first time. Give me a cigarette."

"Do you smoke?"

"No, not usually, but right now I'd like to."

"I'm sorry, I haven't any cigarettes, I'll have to roll you one."

"That's all right with me."

He rolled a cigarette but hesitated a moment before licking it.

"Do it yourself," she said.

He licked the paper, stuck it down, and handed the cigarette to her. She held it awkwardly in her lips. When he lit a match for her, he could see her face in the flicker of the match, and for the first time it seemed to him beautiful.

"What are you looking at?" she said. "I'm not crying . . . We crawled out there through a lot of puddles and it's from that, probably, that my face is wet. Give me a handkerchief, so I can dry it."

He took a handkerchief from his pocket and noticed with

embarrassment that it was dirty, crumpled, and covered with loose tobacco. She wiped her face and returned the handkerchief to him. "Well, are they going to take me right away?" she asked.

"Yes," he said, trying to give the "Yes" the same dry, superior officer's tone with which he had spoken earlier, but this time it didn't come out.

"Will you think of me?" she asked suddenly.

"I will."

"Don't forget. I don't say it just because it's the way all wounded talk, but I'm going to get well quickly, really and truly. I feel it, so you think of me."

"How could I not think of you?" Saburov said gravely. "I'll certainly think of you . . ."

When the stretcher-bearers came in several minutes later to take her away, she stood up and sat down on the stretcher herself, but it was clear that this was hard for her.

"My head aches badly," she said.

They held her under the arms and laid her gently back on the stretcher.

"Are they sending the others already?" Saburov asked.

"Yes, right away, we're going together," one of the stretcher-bearers said.

"Good."

Now the street outside was half in darkness. Saburov realized that he had not yet said anything of what he had terribly wanted to say to her in these minutes. The stretcher-bearers had already taken a few steps, and the stretcher began to move, and still nothing had been said, and no matter how much he wanted to he could say nothing—he did not know how and he did not dare. He felt a sharp, irrational pity for this nurse who had bandaged and escorted so many wounded men and who was now lying helpless herself on a stretcher. To his own surprise, he bent over her, and putting his hands behind his

108

back so as not to hurt her through any careless movement, he pressed his cheek close to her face. Then, not understanding himself what he was doing, he kissed her on the eyes, on the forehead, and on the lips. When he raised his face, he saw she was looking at him with open eyes, clear and understanding, and it seemed to him that he had not simply kissed a helpless girl, who was unable to move or to protest, but that he had done this with her permission—that she had wanted it, too.

Saburov returned to his quarters and ordered Petya to summon Vassiliev at once. Vassiliev came in a few minutes and stood at the door. His face was calm.

"You told me Panasyuk was killed on the German side of the line."

"Yes."

"That's not true."

"He was killed over there."

"No, he wasn't killed there, he's been found between the lines."

Vassiliev was silent. From Saburov's expression, he could tell that something was wrong; but the worst possibility of all —that Panasyuk might be alive and here—had not occurred.

"He was found badly wounded between the lines. How do you explain that?"

"I don't know, Comrade Captain. If he's alive, he could explain better."

"He's killed, but he was killed later. He can't explain anything now . . . How do you explain it?"

"I don't know," Vassiliev said, relaxing. "It must be that he came to and crawled back."

"I can understand that much without your help," Saburov said. "How do you explain that you deserted a wounded comrade inside the German lines?"

"I thought he was dead," Vassiliev answered. "He wasn't breathing."

"No, he was only wounded."

"I don't know, Comrade Captain. I thought he was dead. I listened and listened, but he wasn't breathing, and he was all covered with blood. I thought he was dead."

There was a long silence.

"Next time, listen better," Saburov said coldly. "It's better to bring back a dead man than to leave one who's still alive. Understand?"

"I understand."

"You may go."

"Permit me to say something, Comrade Captain."

"Well?"

"If I had only known . . . but I didn't know. Now I'll kill three Germans in return, just for Panasyuk. I give you my word, Comrade Captain."

"Good," Saburov said. "Now go."

When Vassiliev had left, Saburov took out his field notebook. He had to write his report for the day, the report which would go first to Babchenko at regiment headquarters, then a section of it to Protsenko at division headquarters, and part of it might even make a link in the long chain of dispatches which by morning, in a report of the High Command, would be lying on the table in front of Stalin.

As always in the evenings when he was making up these reports, Saburov thought of the front in all its bigness, the front on which his battalion and these three buildings were just one of an uncounted number of dots. It seemed to him that all of Russia, which had no end and no beginning, stretched endlessly away to his left and to his right, flanking these three buildings where he, Captain Saburov, with his dwindling battalion, was still holding out.

NINE

PERIOD of relative quiet set in on the sector occupied by Protsenko's division. After all that had taken place, this might have seemed a well-earned rest if Saburov had not realized that the silence did not mean at all that the Germans had grown tired or given up their attacks, but simply that they were now concentrating their strength to the south of his sector and trying to break a path for themselves to the Volga—trying to cut Stalingrad in two.

Day and night, from the south, the crash of artillery carried to them, but here it was quiet; that is, quiet in the Stalingrad sense of the word. From time to time the Germans bombed them. Five or six times a day they dropped a curtain of artillery and mortar fire on the buildings occupied by Saburov. Sometimes in one place, sometimes in another, handfuls of riflemen tried to edge their way a little forward and to take back some piece of the ruins. But these were feints rather than real fighting.

The Germans did only what was necessary to make it impossible to move a single man from here to help out on the sectors to the south. The heavy feeling which came from inactivity outweighed any ordinary human pleasure Saburov might have felt that he was still alive and that at the moment he ran relatively less chance of dying than before. During these days the battalion settled down to that special life in the midst of siege which astonished new people coming to Stalingrad by its stability, its calm, and sometimes its humor.

The Germans had finally succeeded, after three days of shooting, in destroying the room in which Saburov had earlier set up his quarters. Fortunately, they had only slightly wounded one telephone operator in doing so. Now Saburov had moved to the basement, into what had been the furnace room. Without exception, the entire battalion had now moved underground and, as a result, life became neater and more orderly.

In the dugout where the dispatch riders were lodged and where the mail was sorted, someone hung a real postbox on a pillar. It had been picked up from the ruins outside the building. It had everything it should have had: there was the usual inscription "POSTBOX" and the post office number, and even a slot which opened and closed. Saburov said jokingly one morning that the only thing missing was the sign "GENERAL POST OFFICE," and this idea apparently pleased the dispatch riders. By evening they had fixed up a little board over the box on which was written in black paint: "GENERAL POST OFFICE—*Incoming and Outgoing Mail.*"

One of the soldiers who had been a well-known watchmaker in Odessa before the war fixed up a workroom just like a civilian watch repair shop in his dugout, setting a piece of broken mirror glass in the earthen wall in place of a window. After the joke with the post office, which pleased the whole battalion, Saburov spelled out neatly on this glass in the same black paint: "Watch Repair Shop—the Exact Time." This was not especially clever, but under trench conditions it rated as a good joke.

For two days Petya was absorbed in the construction of a kind of bath. With the help of the engineers, he built a special dugout. He made a ceiling for it out of several broken doors, constructed out of bricks a flagging of hot stones on which water is thrown in a Russian bath to make steam, and sunk a barrel into the ground for water. It was pretty smoky in the bath and dirty, but nowhere had anyone ever bathed with such satisfaction as here. Even Babchenko, who did not have a bath, came here to bathe. When he walked out, he said he would bring the commander of the division next time, and he did not forget to add that everything should be in order when the boss came.

Aunt Masha—this was what they called the woman whom Saburov had found at the beginning of their stay in the cellar next to his building—became cook for the battalion. She had made up her mind that the battalion would be here forever and that no one would throw her out. The morose despair which Saburov had first noticed in her disappeared, and she turned out to be a simple, good-hearted woman. With the almost light-minded temerity which was the salvation of many Russian people in days of danger, she even gave up talking about how one bomb could kill her and her three children all at once. Now she did not believe the bomb had yet been made which could fall on her or her children.

Three or four times during a night Saburov could squeeze in a half hour to read the books which had been blown out of the building by artillery explosions, and which were picked up later by the soldiers. Among them he found Klyuchevsky's "History of Russia," in five volumes. Saburov said he would consider himself lucky if the siege continued until he could finish the fifth volume. Maslennikov and Vanin laughed and told him that the speed at which he was reading would require the siege to last at least two years.

The chief military operations now took place at night. Little groups of hunters were organized to crawl across the German line trying to catch a "tongue," as they called a prisoner who could be made to talk, or simply to raise a routine nightly disturbance for the Germans. Two nights in a row, Maslennikov took part in these expeditions. He was still in a hurry to distinguish himself, and he argued that he was obliged to engage in these forays himself—he had to do something when three kilometers to the south his comrades were dying. Saburov knew this feeling, too, but at the same time he foresaw that their time would come, so he held Maslennikov back. When Maslennikov went on a night raid for the second time, Saburov did not feel he had the right to forbid it, but he quietly called Konyukov and instructed him not to leave Maslennikov and to take care of him. Konyukov eagerly agreed to go; about Maslennikov he only said: "Don't worry, Comrade Captain, everything will turn out fine."

Konyukov loved working at night. Talking with his comrades, he would express real regret that the Germans had almost given up stringing barbed wire. Once upon a time, he told them, in the other war, you could creep out and cut it, quietly and quickly, to your heart's content. He had been a specialist at it, and he was bitterly disappointed that he could not show his skill.

On the following day, when Maslennikov was still sleeping after his second night raid, Saburov picked up his overcoat and noticed that it was full of holes from shell fragments. During the night a mortar shell had exploded right next to him, and Maslennikov had been saved only by a miracle. When he was getting ready to ask permission that night to go raiding again, Saburov guessed what he was going to ask from the expression on his face, and said: "Tonight your work, Comrade Lieutenant, is cut out for the entire night."

"Yes?" Maslennikov said happily.

"Yes. You've got your coat to mend."

"My coat?"

"Yes, your coat, and until every hole in it is neatly mended, you go on no more night raids, mark what I say."

Maslennikov had his own sense of humor but it deserted him whenever he began to think that someone was teasing him about his youth. He might have taken it better had it not been that his older half-brother, his mother's son, was a flyer with a name so popular in the Soviet Union that Maslennikov did not like to mention it. In the entire battalion he had told only Saburov about his brother, and this in a sudden burst of confidence.

Maslennikov had grown up in a family which worshipped this brother. Maslennikov liked him, too, but at the same time envied him and was bitterly jealous. Sometimes it seemed to him that all his bad luck came from his being eight years younger than this brother. When the civil war broke out in Spain, and his brother went there to fight, Maslennikov was fifteen years old, but he would have given anything in the world to get to Spain. Then later, when his brother was in Mongolia, the time came for Maslennikov to pick his own career and his mother, proud of her older son but frightened for him, implored the younger boy to enter an aeronautics institute instead of a flying school. But at the outbreak of the war, when nothing could hold him back any longer, Maslennikov entered the first infantry school he could find. The boy was ambitious and vain. His vanity was the kind for which it is hard to criticize people in time of war. He wanted passionately to become a hero. For this he was ready to accept any assignment, even the most dangerous.

Saburov had known what ambition can mean in life, and even vanity, but now both had almost vanished for him in a war which he looked on as heavy, bloody, grinding work. He could still understand Maslennikov and not condemn him. He simply tried as far as he could to hold him in check. Sometimes Maslennikov seemed to him almost his own son, younger than he by nine years of life and one year of war—and that meant more than ten years younger.

"You know, Misha," he said when Maslennikov grew sulky

after his joke about the overcoat, "you know, Misha, sometimes when I want to do something too risky I hold myself back by thinking about the war. It's going to be a long war, and the longer it is the more valuable people are going to be who have fought from the beginning and lived through to its end. If I ever command a regiment, then you'll be commanding a battalion, and it's important you should live until then. You've got to live until then. How about it, don't you see that?"

"No," Maslennikov said impetuously. "For all the others—yes, for myself—no."

"You don't agree," Saburov smiled. "Well, all right. After all, it's not important whether you agree or not. You've got to do what I say anyhow, so get on with your sewing."

Maslennikov took the overcoat on his knees, smiled, and began to study the holes in it.

This conversation took place on the evening of their eighth day of quiet. All day and all evening especially heavy gunfire had been heard in the south; Saburov, who could not lose in his temporary feeling of good fortune for himself and his battalion a more general feeling of impending disaster, was in an ugly mood all evening. On the table, the telephone rang. Saburov picked up the receiver.

"Saburov?" he heard Babchenko's voice.

"Yes."

"Turn your battalion over to the commissar. The boss has summoned you; come at once."

Saburov turned to Maslennikov. "Tell Vanin I've gone to see the boss." He put on his hat and walked out the door.

Protsenko was walking with quick steps back and forth across his own dugout located next to the ruins of a building. As was always the case when the colonel could manage it, his dugout had been tightly and neatly built. Protsenko had inspected German officers' dugouts during the first stages of the invasion on the western front, and he built his dugouts with precision, in the German manner. He was not afraid to risk his life when it was necessary, but at the same time he liked to have his dugout strong, five or six layers thick, so that no accidental shell could smash it. He worked hard himself and could not stand laziness in others, and as soon as he set up quarters in any new place, he made his engineers sweat. He liked his dugout to be well-covered, spacious when this was possible, with a table, stools, and some comfortable place to sleep. This was the way of a meticulous man who was not fighting his first year of war, and for whom a dugout had long ago become a permanent home. He could not stand it when officers arranged their quarters with unnecessary carelessness, under enemy fire but without even a place to spread out a map. He could not stand it, in short, when they added to the discomforts which war itself entailed at every step.

All that day furious fighting had been taking place on his left flank. Intuitively and from experience, it had become clearer and clearer to Protsenko in the course of the day that the hour was not far off for the Germans finally to break through on his left to the Volga. This would cut him and his division off from everything that was to the south of them, and, what was worst of all, from army headquarters. A half hour ago, his fears had been confirmed; his communications with army headquarters had been cut. By a curious coincidence, the last thing he had heard, after an endless succession of anxious conversations with the army staff, was the deep bass voice of Matveyev, member of the military council, who had called him to ask how he was holding out and if everything was in order, then had said:

"My congratulations."

"Or what?"

"Didn't you hear the radio?"

"No."

"They broadcast today on the radio that by a special decree

of the government you have been promoted to the rank of major general. So I congratulate you, Comrade General."

Matveyev had spoken in a tired, slow voice. There, probably, to the south, they were having a really tough time, and Protsenko could explain his remembering the government decree and telephoning him about it only as genuine thoughtfulness.

"Thank you," Protsenko had said. "I shall try to be worthy of my new rank."

He had waited, but Matveyev had made no comment.

"I've got everything I need," Protsenko had continued. "Hello . . ." But Matveyev did not answer. "Hello," Protsenko had said a second time, and then a third time. The telephone was dead.

At first Protsenko thought the break in the line was somewhere in his sector and he called the operator at the junction point with the division next to him. But the signal man answered. It would have been better if he had not answered. The line was cut for good. To the left of Protsenko's division the Germans had at last come out on the shore of the Volga, and they had broken all communication lines.

His neighbors gave no sign of life. Army headquarters were silent. Meanwhile, as always, it was essential to send the daily report. There was now only one method of communication open: across the Volga to the other bank, and then along that bank to the south and back across the river to army headquarters. He would have to send someone. At first Protsenko thought of his own adjutant, but he had been all but knocked out by a day of running around, and was sleeping on the floor with his head on his overcoat. Besides, the adjutant was not the man to send at this moment to headquarters. He should send someone who could not only carry the report but who could also find out exactly and definitely what Protsenko was now expected to do. He lifted the telephone and called Babchenko.

118

"Is everything quiet with you?" he asked.

"Everything's quiet."

"Then send Saburov to me immediately."

While waiting for Saburov's arrival, Protsenko worked over the reports from the regiments, and contrary to his usual custom, drew up a general report in his own handwriting and sent it out to be typed. They were still typing it when Saburov came in.

"How do you do, Alexei Ivanovich?" Protsenko said.

"How do you do, Comrade Colonel."

"No longer Colonel," Protsenko said. "Now it's General. Didn't you hear the radio today?"

"No."

"If you didn't hear it, then I'll have to tell you. I'm a general. They promoted me today. The devil knows," he added, pointing to the silent telephone, "I can't lie about it. I really wanted it, but I didn't want to hear it on a day like this, not on a day like this . . . I called you to take the report to headquarters immediately."

"What do you mean, isn't it working?" Saburov pointed to the telephone.

"No, and it won't again, for quite a while. They've cut it. I'll have to make you my living telephone for tonight."

He picked up a local telephone and called the river dock. "Get a motorboat ready, quickly, or a rowboat, whatever you've got."

"Well, Alexei Ivanovich, you'll find out only when you cross the river whether or not headquarters is still at the same old place. Then you'll have to cross the river again wherever they're located now. Well, how about it, is the report ready?" he turned and asked a staff officer.

"It's being typed. It will be ready in five minutes."

"Good. So, Alexei Ivanovich," Protsenko said, "you can soon be off . . . Of course, we'll re-establish communications, but to tell you the truth, I haven't the patience to wait. On my word of honor, I like it better when they're jumping me. Because when they jump you, you know what you've got and what you haven't got, but when it's quiet here and they're jumping your neighbors, that's worst of all; your heart doesn't stand still. It's the same with you, probably, isn't it?"

"I feel the same way," Saburov answered.

"I know," Protsenko said, "so you've got to try to get through, so our hearts can stand still."

He suddenly smiled and turned to the fragment of mirror which was hanging on the wall.

"Tell me, Alexei Ivanovich, is a general's uniform going to look all right on me? What do you think?"

"It ought to, Comrade General—it ought to suit you." Saburov said.

" 'Comrade General,' " Protsenko smiled. "Look, you say to me, 'Comrade General' but, you know, you're probably thinking to yourself : 'He's flattered, the old fool, to hear it.' Is that what you're thinking?"

"That's what I was thinking," Saburov smiled, too.

"And you're quite right in thinking it . . . It's pleasant, it is really pleasant. Only it means a heavy responsibility on me now. We can hand out the titles now,* but the words are something we don't always understand yet. Like a lot of other words, by the way."

Protsenko thought a moment, lit a cigarette, and looked earnestly at Saburov. He was deeply moved. And he wanted to get something off his mind.

"General," he said thoughtfully. "It's a hard rank. And do

---

* Many ranks were restored in the Red Army in 1935, but the popular hatred of Tsarist generals during the Russian civil war prevented the reintroduction of the rank of general until 1940. A decree of May 8, 1940, established the ranks of major general, lieutenant general, colonel general, and general of the army. Until 1940, these ranks had been referred to simply as regiment, division, or army commanders.

you know, Saburov, why it's hard? Because to fight not so badly or even pretty well isn't enough now. Now we've got to fight so that later on, for as long a time as possible, we won't have to fight at all. You know, Saburov, I don't believe in saying that this will be the last war in history. We said that in the last war, and before then we said it often. You have only to read history. After this war there will still be war, after thirty years, maybe fifty . . . But it's in our hands that it shouldn't come quickly, and if it's got to come anyway, that it should be a victorious war. That's what an army is for. Of course, a lot of people are hoping now. Anyone can contradict me who wants to. You, for example, no?"

"I would like to contradict you," Saburov said. "I don't want to think that there can ever again be another war."

"Of course you don't want to," Protsenko said. "I don't want to either. We don't want to think it, but we've got to. We've got to think it, and then, maybe, there won't be one."

The staff officer brought in the report. Protsenko reached in his pocket for his spectacle case, took out a pair of round, horn-rimmed glasses which he wore only when he had to read an important document, read it attentively, word by word, and signed it.

"Get going," he said. "They'll escort you from here as far as the boat, and from then on it's your worry. You'll be sailing on the Volga, and if they don't spot you, you can stuff yourself with beauty. The water underneath, the stars above you. God, would that be beautiful if it wasn't the Volga but the Vistula or the Oder. Well, all right, on your way."

Saburov picked his way in the dark to the landing dock. There was no motorboat; it had been blown up that morning by a mine. A rowboat with four oars slapped its prow quietly on the water. As he boarded it, Saburov snapped on his flashlight for a moment; he saw the boat was white with a blue stripe and with a number. It had belonged to an excursion station on the river. Not long ago, you could have rented it for a ruble or a ruble-and-a-half an hour.

Two Red Army men sat at the oars. Saburov settled himself at the rudder and they pushed off in silence. The Germans were not shooting. It was just as Protsenko had said it would be: the stars above him and the water below, and a quiet night, with rifle fire staccato in the distance, three or four kilometers away, so far that his ear paid no attention to it. In actual fact, it was possible to sit on the gunwale and to think, for these twenty or thirty minutes which divided him from the other bank, where every day and sometimes at night heavy German shells flew over the river and exploded, where dozens of little docks were working from dusk until dawn, where they took the wounded from the battalions and where they sent back every day to the battalions their ammunition, their bread, and their vodka.

To the right and to the left were the Germans who had now reached the river. Russia lay behind, on the east side of the Volga. Saburov had often joked in conversations with Maslennikov, calling himself and his battalion an island power and the other bank of the river "the great continent." Even if you were going to Moscow, you would still have to cross to "the great continent" in order to start, on the other side of the river, and only somewhere to the northwest could you cross the Volga again to get to Moscow. On that side of the river was everything, including Anya. He thought about her now. And he thought that if her wound had been slight, she must be quite near here, at the medical base where she worked.

"Probably it was slight," he thought, not because this was logical, but because she had said: "I will come back to see you soon . . ." Like everything she said, she had said this with such childlike conviction and firmness that it seemed to him it would indeed turn out this way. In recent days he had caught imself two or three times automatically looking around his dugout when he returned to his quarters.

The boat grated on the sand, and Saburov leaped ashore and walked off to find out where the crossing was now located which would bring him closest to army headquarters. It turned out they had moved the crossing a kilometer-and-a-half downstream. So he went back to the boat and they rowed along the shore.

At the crossing the boat nosed up to a temporary wooden jetty. The soldiers stayed in the boat but Saburov shifted to a barge which was just about to cast off for the trip to the right bank. It was loaded with boxes of provisions and entire carcasses of beef and mutton, piled right on the deck. Although there were almost no people on the barge, this mountain of provisions testified to how many there were on the other shore and to how difficult, wearisome, and endlessly complicated was the task of supplying across the river an entire army perched on its other shore.

After a half hour the barge was slowly eased into one of the Stalingrad docks. Saburov learned, to his surprise, that although the crossing had been shifted army headquarters had remained where they were before. Saburov knew from Prosenko, who had been there two or three times, that they were located in specially excavated galleries along the bank of the river, near a grain elevator which had been burned. He would have to get there on foot from the crossing, a little more than a kilometer along the shore. The Germans were dropping mortar fire along the shore in checkerboard fashion, and from time to time shells exploded in front of him or behind him.

Saburov kept walking along the shore, but he could not see the silhouette of the elevator which was supposed to be his landmark. As he walked on, machine-gun fire could soon be heard so close that there was no doubt he was within a kilometer of the front line. He had begun to think that someone had misinformed him, as happens only too often in wartime, and that headquarters must have been moved today to some other place. But when he had come quite close to what was, as far as he could see, the front line, he saw directly in front of him the outline of the elevator on the steep bank of the Volga, and a minute later he ran into a guard standing at the entrance to a tunnel leading into the ground.

"Is this army headquarters?" Saburov asked.

The guard examined Saburov's pass under a flashlight and replied that this was headquarters.

"How does one get to the chief of staff?" Saburov asked quietly.

"To the chief of staff?"

Behind him he could hear a voice he seemed to remember. "Who wants the chief of staff?"

"I do."

"Where are you from?"

"From Protsenko."

"Well, well. That's interesting," said the voice. "Come along."

When they had gone into a tunnel lined with boards, Saburov looked around and saw behind him the same general he had seen on the first night with Protsenko.

"Comrade Commander," Saburov said to him, "may I talk to you?"

"Certainly, right away," the general said. He opened a small plank door and walked in first. Saburov took this as an invitation to follow him and walked in too. Beyond the door was a small room cut into the earth. It was furnished with a couch covered by rumpled oilcloth and a large table. The general sat at the table.

"Would you mind handing me that stool, please?"

Saburov moved up the stool without understanding why. The general raised his leg and rested it on the stool.

124

"An old wound has opened, and I've begun to limp . . . Well, what can you report?"

Saburov reported formally and handed the general the written dispatch given him by Protsenko. The general read it slowly, then looked questioningly at Saburov.

"This means everything with you is quiet?"

"Exactly, quiet."

"That's fine. It must mean they haven't got enough strength to attack at the same time on all the sectors. Have you had heavy losses these last few days?"

"I don't know exactly," Saburov said.

"No, I'm not asking you about the division; the division figures are all written here. How has it been with you in your battalion? You are commanding a battalion, aren't you?"

"Exactly."

"How many men have you lost?"

"In the last eight days we've lost six killed and twenty wounded, but in the first eight days it was eighty killed and two hundred and two wounded."

"Yes," the general said, "that's a lot. Did you wander around this bank a long time before you found us?"

"No, I found you quickly enough, but still I had begun to wonder. At three hundred yards from the shooting, I should have thought, you might have changed your command post."

"Yes," said the general, "we almost did. My staff officers had decided to move tonight, but I came back this evening from division headquarters and stopped them. When it's tough the way it is now—remember this, Captain, because right now it's very tough, it would be foolish to deny it—you can't follow the usual rules of good sense and transfer your command post when it seems obviously the thing to do. The most important thing and the best common sense in times like this is that the soldiers should feel stability, you understand? And stability grows in people from feeling that things don't change

125

and partly from feeling that places don't change. So as long as I can still command from here, without moving, I shall command from here. You're a young officer and I tell you this so you can do the same in your own battalion. I hope you don't think your restful quiet is going to last for long."

"I don't think so," said Saburov.

"Well, don't think it. It won't last. Savelyev!" the general called.

His adjutant appeared at the door.

"Sit down and write out an order for me."

The general quickly dictated a short order which consisted chiefly in telling Protsenko to do everything he could not to let the Germans withdraw any large number of men from his sector. It added a suggestion that he might make several local attacks on his southern flank, where the Germans had broken through to the Volga.

"Yes, and write also," the general said, "congratulations on his promotion to the rank of general. That's all; give it to me to sign."

When he dismissed Saburov, the general looked at him with eyes that were ringed with blue from lack of sleep.

"It seems you've known Protsenko for a long time?"

"Almost since the beginning of the war."

"If you want to become a good officer, learn from him. Watch him. You know he's not really what he seems at first glance. He is sly, clever, and stubborn. In a word, he's a Ukrainian. We have a lot of officers who try to look calm, but he's one of those who really are calm. That's why you should learn from him. He has told me about you and that you did well in the first days when you were encircled. In conditions like that, the most important thing is to be calm. We'll re-establish communications with you, but water is still water, remember that. On the other hand . . ." the general stood up and gave his hand to Saburov, "on the other hand, water some-

126

times does us good, when it is behind us. For example, Odessa, Sevastopol . . . I hope Stalingrad will be another example —only with this difference, that we won't give up this one under any circumstances. You may go."

Walking back from headquarters to the dock, Saburov thought it was, after all, a little strange to have found the commanding general in such a good mood. The calm and deliberateness with which the general had spoken to him had not seemed insincere. They had seemed as natural as truth itself, as if this man really and truly believed what he had said. What had happened that day could well have produced an exactly opposite mood. "Perhaps he knows something we don't know," Saburov thought. "Maybe it's reinforcements, maybe they are preparing something in some other place."

He rejected the idea at once. No, that wasn't it. He understood, suddenly and clearly, the reason for the general's mood: it was simply that the very worst that could happen had already happened. The Germans had broken through to the Volga and cut the army in two. This had been going on for the last few days and he had not had strength enough to prevent it. But now, when the worst had already happened, when the Germans had achieved what they had earlier believed would mean the end of the fighting, the army had not admitted it was beaten but had continued to fight. Headquarters had stayed where it was as if nothing had happened, and into the bargain an officer had arrived from the division which was now cut off and brought the daily report to the commanding general, in spite of everything, at exactly the time when it usually arrived. This was what had produced such a good mood in the general. This was why this man, known in the army for his moroseness, had spent five whole minutes talking to Saburov, an ordinary liaison officer, and had even made several remarks which had, it might have seemed, no direct relation to the business in hand.

Five hours after Saburov had left Protsenko on this mission, he was back again in the same dugout handing the colonel a sheet from a notebook on which the order of the commanding general was written.

"Well, how are things there?" Protsenko asked, after reading the order.

When Saburov told him that headquarters was still at its old location, an approving smile crossed Protsenko's face. It was clear he shared Saburov's feelings; he, too, was pleased that the staff had stayed where it was. The apparent rashness of such a decision was actually good common sense which, it would seem, does not always coincide in war with what is logical.

On the road back from Protsenko to his own quarters, Saburov stopped at Babchenko's dugout. They had told him at division headquarters that Babchenko had telephoned and asked for him. Babchenko was sitting at his table and working on a report.

"Sit down," he said without raising his head and continuing to work. This was his custom. He never interrupted what he had begun when subordinates, summoned by him, arrived. He considered this inconsistent with his authority.

Saburov, who was used to this, asked Babchenko cheerfully for permission to go out and smoke. Hardly had he gone out the door when he ran into First Lieutenant Yerenin, commander of a signal company, who had been fighting with the division since the beginning of the war.

"Hello," Yerenin said to Saburov, shaking his hand firmly. "I'm leaving."

"Where are you going?"

"They have sent me to study."

"Where?"

"In courses at the Academy of Military Communications. Funny, isn't it, to go there from Stalingrad. But an order is an order, so I go. I came in to say good-by to the lieutenant colonel."

"When are you going?"

"Right away. As soon as the boat comes, I'll be on my way."

Saburov thought the arrival of Yerenin, whom Babchenko had known for a long time and who now had to take his leave, would force the commander of the regiment to tear himself away from his papers. So he walked into the room behind Yerenin.

"Comrade Lieutenant Colonel," Yerenin said, "excuse the interruption."

"Yes," Babchenko said, still not looking up from his papers.

"I am leaving, Comrade Lieutenant Colonel."

"When?"

"I am leaving right away. I came in to say good-by."

"Is your travel order ready?" Babchenko asked, still without looking at Yerenin.

"Yes, here it is." Yerenin handed him a paper.

Babchenko, still without lifting his eyes, signed the paper and handed it back to Yerenin. A silence followed. Yerenin shifted from foot to foot and stood for several minutes in uncertainty.

"Well, yes, that's what it is, I'm going," he said.

"Well, all right, go along."

"I just came in to say good-by, Comrade Lieutenant Colonel."

Babchenko raised his eyes at last and said: "Well, all right, I wish you success in your studies," and he gave Yerenin his hand. Yerenin shook it. Somehow he wanted badly to say something more but Babchenko, after shaking his hand, paid no more attention to him and buried himself again in his papers.

"Good-by then, Comrade Lieutenant Colonel," Yerenin said again, hesitantly, looking at Saburov. His look was not so much hurt as upset. He had not really known how he would say good-by to Babchenko and what his farewell would consist of, but he had not thought it could take place so coldly.

"Good-by, Comrade Lieutenant Colonel," he said for the last time and very quietly.

Babchenko was not listening. He had come to the final revision of what he had been writing and he was carefully drawing a line with a ruler on the paper. Yerenin shuffled his feet for a little longer, then slowly turned to Saburov, and after shaking his hand with a special warmth walked out. Saburov accompanied him through the door and there, in the exit from the dugout, embraced him warmly and kissed him. Then he walked back to Babchenko.

He was still writing the report. With irritation, Saburov looked at him, at his stubbornly lowered face and his temples which were beginning to grow bald. Saburov did not understand how the lieutenant colonel could feel nothing at this moment, how he could let a man go like this who had fought with him a full year, who had risked his life with him, who had eaten from the same mess tin, who might possibly have saved his life on the battlefield. This was the insensitiveness to people and to their fate which Saburov sometimes found in the army, and always with surprise.

He was so conscious of the hurt which Yerenin had just felt that when Babchenko finally talked to him, interested in learning at first hand what was going on at headquarters, Saburov answered in an unusually dry, reserved manner. He wanted only one thing: to finish the conversation as quickly as he could so that Babchenko could get back to his papers without ignoring him as he had ignored Yerenin.

On his way back to the battalion, Saburov thought that it was a strange thing indeed that they should suddenly lift a man out of Stalingrad in the bitterest days and send him to study at a military school. In spite of what seemed at first glance the futility of this, it was really a part of the general and enormous march of events which nothing could stop now.

TEN

A T home, in his quarters, a guest was waiting for Saburov. Across from the commissar at the table sat a stranger, a middle-aged man with glasses, and with two bars on his shoulder. When Saburov came in, both the stranger and the commissar stood up.

"Alexei Ivanovich, let me introduce to you Comrade Avdeyev, from Moscow, a newspaper correspondent."

Saburov greeted him. "Did you leave Moscow a long time ago?" he asked with interest.

"Yesterday morning I was still at the Central Airport in Moscow," Avdeyev said.

"It seems to me I've read your articles sometimes in *Izvestia*, haven't I?"

"Yes, mostly there."

"Yesterday in Moscow, and here today," Saburov said enviously. "Well, how is Moscow getting along without us?"

Avdeyev smiled. No one, it seemed, could keep from asking his question.

"All right, it's still standing. Still standing, just as it used to." This was the answer he always gave. "You come from Moscow?"

"No, but I studied there. Have you been here long?"

"Just as you went out," Vanin said, "he appeared. We've already talked a little bit."

"Who sent you to us?"

"The commander of your division. But at headquarters the also advised me to come and see you."

"Really?" Saburov said.

"Yes, I was told to visit the Saburov Battalion."

"Well, well, so we've already received an official name, Saburov said, trying to hide his pleasure by joking about it.

"What did they tell you when they sent you to us?" he aske bluntly. "It would be interesting to know."

"They said that you had taken three buildings in a difficul operation and that you haven't given any part of them bac to the Germans in sixteen days."

"That's true, we haven't given any of them back," Saburo said, "although, of course, for the last week they haven't trie especially hard to take them back. If you'd landed here seve or eight days ago, then you'd have seen something interesting But now it's quiet."

Avdeyev smiled. How many times in his life as a front lin correspondent he had heard those words: "You should hav come to us a while ago." It always seemed to people that wha was going on at any given moment was not really interesting and that what deserved attention had either already take place or was still before them.

"Never mind," he said. "I'll hang around a little, and collec some material. As a matter of fact, it's good that it's quiet, i will be possible to talk with your men."

"Yes," Saburov agreed, "you couldn't have done much talk ing then."

They looked at each other. "Well, what are they writin, about Stalingrad, what do people say in general?" Saburo

132

asked with the eagerness of a man who has not seen a newspaper for a long time.

"They write a lot," Avdeyev said, "and they talk even more, and most of all they think . . . A little while ago I was at the northwestern front. Up there a lot of officers envy you. They say: 'Look, here we sit, while down at Stalingrad . . .' In most cases, you know, they don't doubt for a moment that it's hell down here, but just the same they really want to come."

"Are you here for long?" Saburov asked.

"No, not long, a day or two, then back to the southern sector."

"Right," Saburov said, "down there it's more exciting now."

"With whom would you advise me to talk here in your battalion?"

"Well, I wonder. You might talk to Konyukov. We've got an old soldier by that name. Then there's another, named Vassiliev, who just did quite a successful scouting job. Or you can take them all, by company. Gordienko is in command of Company One. Maslennikov, my chief of staff, a young but very good officer—do you want officers, too?"

"Of course."

"Then talk to Maslennikov."

"I want to talk with you especially," Avdeyev said.

"With me? Of course you can talk with me," Saburov answered, "only with me later. Get acquainted with the battalion first. You can get to know the commander of a battalion only after you've found out what kind of a battalion he has. And what he tells you about himself—that's less important. Isn't that true, Commissar?" he said, turning with a smile to Vanin.

"It's true," Vanin said. "But if the commander of this battalion forgets to tell you about himself, then I'll remind him."

"What time is it?" Saburov looked at his watch. "Four o'clock. I've been gone a long time . . . I need to sleep. How do you feel about it?"

"I'm not against it," Avdeyev agreed.

"If you stay, we'll bring you in a cot here tomorrow, but tonight you'll have to sleep with the chief of staff or with the commissar. They are both built on reasonable lines, they'll leave room for you. You could turn in with me, but I'm afraid that would be a mistake."

"Yes, I'm afraid that's so," Avdeyev said, looking at Saburov's powerful figure.

Saburov had prepared to go to sleep and was standing in the middle of the room wondering where he could get one more blanket for the guest. His glance fell on a bottle standing on the table and he suddenly felt like a drink. He felt like sitting and drinking for a while and asking this man from Moscow every question that came into his head.

"Do you really want to sleep?" he asked.

"No, not especially."

"Then, maybe, instead . . . did you feed him, Commissar?"

"Yes, a little bit."

"Well, if only a little, then that doesn't mean he has been fed, it means he hasn't eaten. Come on, let's have supper, if you're not really sleepy."

While Petya set the table, Saburov threw short and unexpected questions at his guest.

"How is it, are the barricades still up in Moscow?"

"No, they've taken them down."

"But there are still fortifications? Have they added to what there was?"

"As far as I know, they've added to them," Avdeyev said.

"But aren't there men there, in any case, manning them?"

"As far as I know, there are."

"That's good. That means, then, they really are fortifications . . . They are manned all the time?"

"As far as I know, all the time."

"Good. Have you been to the opera?"

"I have."

"To see what?"

"Eugene Onegin."

"That's interesting," Saburov said. "Not that I'd like so much to see it myself. Opera doesn't interest me much, but the fact that it's still on, the fact that people sit in the audience, just as they used to, that's what interests me. I'd like to catch a look at it . . . You know, in general I don't like opera much."

"Neither do I," Avdeyev said.

"The singers are so big, and they all play little girls' parts. It doesn't come off somehow. Maybe now, with the war, they've grown thinner?"

"No, they haven't grown any thinner," Avdeyev smiled.

"Well, never mind," Saburov said, "when I close my eyes it's nice to listen anyway. And I'd like to see it. Do the traffic cops still wear white gloves, the way they used to?"

"You know, I never noticed. There are some things you just don't notice."

"Yes, it's not important," Saburov said, "although on the other hand, maybe it is important. Probably there are a lot fewer automobiles in the streets?"

"Fewer, but more people again, not the way it was in December. Were you there in December?"

"Yes, it was nice there in December. I went up once for the day. Moscow was so empty and quiet."

Petya brought in a frying pan with meat sizzling in it.

"That's American canned meat," Saburov said, "help yourself. Do you drink?" he said, with a little hesitation, putting a "land mine" in front of Avdeyev.

Avdeyev had grown used to having people ask him this question, even on the front, where people usually do not ask if you drink or not. Whether it was his middle-aged, scientific ap-

pearance, or his powerful, double-lensed glasses, which gave
him an especially intellectual look, or his slow, lingering way
of talking, or maybe all these together, he often made people
who did not know him think of him as a very serious, perhaps
even a stuffy, man. In addition, it seemed, people were careful
of the jokes they told in his presence, of swearing, and of taking another drink. Answering Saburov's question, Avdeyev
screwed up his eyes slyly behind his glasses and smiled a little:
"Of course I drink," he said.

They drank a "land mine" each, then a second. Saburov
was desperately tired. The vodka did not go to his head but
only gave him a wonderful awareness of the warmth, comfort,
and friendly atmosphere around him in the dugout.

"You know, I advise you go to Company Two tomorrow,
we've got some awfully good men there; talk especially with
Konyukov. Go and look for yourself. You know," he said,
stopping short as if an unexpected thought had suddenly come
to him, "although maybe we live here in greater danger, gen-
erally speaking, than you, still war must be much more frightening for you."

"Why?"

"Well, you do your work later, when you get back to Moscow, or at the telegraph office, or at staff headquarters, and
here you only look at things, in order to write about them
later. That's what must be frightening. You know why it isn't
so frightening for me? Because I'm busy, I haven't time to
breathe. Here they're shooting, shells are going off, and I'm
talking on the telephone and it's hard to hear; I've got to report, but the operator isn't listening, and I swear at his mother,
and well, you understand, with all this it's almost as if I forget
that the shells are going off. But for you, here, there's nothing
to do; you just sit and wonder: will they land on you or not.
That's what must be frightening for you. Don't tell me it
isn't."

136

"Yes, maybe you're right," Avdeyev said.

They were both silent for a little. "Shall we go to sleep, maybe?" Saburov asked.

"In a minute," Avdeyev answered reluctantly. He did not want to interrupt the conversation. After a year of war he had become firmly convinced that people had grown simpler, purer, and more intelligent. Maybe they had really stayed just as they were, but the good in them had come to the surface. It was perhaps because they were no longer being judged by all the conventional standards: whether a man attended meetings or not, what he said on official occasions, whether he was polite, whether he was obliging, whether he knew how to carry on a conversation, whether he could appear to be attentive and amiable when he didn't feel that way. Suddenly the war had come and all this seemed to be not very important, and people in the face of death stopped thinking about how they looked and how they seemed to others. For this there was no longer any time, nor any interest.

During this year of war, Avdeyev had heard more frank talking than ever before in his newspaperman's life. No matter how tired he was, whenever conversation promised to become personal and philosophical, he tried to stretch it out as long as he could.

"Let's go to sleep," he said, "but I only wanted to ask you . . ." Saburov never found out what he had wanted to ask, because Petya came in at this moment and announced that a scout had just come in. Saburov looked at his watch; it was five o'clock in the morning.

"Who went out today?"

"Vassiliev," Petya answered.

Saburov laughed. "Last time, too, he came back on the dot of five. A punctual fellow. Maybe he'll have an N.C.O.'s documents again, and another German tommy-gun. Well, let him come in."

Vassiliev walked in. There was no tommy-gun in his hands. After he had saluted the captain, he put some papers on the table. This time, they were those of a German sergeant.

"That's fine," Saburov said. "Where did you get him?"

"At Number 4. He was checking the guard. I got him between two sentry positions."

"Did you capture him?"

"No, Comrade Captain. I killed him. I couldn't have got him back."

"Didn't you bring his gun?"

"No," Vassiliev said, cursing to himself the German major who had refused this time to give him a revolver. Now the German's stingy stupidity would make him tell an extra lie, and extra lies were never safe. "He had a revolver and I took it. I put it in my belt but it dropped out somewhere, while I was crawling. I was bringing it back for you, Comrade Captain—it was steel-blue, and new." Vassiliev had actually seen a new, steel-blue revolver lying on the major's table.

"So," Saburov said, examining the documents. "Sit down, on the stool there."

Vassiliev's heart missed a beat: why was he being asked to stay?

"This is a correspondent," Saburov said. "He wants to talk to you. And this is the same Vassiliev I was telling you about. Well, you two sit here and talk while I go and check the guards." He walked to the door.

"How many times have you gone on reconnaissance?" Avdeyev asked.

Saburov stopped at the door. "Better not ask him about this trip, but about the other one he went on before. It turned out pretty tragically; it will interest you."

Saburov walked out. Avdeyev looked at Vassiliev. He saw a man about thirty years old with a face that told him nothing, and with quiet, lazy eyes.

138

"In other words, you've been out twice?"

"Yes."

"Tell me about the first trip, the one the captain was just talking about.

"What should I tell you?" Vassiliev asked. When he learned this man was a correspondent, he had brightened up. It gave him a malicious pleasure to think of his exploit being written up in *Izvestia* or in *Pravda*.

"Tell me it all in order."

"What can I tell you?" Vassiliev said. "We went out at eleven at night, the two of us, and we got through; the Germans didn't fire. We caught an N.C.O., and I stuck him with a bayonet. Then we crawled back. There were two of us. On the way back, my comrade got killed—that is, it turned out that way later. At first he was just badly wounded but he could still crawl. I thought he had been killed."

"So," Avdeyev said. "No, you're not telling it to me right."

"What do you mean, not right?" Vassiliev asked calmly, but with anxiety inside him.

"Not right," Avdeyev said. "You're telling it to me just the way the captain, probably, reported it to headquarters. That isn't what I want. Tell me, step by step, how you went along, what you felt when you were crawling, how you killed the German, what you felt like then, how you crawled back, what was going through your head—tell me all these things."

"Well, that's how it was. They gave us the job—Panasyuk and I went out. We went . . ." He stopped short. He felt suddenly confused and uneasy at heart, just as if this quiet man with thick glasses across from him knew everything and was asking questions just to check up on him. It was as if a detective were sitting in front of him, but that was clearly not so; everything was all right, this was a reporter, he would only have to describe it all, quite simply . . . "Well, we went along. First we went up to the line . . ."

"What were you talking about then?" Avdeyev asked.

"Talking about? Nothing."

"Well, what were you thinking about then?"

What had he been thinking about? He remembered how he had thought about where it would be easier to kill Panasyuk—here, crossing the line, or closer to the Germans. Then he had thought about how to crawl on without attracting German fire. What else had he thought about? He had thought about his father.

"Yes, what were you thinking about?" Avdeyev repeated.

Vassiliev had often had to lie, but he did not know how to make this up. "I wasn't thinking about anything."

"It couldn't happen," Avdeyev said. "A man always thinks about something. Try to remember; it would interest me."

"I didn't think about anything," Vassiliev said stubbornly. "I thought about how to do the job," he added, "that's all."

"Well, all right. What did you feel when you crawled up to the German?"

What had he felt?

"That was inside the German lines," Avdeyev went on quietly. "Did you whisper to your comrade, or make signs to him what to do? Don't you remember?"

Vassiliev remembered how Panasyuk had been crawling a little in front of him and to the left, and how he had moved a little more to the right to give himself room to strike sideways with the bayonet, and how he had struck, and how Panasyuk had grabbed with his hands at the bricks in front of him. They had made a little noise. And he remembered how he had held Panasyuk's arms, so he could not make a noise in his death agony, because the Germans might fire at the noise. But all this, naturally, he could not tell about.

"No, we didn't do anything, and we didn't whisper, we just crawled," he said.

"All right," Avdeyev said. "But when you had crawled right up to the German, what did you feel?"

"Well, he was right next to us," Vassiliev said, remembering again how he had pushed the bayonet into Panasyuk. "He was right next to us, so I stuck my bayonet in his side."

"You jumped up and struck him?"

"No, why jump up? That is, yes, of course, I jumped up and hit him."

"What was your comrade doing then?"

"Nothing," Vassiliev said. "He was helping me."

"How?"

"Well, he helped later, when we searched him."

"How did you crawl then?"

"Well, we crawled, the way you usually crawl. Then he was killed, Panasyuk . . ."

"How was he killed?"

"They started to shoot and they killed him."

"Didn't he say anything, when they hit him? He was just wounded, wasn't he?"

"Yes, just wounded, but he didn't say anything. I thought he was dead."

These questions were beginning to give Vassiliev a hollow feeling in the pit of his stomach. He felt no remorse about Panasyuk. But having the whole affair dragged out of him, word by word, and not being able to fabricate his story as he went along reduced him to helpless exasperation.

"Then I came back and reported to the captain," he said in an effort to bring the story to an end.

He was afraid Avdeyev would ask him some more questions, but the reporter only said: "Well, all right then, thanks. That's all," and he wrote something in his notebook.

Vassiliev stood up. "May I go?"

"Yes."

He went out.

"Did you have your talk?" Saburov asked when he returned. "How did the scout turn out?"

"All right," Avdeyev said slowly, "all right."

"Are you going to write about him?"

"I don't know. No, I don't think I will. When people talk to me, it's very important for me to get at their feelings and what they think about. But while he was talking, I couldn't get any clear picture of him. He talked almost as if he were saying someone else's words. No, I won't write about him."

"That often happens," Saburov said. "A fellow does something, and then can't talk about it."

"No," Avdeyev said. "it's nearly always possible to get a man's story if you know how to ask the right questions. Sometimes, a soldier doesn't want to talk, but that doesn't mean he can't. He just doesn't want to. Often, when this happens, it means that a man is willing to tell a short lie but knows it will sound badly if he starts to elaborate it under questioning. Then he doesn't describe what happened to him, and not because he can't, but because it never really happened."

"Well, this happened all right," Saburov said.

"Probably so, I don't know. But there's nothing to write about. Not one word came alive."

"Well, never mind," Saburov said. "Tomorrow you can talk with the others. And find out for yourself whom it's worth talking with. I have a lot of good people; almost all of them are good. You probably hear that often from officers, don't you?"

"Often," Avdeyev agreed.

"Well, anyway, it's true. I don't know what sort of men these were before the war or what they'll be like afterwards, but now they're really good, almost all of them. And I think that most of them will stay good—those, of course, who live. Do you know, I'm almost certain of that . . . Well, let's go to sleep."

142

Saburov walked over to Vanin, who had dozed off long ago, lifted him up, and moved him to the edge of his bed.

"Why do you do that?" Avdeyev said. "You'll wake him up."

"No," Saburov said, "he'll sleep. If the telephone rang he'd wake up like a shot, but like this you could spin him around three times. I know from experience. Lie down, half the bed is ours."

Avdeyev took off his boots and lay down without undressing, covering himself with his coat. Saburov sat on his own bed, took off his blouse and his trousers, folded everything neatly, lined up his boots, and placed the strips of cotton cloth in their tops. Then, covering himself with a blanket, he lit a cigarette.

"When I can, I always undress," he said. "I served once on the frontier, so I keep everything in order, the way frontier guards do. It takes me fifty seconds to dress. I've timed it. In my opinion, the war will last a long time. So I sleep under a blanket, too . . . What's the matter, don't you approve?" he asked with a smile.

"Certainly, I approve," Avdeyev said, "I approve and I wish you a pleasant night."

Saburov sank back on his pillow and inhaled deeply several times. He didn't feel like sleeping. The door of the dugout was apparently open and from outside he could hear the steady, sad rustling of the rain—the last rain, perhaps, of the year.

ELEVEN

ARLY in the morning Avdeyev went out to Company One with Vanin. Saburov stayed; he wanted to use the quiet to catch up on some chores. He and Maslennikov sat for two or three hours over the preparation of various military reports, some of which were actually necessary and some of which seemed to Saburov useless, in force only by virtue of some peacetime passion for all kinds of paper work. When Maslennikov went out, Saburov sat down to a job which he had postponed for a long time and which hung heavy on his conscience: answering letters which had arrived for soldiers who had been killed. Almost since the very start of the war, he had taken on the difficult obligation of answering these letters. It distressed him to realize how we try, when a man dies, not to let his family know about it for as long as possible, to delay answers to their letters as long as we can, and if it is possible not to answer them at all. The motive behind this always seemed to him nothing better than a simple desire to by-pass someone else's grief, to try not to touch it in order not to have to share it.

The first letter was from the wife of Parfenov.

"Petya, my dear," his wife had written him . . . (It seemed

they had called him Petya; he had not known this.) "We miss you terribly and we're waiting for the war to end so you can come back. Galochka is a big girl now and already walks by herself and hardly ever falls down." Saburov read the letter carefully to the end. It was not long; greetings from his family, some words about work, a hope for a quick victory over the Fascists, and at the end two lines of a child's scrawl, written by the older son, and then unsteady lines drawn by a child's hand held in its mother's hand, and under these: "Galochka wrote this herself."

What could he answer? Always in these cases Saburov knew there was only one thing to be said—he is killed, he is dead. But he always thought for a long time about it, as if each time he were writing his first answer to one of these letters. What could he answer? In actual fact, what was there to say?

He remembered the little Parfenov lying on his back on the cement floor, his white face, and the knapsacks piled under his head. This man, who had died on his first day of fighting and whom he had hardly known before then, was for him a comrade-in-arms, one of the many, far too many, who had fought side by side with him and had died while he himself had somehow survived. He had become used to this, as he had become used to war, and it was simple enough to say to himself: here he was, his name was Parfenov, he fought and was killed. But there, in Penza, at 24 Karl Marx Street, these words, "He is dead," would not be words but a catastrophe, the end of all hope. After these words, at 24 Karl Marx Street, a wife would cease to call herself a wife and become a widow, children would stop calling themselves children and become orphans. This was not just grief, this was a complete changing of all life, of all the future. And always when he wrote such letters, he was most afraid that whoever read them might think that they had been easy for him to write. He wanted each letter to seem, when it was read, as if it had been written by a comrade in grief, a man as sorrowing as they who were reading the letter. Then it might not hurt so much, it might not be so sad to read the letter through.

People sometimes need to be lied to; he knew this. They want passionately a hero's death for the man they have loved, or to know, as it is usually written, that he died the death of the brave. They want him not to have died simply, but to have fallen doing something important, and they want above all else to think that he remembered them before his death.

Saburov always tried to satisfy this desire when he answered letters, and when it was necessary, he lied. He lied more or less as the situation demanded; these were the only lies which never bothered him. He took up his fountain pen, tore a sheet of paper from his notebook, and began to write in a quick, large, bold hand. He wrote how he and Parfenov had served together for a long time, how Parfenov had died heroically in night fighting inside Stalingrad (and this was true), and how before falling he had shot three Germans (and this was not true), and how when he died in Saburov's arms he had remembered his son, Volodya, before his death and had asked that his son be told not to forget his father.

When he had finished the letter, Saburov picked up a photograph lying in front of him and looked at it before enclosing it in the envelope. It had been taken in Saratov, when the division was being reformed, by a street photographer; the little Parfenov stood there, drawn up to full height in a martial pose, his hand resting on his leather holster—no doubt the photographer had insisted on this.

The next letter was to Sergeant Tarasov of Company One. Saburov knew only that Tarasov had also been killed in the first fighting, but how and under what circumstances he did not know. This was a simple letter from the country, a peasant woman's letter, written in big letters on a piece of notebook paper ruled in squares. But every word in it breathed love and grief, awkwardly expressed but no less powerful. Although Saburov did not know how Tarasov had fallen, he wrote anyway that he had been a fine soldier, that he had died the death of the brave, and that he, his commander, was proud of him. Having finished this, Saburov took up a third letter, and when he had finished it telephoned to Company One where the commissar and Avdeyev had gone.

"They've already gone back," the company commander, Gordienko, said.

"Did they climb around a lot?" Saburov asked.

"Quite a lot."

Saburov heard Gordienko chuckling into the telephone. He put down the receiver with a sigh of relief.

There were four of them at dinner. Besides the commissar and Avdeyev, Maslennikov came. Vanin was his usual self, but Avdeyev was tired out. Back at his quarters, he was feeling that light and happy sensation which comes to every man in war when the consciousness of danger is replaced by a feeling of relative safety. After dinner they started talking about this.

"You know, to put it frankly, the feeling of danger and the possibility of dying is a really exhausting business; you can get tired out from it, isn't that the truth?"

"True," Saburov said.

"A soldier sometimes reminds me," Avdeyev said, "of a diver who goes down into the water gradually, with the pressure increasing all the time. It's just the same here, the danger increases by degrees and you grow gradually used to it. In the rear, people often don't understand that danger isn't a constant quantity and that everything at the front is relative. After an attack, when one of your soldiers falls into a trench, it seems to him safety. When I come from a company back to your battalion headquarters, your little hole here looks like a fortress to me. When you drop in at army headquarters, it seems to you like a vast silence there. On the other shore of the Volga, even though it's being shot up all the time, it would seem like a resort to you, or almost a resort, anyway, although even that shore would seem terribly dangerous to any man arriving there for the first time from the rear. What do you think, isn't this so?"

"True. Of course, it's true," Saburov said. "With one reservation as to Stalingrad: here army headquarters itself is sometimes just as near the Germans and just as much in danger as we are. Considering the quiet we've got now, on this sector, it's even more dangerous."

After dinner Saburov put on his overcoat and said: "Well, I'm going over to Company Two."

Avdeyev understood this as an invitation, or even perhaps a challenge. He stood up and quietly put on his coat.

"Where are you going?"

"With you," Avdeyev answered.

Saburov looked at his tired face and wanted to object. Then he realized that once this man had understood a simple sentence, not even addressed to him, as a proposal to go along, he would insist on going now even if someone tried to talk him out of it. Saburov didn't feel like useless argument anyway, so he merely said: "Well, all right, let's be off."

The Siberian, Potapov, was still in command of Company Two. When he saw Saburov with a stranger, probably from headquarters, Potapov followed the custom of the front by inviting them to eat with him in his dugout. Whatever God could give them, nothing special, really nothing at all, just some of our Siberian boiled meat dumplings, and nothing else.

Saburov knew that if Potapov had dumplings, they would be something wonderful. In the way Potapov had said "nothing special," there had been that peculiar front-line pride with which junior officers always invite their seniors to eat with them. Whenever possible, they tried to fix things so that their

148

cooks were better than those of their superior officers, and they often succeeded.

But Saburov and Avdeyev declined the dumplings, and walked along a trench to find, behind the front wall of the building, the squad which Konyukov commanded. The trench had been dug below the wall itself, along the foundations, and cleverly camouflaged with piles of broken bricks and earth. Two good communication paths led back under the building to a dugout which had been covered with charred beams. Two machine-gun nests had been set up, as well as a place for sharp-shooters. Along one side shelves had been cut into the earth bank to hold all manner of soldiers' reserves: mess tins, tobacco, and other things.

"Never mind, go on smoking," Saburov said when the soldiers, seeing him, began to put out their cigarettes. "Well, how are things, Konyukov?"

"Very good, Comrade Captain."

Konyukov had not lost his disciplined manner, but after a half month of fighting a certain woodenness in him had softened. In the face of danger he seemed to feel himself on a more comradely footing with his superiors.

"How about it, have you grown used to the bombs?"

"That's just it, I've got used to them. If you didn't get used to them, allow me to report, you might just as well go jump into the Volga. He (in soldier's speech "he" invariably meant the Germans) drops them, and he keeps on dropping them. He's teaching us, he's giving us practice; how could you keep from getting used to them?"

"This is Senior Sergeant Konyukov," Saburov said, turning to Avdeyev. "On the 27th I recommended him for a decoration for bravery."

Konyukov smiled happily. To tell the truth, he had already heard from his company commander that he had been recommended for a decoration, but the fact that his battalion commander repeated it out loud and in front of all his soldiers was especially pleasing to him. As often happens with people in moments of emotion, he could not remember what he was supposed to say in this situation, and came up instead with something he had learned a long time ago in his earlier war. "Glad to do my best," he snapped out. On the last syllable he bit his tongue so that the phrase did not conclude with the pre-revolutionary ending: "Your Honor." *

"This comrade is a battalion commissar from Moscow," Saburov said. "Tell him, Konyukov, what you did on the 27th. Meanwhile, give me your field glasses."

Konyukov took off from around his neck a large pair of Zeiss field glasses, picked up by him on the first day after the buildings had been taken. He handed them to the captain. He always wore them on his chest, which made him look almost like an officer and not at all like a sergeant. He was proud of them and now, handing the glasses to Saburov, he felt a little worried, for he remembered from the last war how commanding officers loved to appropriate interesting and useful trophies from their subordinates.

While Saburov perched himself on an outcropping of the wall and examined carefully through the glasses the ruins of the neighboring street, Konyukov proceeded in leisurely style with his tale. He himself considered the 27th to have been his specially lucky day and he talked about it with deep satisfaction. On that day he had been a courier, and seven times before nightfall he had crawled across an open space from Company Two to Company One and back again, along a stretch where every other courier had been killed. He talked about it with the picturesque expressions of an old soldier.

"I'm crawling along, you see, and over me the bullets are

---

* Before 1918 Russian soldiers acknowledged any commendation by an officer with the words "Glad to do my best, your Honor." Red Army soldiers are now instructed to say instead: "I serve the Soviet Union."

flying back and forth, and on my back I've got a kind of knapsack, and in it there is some tobacco and a crust of bread because, after all, even though it's easier to crawl without them, still you can't leave bread or tobacco behind. You never know where you'll get to; maybe you can't crawl back again. Or you might be wounded along the road, and you'd have a smoke and a crust to chew at least. Now on top of the knapsack on my back there's a frying pan, because what kind of eating is there without a frying pan? So I crawl along and the frying pan starts to swing from side to side and rattle. It isn't rattling because it's badly tied on but because the bullets are hitting it —you see, it stuck out pretty high—and as I'm crawling along I suddenly feel that something's burning on my back.

"I take out my knife, pull my belt around, and cut the pack off. It falls down next to me, and, would you believe it, it's smoking. The Germans have set it on fire with incendiary bullets, and all I can do is start laughing. Somehow it seems funny: what do they think I am, a tank? They certainly set my turret on fire. Well, so I throw the pack away and crawl along, only the tobacco is gone, all burned up. I keep on going farther. There's a perfectly flat place along the path which is full of mud, and I crawl through the rain and snow there so tight to the ground that I scoop the mud up with the tops of my boots. And they keep on firing at me. Well, here I am pressed down to the ground . . ."

Here he looked around at the soldiers listening to him. They were hearing the story not for the first time, and their faces showed that a joke was coming. They knew it already and it always gave them great amusement.

"I tell you, I'm crawling along pressed down to the ground, tighter than I squeezed down on my young wife the first year we were married. It's God's truth. I cross myself." Konyukov did cross himself gravely while his listeners laughed. "And then I sneak along behind the ruins where they couldn't get me with a machine-gun, but still they don't want me to get out alive. It was insulting to them. Here it is the second war in which they try to get me and still they can't do it. They aim and miss. So they start peppering shells at me. All around nothing but mud. The shells go off and the splinters fly around and splash like sheep running through the mud . . ."

"Why don't you go on talking here?" Saburov interrupted. "I'll be back right away." He handed the glasses back to Konyukov, who was overjoyed to get them, and crawled out of the trench towards the next platoon.

Thirty minutes later, as he was preparing to come back again, he heard from his left several long bursts of machine-gun fire. He had just begun wondering what they meant when one after another five or six German shells whistled over his head and exploded at approximately the same spot, where Konyukov had been talking. Saburov waited a minute and then crawled back. He found Konyukov and Avdeyev sitting across from each other in the bottom of the trench.

"You see, I told you so," Konyukov was saying. "As soon as we slapped him, he slapped back."

"Yes, you're right." Avdeyev answered with some feeling. "You certainly were right, and that's the way it should be."

"What's happening here?" Saburov asked. "Those didn't land on anyone, did they?"

"No, they only spoiled his cap," Konyukov said, standing up and laughingly picking up with two fingers Avdeyev's cap, which had been lying upside down on the side of the trench. "He took it off when he started to aim and put it up there. Look, the Germans hit it as neat as a hen puts eggs in a basket of linden bark."

Two small shell splinters had pierced the cap. They had not gone completely through the cloth but only nipped it, just as if moths had eaten into the fabric. Saburov took out the splinters and looked at the cap.

152

"No one will believe you if you say shell splinters hit it. Everyone will say it was moths."

"I won't be talking about it," Avdeyev said.

"That means it was you who fired?" Saburov asked.

"Yes, at those ruins. They told me Germans were sitting there."

"That they were; they were sitting there," Konyukov repeated, "that's why they answered you, because they were sitting there."

"You see," Avdeyev said, "everything was quiet and now it isn't. Why do you shoot so seldom? Are you saving ammunition?"

"The devil with ammunition," Konyukov said, "we're not saving bullets, but why shoot when you can't see them? As soon as we can see them, we always shoot, but when you can't see them . . ."

"Have you finished your conversation?" Saburov asked.

"Yes, I guess so, let's go on."

When they had gone as far as Potapov's dugout, Avdeyev turned to Saburov and said suddenly: "Do you know, I fired at them deliberately, on principle."

"You mean you wanted to kill a German yourself?"

"No, don't get sore, maybe I'm mixing in your business, but it seemed to me it wasn't right . . ."

"What wasn't right?"

"Well, all that quiet. That kind of armistice."

"Why?"

"Perhaps it's true that when you can't see the Germans there's no point in shooting at them," Avdeyev said. "But it seemed to me suddenly that maybe they weren't shooting for another reason."

"What other reason?"

"Because maybe they didn't want to be answered. Maybe they like it to be quiet. So I fired several bursts, and the Ger-

153

mans banged off right away with some shells. So it works out: we won't shoot, and they won't shoot. The way I feel, that's not good. What do you think?"

"Maybe you're right."

"Why did I think of all this?" Avdeyev said. "Last spring, on the western front, I noticed how every time after an attack there would come a kind of quiet. They kept silent just the same way, sometimes longer than was necessary, it seemed to me."

"Yes, maybe you're right," Saburov said thoughtfully. It occurred to him that this man was, actually, obviously right. After heavy fighting and the chance of being killed at any moment, every soldier and maybe even he himself, perhaps unconsciously, wanted not to break the silence for a little while, not to go on swapping shells and machine-gun bullets, when he didn't have to. This was natural, and at the same time it was wrong. "He is right," Saburov thought. He would have to give an order that in addition to nightly raids they should not only answer all German fire in the daytime, but also from time to time disturb the Germans if necessary with blind firing, just to keep them jumpy and nervous.

They found Potapov waiting for them on the threshold of his dugout. He talked again about his boiled meat dumplings. While they had been gone he had coached his cook, and now he was determined to get them to eat.

"Please, Comrade Captain, I urge you to, if only to celebrate the arrival of a guest," Potapov began. At just this second three or four heavy shells exploded all at once behind the dugout. Saburov pushed Avdeyev through the door and squeezed himself against the wall. After the first ones, another dozen shells fell in front and behind, then a mortar began to fire, then shells again, and again mortars, and so it continued for a quarter of an hour. Potapov was giving commands to messengers, trying to shout above the racket, and the messengers ran off to the platoons.

Saburov looked at the sky. Like a wedge of wild geese, the German bombers were coming over. From this distance it was hard to count them, but it seemed to him there were at least sixty. After a minute's pause, the artillery began again. Black fountains rose toward the sky behind the dugout.

"Well, I guess the quiet's over," Saburov said softly, more to himself than to Avdeyev. "Potapov!" he called.

"At your service."

"The battalion commissar will stay with you until the artillery barrage has finished. Pick out one of the pauses and send him back to me with an escort. I'm going back to battalion headquarters."

"Comrade Saburov, I'll go with you," Avdeyev said.

"No," Saburov said curtly. "We won't even talk about it now. Potapov will pick the moment and he'll send you back with an escort."

"But wouldn't it be better if . . ."

"No, that's all. Don't argue. I'm the boss here. Petya, let's go." Climbing out of the trench, Saburov and Petya ran quickly back to battalion headquarters.

The quiet had really ended. Saburov, crawling from shell hole to shell hole, thought to himself that if a German attack did not start at the most inside fifteen minutes, then he had learned nothing at all in this war.

TWELVE

IT WAS morning. Five days and nights of fighting had followed the lull. Vassiliev was lying on the bottom of a trench, protected from the rain by a canvas flap. He was lying on his back, and he opened a corner of the canvas to look at the gray, dull, autumn sky. He had returned the night before from a successful reconnaissance trip, the third he had made recently, and as a reward he had been told to go off and sleep as long as he could. He had slept like the dead for three hours, but then he woke up and lay where he was, his eyes open, thinking.

He had made a deal with the Germans to set a trap for tonight in the ruins of a building in the middle of no man's land. It was a typical military trap, not too clever and not too simple, the kind in which soldiers usually get caught unless there is some special accident or slip.

He had returned this time with an officer's documents and revolver, to make his story even more plausible than usual. After he had listened to Saburov's thanks, he had reported to him that one passage between the southern ruins (this is what the former motion picture theater was called in the battalion) and the black house (this is what the former bank was called)

156

had been only carelessly mined by the Germans and was not guarded.

"If we could make a night attack through there, we could cut off an entire German company, and capture it," Vassiliev said. "There's no doubt about it, Comrade Captain. But you'll want to check it. You ought to see for yourself whether I'm right or not. You can get through almost to the rear of the Germans by that route. And another night, we could make a heavy attack through it."

The idea of making a night attack and capturing a German company, just now when things were not going well for the defenders of Stalingrad, was sure to be enormously attractive to Saburov. The only doubt was whether he would agree to explore the route first with one or two men. Vassiliev thought he would, and he had told this to the Germans and arranged for a trap to be set tonight in which they could literally capture Saburov with their bare hands.

Vassiliev had stood in front of Saburov and outlined his plan for verifying the route. He spoke in the casual tone of a man who has no special fears or worries, but in his heart he had been anxious——would Saburov agree or not? Saburov had agreed.

"What time will it be quietest there?" he had asked.

"From eleven to midnight."

"Go back to your quarters and sleep yourself out," Saburov had said. "Come back for me at eleven o'clock."

It was dirty and wet in the trench. Water was running down its sides. Rain had collected in the canvas flap and was falling in heavy drops through a little tear in the cloth. The late autumn rain had been falling for three days in a row; everything was now so wet that there was no dry cover left. Vassiliev lay there, looking at the sky and thinking that he could not go on forever doing what he had done in the last few weeks. Sometimes he caught himself envying the soldiers lying next

157

to him, listening to the same shells flying over them. The Germans were firing at them, but they were firing back at the Germans. He was in the same danger as they, and he felt the stupidity of this position. After all, he had studied a year in the special school at Krakow; he had a place in the sun coming to him as soon as the Germans won their victory. But he might be killed here in the mud and the rain by a German shell splinter, and he would "die the death of the brave," and the men next to him would mourn him and honor him as a man fallen for his fatherland against the Germans. What could be stupider than that?

When he had arranged the trap the night before, the Germans had told him he would be able to stay on their side for a while and take a rest, after the trap had been sprung. Even if they gave him only a short rest, he would know how to stretch it. After all, the war would soon end, and if it didn't maybe they would send him back to work in some rear area, where some regiment was being reformed, at some quieter work.

If anything could have increased his hatred for the world around him, it was this fear for his life which had grown so strong during the last few days. He was afraid of dying stupidly, by some accident, and this made him hate everything around him even more than before.

This was no new feeling for him. It had begun a long time ago, in his childhood. His mother and father had not taught it to him, and later he had despised them both, especially his father, because they hadn't. His mother, after all, had been only a plain, quiet woman. His father's hand had always been the heavy one in their home; he was a powerful man, and sometimes a rough one. But the father had never known hatred. He had not loved the demobilized Red Army soldier, Stepanyuk, who had opened a branch of "The Society of the Godless" in his village. He had not loved the president of the village soviet, who had wanted to close all the churches. He had not

158

ved two or three more men, who in their turn had not loved
im. But all these taken together, calling themselves Soviet
Russia, he could not hate. He called it "Russia" himself, or
ometimes "little Russia," and he loved its hills, its pastures,
s woods; he loved his own village, Gorodisha; he loved the
eople who lived in the houses next to his.

When Vassiliev used to ask his father about the past, the
nswers were always cool, almost indifferent. The priest was
nhappy about wrongs people did to each other, but he used
o say that wrongs there had always been and probably always
ould be. He had christened, married, and buried so many
eople in his lifetime that it seemed to him people didn't
hange much. They went right on being born, getting married,
nd dying, and whether they were right or wrong in relation to
im, Father Nikolai of the Gorodisha Church, God would de-
ide later in judgment over them and over him. He never
aised his hand for or against power, because everything
round him was Russia, and so power over it stayed Russian,
nd he did not assume for himself the right to judge this or to
hallenge it.

In this the son was not like the father. From school days he
egan to hate. He was a bad student and did not like any sub-
ect very much, and he hated those who studied well and who
rew interested in something. He finished elementary school
ith a bad record, and was turned down when he tried for more
ducation. Gradually, he had become a failure and a sour man.
Obstacles which in those times were set up against him as the
on of a priest aroused in him no desire to overcome them, to
tudy harder than others, or to become more intelligent. No,
hey were not so much stumbling blocks for him as they were
xcuses. Well, of course, he told himself, people didn't like
im just because he was the son of a priest; he had failed his
xaminations because he was the son of a priest; he had not
een allowed to go on studying because he was the son of a

159

priest. If it had only been the old times, before 1917 . . . He had not known the old times, but he felt that since people did not like him now, they would probably have liked him then, and they would have helped him rise above all the others who were now rising above him. When his father, in moments of exasperation, told him that he would have come to no better end in the old times than now, and that he was just no good, he took this for an old man's grumbling. It seemed to him that he would have been a great man under the old regime, and that only the fact that now things were different, the laws different, the power in different hands, kept him from being a great man. So he hated this power, and these laws, and these times. Gradually he came to feel that everything was permissible to him: he had the right to steal because he felt that this new power was slowly killing him. Because he himself was good for nothing and unlike others around him, he came to believe that he alone was real, and that what was worthless was all the rest, because they were unlike him.

This ended where it was bound to end, in criminal activity, and there were enough political motives for it so that, when he was caught, it came under the statutes against counter-revolution. Working on a state farm, he had stolen spare automobile parts just before harvest time, and when the theft was about to be discovered, he set fire to the warehouse in which they had been stored. He was sentenced to be shot; the sentence was later changed to a long term of imprisonment.

He had escaped from his concentration camp in the first month of the war, determined to get somehow to the German side of the line. The invasion helped him, and in August, 1941, he showed up on their side, somewhere near Smolensk. He described himself to the German officer who questioned him as a fugitive enemy of the Soviet regime, and he recited a few quotations from a book by Nietzsche which he had once read in his father's library.

160

The Germans didn't care whether he could quote Nietzsche. He could be useful to them under any circumstances, and they took him without examining him too closely. This was how his espionage school in Krakow began, and then, his work. From this point on he could not turn back, and this fact, together with the Germans' discipline and his own consuming hatred, had led him to act in war more daringly and more decisively than he could ever have dreamed of acting before. Sometimes he even began to fall in love with his work. But now, here in Stalingrad, he had grown really tired of the feeling of constant danger. Any close explosion filled him with the simplest kind of terror. Now he wanted only rest, whatever it might cost him.

A German shell interrupted his thoughts. It exploded a dozen steps from his trench. The blast ripped the canvas, and its wet, muddy end dropped on Vassiliev's face. Clods of heavy mud slithered down into the trench. "It's started," Vassiliev thought with exasperation. For the last five days it had always started at the same time, at six o'clock in the morning, with sunrise. The cannon fire continued for fifteen minutes, then there could be heard the distant rumble of tanks. Someone yelled: "Get ready," and Vassiliev grabbed his tommy-gun like the others around him and stood up in the trench.

From here everything that was happening in front could be clearly seen. The tanks came down the street and turned at Company Three, the next one to theirs. Against Vassiliev's company came tommy gunners. There were a lot of them this time, more than usual. When others began to shoot, Vassiliev also fired. He was forced to fire by the evil thought that to the Germans at this moment he was less than nothing, and that if they got up to the trench they would kill him in the same fever they would kill the others around him. As often happens to people who know that they may soon be in safety, his present danger had now a special terror for him. He was within one

day of at least temporary release from this dreadful peri
So he fired madly with his tommy-gun, whispering over an
over to himself words he had used since childhood: "My Go
my God, my God."

Saburov was wakened by the same thunder of cannon fir
Before he even opened his eyes, he fumbled for the coat folde
by his side, put it on, and sat on the edge of the couch. For th
first time in the war, his head was spinning like a top. Poin
of flame danced in the air, formed themselves into circles c
fire, and whirled before his eyes like pinwheels.

He stood up, walked over to the lamp, and looked into
mirror which he took from the table. "I don't have to shav
yet," he thought. His face seemed to him no longer white, bu
green. It was stuffy in the dugout, but at the same time raw
Moisture was hanging on the walls. Putting the mirror back o
the table, he let it slip and it broke on the floor. He picked u
the largest piece, in which he could still see himself, and place
it back on the table.

"Breaking a mirror brings bad luck," he said to himsel
and he laughed. Things had now come to such a pass that a
dreams and predictions of bad luck were fulfilled without ex
ception. Every day, one misfortune or another was sure t
happen. It was not hard to be superstitious under such condi
tions. He remembered how Avdeyev had gone out of the dug
out two nights before and then come back for his knapsack
laughing at the time because this was supposed to bring ba
luck. But that very night he had been shot in the arm abov
the elbow and he had had to be moved across the Volga.

He rolled a cigarette and struck a match. The match did no
light. He struck another, and still another, then ten in a row
He spat in disgust, and threw both the cigarette and the match
box on the floor. So much carbon monoxide had collected in th
dugout that matches would not light. He had moved here tw
days ago. On the first day of the German attack after the spel

f quiet, several direct hits had demolished the furnace room. He had moved into another basement room, but the following ay, towards evening, it had been destroyed, too. It was then hat he had moved here. This dugout was even below the basement level. Here at one time had been sewage pipes running nder the earth. His engineers in a night had widened the unnel and made a dugout. It was the third command post he ad set up in five days. He could not understand it. Either he Germans had become incredibly lucky or they had their wn eyes and ears here in his battalion. He tried to brush this hought away. His disposition made him like to trust people, nd he didn't want even to think of the possibility of treachery. t seemed to him that here and now, in Stalingrad, where they ll stood together in the face of death, there simply could not e treachery among them. It was probably an accident, a urious coincidence. It works out that way in war, as a matter f fact, he thought, such strange coincidences actually do appen.

He walked out of the dugout and clambered up to an observation post from which he could begin to direct the repulse f the German attack. His telephone contact broke down three imes; in a single hour two signal corps men were killed. Finaly, they beat the Germans back. But the day promised to be a ough one. Saburov went back to his dugout, called Maslennikov, and gave the instructions required to get ready for new ttacks. He had hardly finished talking with Maslennikov when a military lawyer from division headquarters, an investigator whom he knew, crawled on all fours into the dugout. Saburov got up from the cot and greeted him.

"Well," he asked, "are you going to cross-examine Stepanov?"

"Yes."

"Things are pretty hot today, there won't be time."

"Well, what if there isn't any time? There's never any time.

Nobody knows when there will be any time," the investigato objected. "We'll never get anything done."

"Dust yourself off," Saburov said. Only then did the invest gator notice that he was covered with dirt.

"Did you crawl here?"

"Yes."

"Lucky you got through all right."

"Yes, almost," the investigator said. "You haven't got shoemaker in your battalion?"

"What for?"

"Look, it's as if they were making fun of me; they shot of half my heel." He held out his foot; the heel of his boot ha been neatly sliced in half.

"We haven't any shoemaker. We had one, but he wa wounded yesterday. Where is Stepanov? Petya!" Saburo shouted. "Show this officer to the soldier on duty. Stepanov there, helping him."

"What do you mean, he's helping a soldier on duty?" th investigator asked in surprise.

"Well, what else was I to do with him? Put him under guard I haven't got enough men even without that."

"But he is under investigation."

"All right, let him be under investigation. I tell you, haven't any men. There's no one here to stand guard over hin while we wait for your decision and, frankly, I'm damned if see any reason for it anyway."

The investigator went out with Petya. Looking after them Saburov thought that war was full of strange situations, som of them stupid ones. Of course, this investigator was only do ing his job. Maybe Stepanov should be court-martialled, bu the investigator had crawled up here on his stomach to questio him. To get a few answers, he had risked his life. He could have been killed five times over on the road, and he could b killed while he was asking his questions, and when he went bacl

164

o division headquarters, maybe taking Stepanov with him, then they could both be killed on the way back with exactly the same ease. In spite of this, he was doing everything that he should do, according to the rules.

The investigator led Stepanov, under guard as regulations required, into a corner of the basement, with broken windows and a hole in the wall looking out at the cloudy sky. The wall had been shattered in two places by the shells, and on the stone floor were large, dark blood stains. Evidently someone had been killed or wounded here. Stepanov sat on his heels by the wall, the investigator on some bricks in the middle of the cellar. He wrote in a notebook balanced on his knee.

Stepanov was a collective farmer from the neighborhood of Penza, a soldier of Company Two. He was thirty years old. He had a wife and two children at home. Almost as soon as he had been called up by the army, he had landed here in Stalingrad. The evening before, during the last German attack, he had been sitting with another soldier named Smuishlayev in a deep "swallow's nest," shooting at German tanks with a long antitank gun. He had missed his aim twice in a row and one tank, moving in the lead, had ground its caterpillar treads over his head and passed beyond the trench, leaving it heavy with the smell of gasoline and exhaust fumes. Smuishlayev yelled out something incomprehensible and savage, jumped up in the trench, and threw a heavy antitank grenade directly behind the tank and under its tread. It exploded, and the tank stopped. At just this moment the second tank came roaring over the trench. Stepanov dove head-first to the bottom of the trench, and he was only covered with dirt. Smuishlayev could not make it. By the time Stepanov could stand up again, the dirt in his "swallow's nest" was mixed with pieces of Smuishlayev, or rather the lower part of him, below his belt. The upper part of his body had been cut off and crushed by the tank. When this bloody piece of his companion's body fell into the trench, right next to Stepanov, he lost control, and without a thought in his head he crawled out of the trench. He kept on crawling, in the direction of the Volga, thinking of nothing, trying only to get as far away as he could.

By nightfall he was already in the custody of the regimental staff. He was not in a position to hide anything, and he simply told what had happened. Babchenko had sent him back under guard to Saburov, forwarding through official channels to division headquarters a report accusing him of desertion.

Saburov had been told about this incident, but in the confusion of the fighting he had not had a chance to talk to Stepanov about it, and now here was the investigator who had come to examine the case because of Babchenko's report. Stepanov sat in front of him and gave the same answers he had given the night before to Babchenko. The investigator was slower than usual and asked a lot of questions. He did this because he had not the faintest notion what to do with Stepanov. The man was a deserter, but he had done nothing with wrong intent. He had suffered extreme shock, he had not stood it, and he had run away. Maybe if he had run all the way to the shore of the river he would have mastered himself and come back again. So thought the investigator and so thought Stepanov, now that he had completely recovered. But the fact of desertion remained a fact, and because of general regulations it was impossible to let it go unpunished.

"I would have come back, by God," Stepanov said with great conviction after a short silence, and when he expected no more questions. "I would have come back myself."

At this moment the rumbling cannonade around them stopped short, and machine-gun fire could be heard close to them. Petya ran through the basement from Saburov's headquarters, yelling as he went: "The Germans have broken through. The captain says for every man who has a rifle to get in the fight," and he ran on.

The investigator was no longer a young man, and he was really only a civilian dressed up in uniform. He took off his glasses, wiped the lenses, put them on again, and picked up a tommy-gun from the ground. Slowly and deliberately, he crawled through the breach in the wall into the light. The soldier guarding Stepanov looked at him a little doubtfully, then at the hole in the wall, then again at Stepanov. He said quietly "You sit here for a while," and then disappeared after the investigator.

This was the second severe attack that day, and twenty or thirty German tommy gunners managed to break through into the courtyard of the building. Inside the courtyard, the firing was at point-blank range. Everyone at battalion headquarters and around it went into action.

Saburov himself climbed up to the basement and directed the fighting as far as such hand-to-hand combat could be directed. In a half hour the majority of the Germans had been killed, and the rest were driven beyond the wall of the courtyard. The investigator and the guard climbed back through the breach in the basement wall and sank down exhausted on the bricks. Blood was flowing from the investigator's wrist, which had been slightly nicked by a bullet.

"You should bandage that," the guard said.

"I have no kit with me."

"No?" Stepanov said. He fumbled in the pocket of his blouse, and pulled out his own first-aid kit.

He and the guard bandaged the wounded man's hand. Then Stepanov went back and sat down again by the wall. Only now did they remember that the cross-examination had been interrupted by the attack, and that now, obviously, it should be continued. But the investigator's heart was not in his work. In order to stretch out the time and to rest a little, he pulled a tobacco pouch from his pocket with his good hand, and rolled

167

a cigarette with difficulty, steadying it with his bandaged fingers. Then he looked at Stepanov and the guard, and with the automatic reflex which makes men who have been a long time at the front divide their tobacco he handed them the pouch. "Take some."

Following the guard's example, Stepanov took a pinch between his fingers, and pulling out a carefully preserved piece of newspaper, tore off a strip and rolled a cigarette. All three men smoked. This silent smoking went on for ten minutes. During this time, the cannonade began again. Under its rumble, the investigator began to hurry up his questions. He held his notebook with difficulty in his wounded hand. The questioning was soon finished, and only the report remained to be written. At this minute, just as it had happened before, the cannon fire ceased and the German attack began again.

Hearing bursts of tommy-gun fire, the investigator quietly picked up the gun again, held it in his good arm, and without even looking around climbed out of the cellar. The guard followed him.

Stepanov again remained alone. He looked anxiously from side to side. Beyond the wall could be heard close firing. Again he looked around him. Then he crawled through the breach where the guard had just disappeared. Coming out into the light, he saw a rifle lying on the ground next to the body of a dead Red Army soldier and he grabbed it. He ran several steps and then threw himself face down on the bricks not far from where the investigator and a handful of soldiers were firing from a prone position. When the Germans ducked out from behind the wall to their left they all began to shoot at them. Then Stepanov stood up, ran several steps farther, turned his rifle around, and clubbed a German who was running straight at him. Again he fell flat on the ground and fired at the Germans still moving at the other end of the courtyard. The Germans were also firing. This time they succeeded in getting a dozen

168

men into the enclosure. After a few minutes all of them had been either killed or wounded.

The attack ebbed away, and shots could now be heard only some distance beyond the wall. Stepanov stood up, and not knowing what to do, walked over to the wall where the investigator and the guard were lying. The guard also stood up, but the investigator did not move; he had been wounded in the leg. Stepanov lifted him, and saw that the leg had been almost cut in two by tommy-gun bullets and was bleeding badly. Slinging the investigator over his shoulder, he carried him back to the basement. He lowered him to the floor and placed two or three bricks under his head.

"See if you can find a nurse or a stretcher bearer," the investigator said to Stepanov.

Several minutes later Stepanov came back with a stretcher bearer who bent down over the wounded man and began to bandage his leg. He did not groan but lay there quietly waiting for the pain to stop. The guard fished out of his boot top a tin box of "makhorka," * rolled himself a cigarette, then gave a pinch of it to Stepanov, asking the wounded man: "Shall I roll one for you?"

"Please," he answered.

The guard rolled another, licked it, placed it in the wounded man's mouth, and lit a match. The investigator drew the smoke greedily into his lungs.

On his way back to his own dugout, Saburov came through the basement. Today he was really tired. In spite of his physical strength, he could hardly carry his automatic rifle, and he dragged it along behind him with its butt end on the ground. "Smoking?" he said. In the corner of his mouth was stuck a dead cigarette which he had started to smoke in his dugout before the fighting and which he had forgotten about. "Smok-

---

* "Makhorka" is a kind of cheap Russian tobacco, of inferior quality.

ing?" he repeated, and then he remembered about his own un-smoked cigarette. "Give me a light."

Only after he had come up to the guard did he recognize the men in front of him. He looked at Stepanov, then at the wounded man, and asked: "Is it bad?"

"Pretty bad."

"I'll tell them right away to get you out of here. It's going to begin again." He looked sympathetically at the white, blood-less face of the investigator, and not knowing what else to say, asked: "Did you finish with your cross-examination?"

"Yes, we finished," the investigator said, nodding at Stepanov.

"Well, what's your conclusion?"

"What conclusion could there be?" the army lawyer said. "We'll go on fighting. That's all there is to it."

He took his notebook, tore out his formal report, and wrote on its bottom: "Sufficient evidence of crime to warrant turn-ing over to a court-martial does not exist. Accused to be sent back to the front line." He signed his name.

"Sent back to the front line," he repeated aloud, and he smiled over the pain as he remembered what had just happened to them.

"Yes," Saburov said, laughing in his turn, "you won't have to send him far, maybe a hundred paces. Well," he turned to Stepanov, "go on over to your own company. Whose rifle have you got?"

"I took one from one of our dead, Comrade Captain."

"Well, consider it yours. You can go. Tell Potapov I sent you."

It was an especially tough day, one of those days when emo-tional tension is stretched to such a degree that it is almost im-possible to overcome an irrational desire for sleep, even in the heat of battle. After two morning attacks, a third followed at noon. In the part of the courtyard facing the Germans stood a small, half-destroyed storage building. It had been well constructed with heavy walls and a deep cellar. It stood apart from the other buildings occupied by Saburov, somewhat in front of them and to one side. It was at this building that the Germans directed their third attack.

When four or five tanks had succeeded in coming flush up to this storage building, they took cover from artillery fire behind its walls and began to pump shells directly inside it. German riflemen followed and in fifteen minutes the last shot sounded inside the little building. Saburov's first impulse was to try to take the building back at once, in full daylight, but he restrained himself. He made a sober decision instead: to concentrate all his fire behind the building, thus giving the Germans no chance to bring up strong forces before darkness, and to time his counterattack with darkness itself, when determination and familiarity with storming operations at night would serve for him as substitutes for the manpower he simply did not have.

When he reported by telephone about the loss of the storage building, Babchenko made no suggestions but cursed everyone's mother for a long time and in a vile spirit. In the end, Babchenko said he was coming over himself at once. This failed to cheer up Saburov. He sensed a row with Babchenko, and his fears were justified. Babchenko crawled through to the dugout, stooping over, sweating, angry, covered from head to foot with dirt.

"Well, I got here," Babchenko said. "How many meters deep are you here?"

"Three," Saburov said.

"Why didn't you go still deeper?"

"I don't need it any deeper," Saburov said. "They won't get us here."

"You've burrowed into the ground like a mole," Babchenko grumbled in the same surly voice.

Actually, he had nothing to complain about. Saburov had not dug this command post specially, but had only widened the tunnel already built for sewage pipes, and the fact that his dugout was deep and safe even from direct hits was a good thing. But Babchenko had wanted to say something insulting because the Germans had taken back the storage building.

"You've buried yourself," he repeated.

Saburov was tired, filled with bile, and certainly no less upset than Babchenko about the loss of the warehouse. He knew the thought of this loss would torment him like a splinter in his mind until the evening, until he could take the building back again, and so in answer to the lieutenant colonel he said defiantly:

"Well, Comrade Lieutenant Colonel, are you ordering me to move the command post up above?"

"No," Babchenko said, conscious of the irony in Saburov's words. "You shouldn't have lost the warehouse, that's what."

Saburov said nothing. He was waiting for Babchenko to continue.

"What are you thinking of doing?"

Saburov outlined his plan for a night counterattack.

"Well," Babchenko said, looking at his watch, "it's two o'clock now. That means they're going to sit there until dark. Have you read the command not to retreat one step backward? Or maybe you don't agree with the command?"

"At six o'clock I will begin the attack," Saburov said, trying to control himself, "and by seven I will hold the warehouse."

"Don't tell me that. Have you read the command not to retreat one step?"

"Yes," Saburov said.

"But you gave up the warehouse?"

"Yes."

"Drive them out at once," Babchenko shouted in a voice

hat was not his own, jumping up from his stool. "Not by seven, but right away."

From his face and gestures, Saburov realized that Babchenko was teetering on the same thin edge of fatigue and nervous exhaustion on which he stood himself. To quarrel with Babchenko at this minute would be useless. If it were simply a question of Saburov's being ordered to proceed alone and at once to that warehouse in full daylight, then he would stand up and go with a bitter feeling that if nothing could show his regiment commander how wrong he was except his own death, then, all right, he would show him. But to mount a counterattack now would require men. That meant he could show Babchenko how wrong he was not by losing his own life, but only by sacrificing others.

"Comrade Lieutenant Colonel, permit me to . . ."

"Well?"

Saburov repeated all the reasons which had made him decide to postpone the attack until night. He added his pledge that he could hold the entire square behind the warehouse under such fire throughout the day that not a single German could be added to those already inside the little building.

"Tell me, have you read the command that we are not to retreat one step backward?" Babchenko asked again, with the same merciless obstinacy.

"I've read it," Saburov said, drawing himself up and keeping his eyes on Babchenko's face with a look as evil and heartless as he saw in the other's eyes. "I've read it, but I just don't want to send men where it isn't necessary to send them when it would be possible to take it all back almost without losses."

"You don't want to? I order you to."

The thought suddenly flashed into Saburov's mind that right away, at this very minute, he must do something with Babchenko, force him to keep quiet, not let him repeat these words, in order to save the lives of many people. He should call

173

Protsenko and report to him that to do as Babchenko wanted was out of the question. Then, whatever might happen, let it happen, let them do what they wanted to him. But habit and discipline flowed back into him and kept him from doing any of this.

"Very good," he said, continuing to stare relentlessly at Babchenko. "Shall I carry out your command?"

"Carry it out."

Everything that happened after this stayed for a long time in Saburov's memory like a bad dream. They climbed out of the dugout and in a half hour Saburov rounded up all the men who were at hand. Babchenko telephoned an order to support the counterattack with the five field guns still left in the regiment, which could hardly help much under the circumstances. So the counterattack began.

Although the battalion had begun to fight with full ranks twenty days before, to organize a counterattack now in the daytime and in the middle of general fighting Saburov could collect only thirty men. This was the entire reserve on which he could count in his battalion.

Babchenko was in a hurry. The words "not one step backward" he understood literally, not wanting even to consider what today's losses had already cost or what they would cost tomorrow, when the Germans would resume their attacks. This counterattack had not been prepared; at its start they had not succeeded in dragging over from their left flank even the mortars which would have been at least some help; but Saburov with his thirty soldiers, running from wall to wall, from shell hole to shell hole, opened an assault on the building.

It all ended as he had expected. Ten men remained lying among the ruins. The rest found themselves some kind of cover not far from the warehouse, and nothing on earth could make them stand up again. The attack failed and it was obvious that under such conditions it could never have succeeded.

While the men were still hugging the ground, the Germans began to drop mortar shells on them. To go on lying there where they had dropped, with no hope of cover, meant certain death. The shells grew in number. One of them, exploding right next to him, bruised Saburov slightly, and the whole left side of his face suddenly felt numb, as if packed with cotton wadding. He was cut by a brick splinter, and blood ran down his face, but he did not notice it. When the shell fire had become unbearable, Saburov signalled to the others and began to crawl back.

On the way back still another was killed. An hour after the beginning of this project, Saburov was standing in front of Babchenko behind the low projecting entrance to the building where the lieutenant colonel, taking almost no cover himself, had watched the attack from as close a position as he could find, under fire the entire time.

Saburov saluted and dropped his rifle on the ground with a clatter. His face smeared with blood and mud was so terrifying to look at that Babchenko at first said nothing. Then he said: "Take a rest."

"What?" Saburov asked, not hearing.

"Take a rest," Babchenko repeated.

Saburov again did not hear. Then Babchenko shouted directly into his ear.

"I guess I've got a slight concussion," Saburov said.

"Take a rest," Babchenko shouted for the fourth time, and he walked off towards the dugout.

Saburov moved after him. They did not descend into the dugout but sat on their heels by the side of a spur of the wall where the guardhouse was. Both were silent; neither wanted to look the other in the face.

"Blood," Babchenko said. "You wounded?"

Saburov took out of his pocket a dirty, earth-colored handkerchief, spit on it several times, and wiped his face. Then he felt his head.

"No, just bruised and scratched," he said.

"Call up from the company everyone you can get," Babchenko ordered. "I'm going to lead an attack myself."

"How many men?" Saburov asked.

"As many as there are."

"There won't be more than forty," Saburov said.

"As many as there are, I already said," Babchenko repeated.

Saburov sent out an order for more men and also for the mortars to be dragged nearer; they might be able to help. In spite of his stubbornness, Babchenko knew perfectly well that it was his own fault the attack had been unsuccessful, and that the next attack would have no better chances. But after men had died uselessly before his own eyes, and at his command, he considered it essential to try to do what his subordinates had failed to do, to prove at any rate that what he had demanded of them was entirely possible.

While the mortars were being dragged up and the men assembled, Babchenko gave his last command before the attack and then returned to the fragment of wall from which he had observed the first attack. He began to examine carefully the stretch of courtyard lying in front of him, checking from just which points it would be easiest and safest to begin the attack. Saburov stood silent beside him. Forty steps away a heavy German shell exploded with a dull thud.

"They've spotted us," Saburov said. "Let's get out of here, Comrade Lieutenant Colonel."

Babchenko said nothing and did not move. A second shell went off on the other side of them, also not more than forty paces away.

"Let's get out of here, Comrade Lieutenant Colonel, they've spotted us," Saburov repeated.

Babchenko went on standing there. He felt himself challenged. He wanted to show, right after sending people into an attack, that he had asked of them only the same readiness to die as he demanded from himself.

"Let's go," Saburov almost shouted a third time when another shell went off right next to them.

Babchenko quietly turned to him, looked straight in his eyes, spat between his feet, and took a pinch of tobacco from his pouch and rolled himself a cigarette with firm, untrembling fingers.

The next shell exploded right in front of the wall. Several shell splinters buried themselves in the masonry above their heads, sifting dust down on them. Saburov noticed that Babchenko jumped, and this natural, human reflex prompted Saburov in his turn to say the simple, friendly words: "Philip Philipovich, let's get out of here, yes?"

Babchenko remained silent. Then, remembering his cigarette, he took a lighter out of his pocket, snapped it several times, and lit the cigarette, turning his back into the wind and bending over low to catch the flame. Maybe if he had not turned he would not have been killed but, turned and crouching, he was struck directly in the head by a piece of a shell exploding five steps away. He sank quietly at Saburov's feet; the body quivered only once, and he was dead. Saburov squatted on his heels beside him, lifted his battered and bloody head, and thought with a cool indifference which surprised him—this was just what should have happened. He pressed his ear to Babchenko's breast; the heart was no longer beating.

"Dead," he said.

Then he turned to Petya who was lying a few steps away behind the wall and said: "Petya, come here a minute, help me."

Petya clambered over to him. They took Babchenko by the

177

shoulders and the legs and, bending over, carried him quickly into the dugout.

"The mortars have been dragged up," said a lieutenant running up to Saburov. "Shall we open fire?"

"No," Saburov said, "drag them back again."

He called for Maslennikov and ordered him to cancel all the preparations for attack and to send the men back to their posts. Then he telephoned regiment headquarters. The commissar answered the telephone. Saburov reported that Babchenko had been killed; he explained under what circumstances, and then said he would send the body back to regiment headquarters as soon as it grew dark.

He was sorry, of course, that they had killed Babchenko, but at the same time he had a fully conscious, completely clear feeling of relief. Now he could handle things as he considered necessary, and now the stupid counterattack thought up by Babchenko for his own prestige would not be repeated. He issued orders to send help to the wounded men and to prepare for a counterattack on the storage building during the night.

Meanwhile the Germans started nothing new. In his bones Saburov felt that on their side, too, everything was over for today, and that there was no reason to expect a new attack before the next morning. He talked on the telephone with his companies and then lay down, having left an order to be wakened at five, just before it would be dark.

THIRTEEN

O sound woke him, but a feeling of being stared at. In front of him stood Anya. She was looking at him with big, child-like eyes. He sat up and quietly looked at her.

"I asked your orderly to wake you up," Anya said, "but he didn't want to. I've been here a long time. I've already got to go. But I wanted very much to see you." She held out her hand to Saburov. "How are you?"

"Sit down," Saburov said, moving over on the cot. Anya sat down.

"I see you've recovered completely."

"Yes, completely," Anya said. "You see, I was only slightly wounded. It was just that I lost a lot of blood. You know," she added quickly, as if not to let him talk, "I've found my mother. We are together again now."

"Together?"

"Well, not quite together. She's over there in a village, living in a peasant house, near where our medical aid station is located, and I spend the nights there with her. That is, not the nights, because I sleep in the mornings when I get back from crossing the river."

"Have you been coming back here a long time already?"

"This is the first time here, but it's my fourth day back at work. I told mother all about you."

"What did you tell her?"

"Everything I know."

"And what do you know about me?"

"A great deal," Anya said.

"Well, such as?"

"Quite a lot, almost everything."

"Everything?"

"I even know how old you are. You told me the truth that time. You're twenty-nine. Your orderly told me so."

"I'll have to discipline him for revealing a military secret," Saburov said, trying to sound severe. "What else did he tell you?"

"He told me you almost got killed today."

"And what else?"

"What else? Nothing else. I didn't have time to ask him. We're moving the wounded all into one place. Have you many?"

"Yes, a lot of wounded," Saburov said, frowning. "A lot of them. You say you didn't have time? If you had had time, would you have asked more questions?"

"Yes, I certainly would."

"Well then, ask me them." He looked at his watch. "I've got time."

"You'd better sleep. I woke you up."

"How did you wake me. I woke up myself."

"No, it was I who woke you. I looked at you such a long time that you woke up. I did it on purpose. I wanted you to wake up."

"That means you must have some magnetic power in your eyes," Saburov said. He knew he wasn't saying what he wanted to. He added at once, in another tone: "I am very glad to see you."

"I am, too," Anya said, and she looked straight into his eyes.

He understood then that the unexpected kiss that night, when she was lying on the stretcher, had not been forgotten by her, and that in general she had forgotten nothing of the little there had been between them, little indeed but very important. He felt this now when he looked at her.

"I have been all tied up here," he said. "I've seldom had a chance even to think about you, it has been so . . ."

"I know," Anya said. "Several times we've had your soldiers at our medical aid station. I asked them how things were here."

Anya plucked with her fingers at the edge of her tunic. Saburov knew this was not from embarrassment but because she wanted to say something that was important to her and was trying to choose her words.

"Well?" he asked unexpectedly.

She was silent.

"Well, what is it?" he repeated.

"I've thought a lot about you, a great deal," she said with her customary grave frankness.

"And what conclusion did you reach?"

"None. I simply thought about you. I wanted very much to talk to you again."

She looked at him questioningly, waiting for him to answer her, and he could feel that she was waiting for him to say something good, something wise and comforting: that everything would come out all right, that they would both come through the war alive, the kind of grown-up talk which would make her feel like a little girl under his protection. But he didn't want to say anything, he wanted simply to put his arms around her. He put his hand on her shoulder, just as he had on the steamer, and pulled her gently toward him, and said: "You know, I thought you would come."

With these words she felt that he also remembered the kiss when she was on the stretcher. She felt that it was this memory which made him say: "You know, I thought you would come."

"Do you know," she said, "probably this happens to everybody. A day comes and you've been waiting terribly for something on that day, and then it happens. Today I've been waiting since morning to see you and I haven't noticed anything else around me. During the daytime the shooting was fierce but I hardly noticed it. Maybe that means that if I keep on coming to see you I will become brave; what do you think?"

"But you're already brave."

"No, not so brave, usually, but today I am."

He looked at his watch. "Is it beginning to get dark outside?"

"Yes," she said, "probably. I didn't notice. Probably, I suppose so." She gave a start. "It's time to begin moving the wounded; I must be off."

He was glad to hear her say "I must be off" because he saw from his watch that it was time for him to get ready for the attack, and he was glad that she would be the first to go.

"You won't manage them all in one trip?"

"No," she said. "I'll be back two more times today. If we manage before morning we'll be lucky."

Saburov stood up and said: "The commanding officer of our regiment was killed today. Did you know about it?"

"Yes, I know. Right next to you, they told me. Were you injured today?"

"Only slightly." He looked at her and realized for the first time that she had been talking more loudly than usual, probably because she had heard about his concussion.

"Did Petya tell you that, too?"

"Yes. Will I see you again today?"

"Yes, yes, of course," Saburov said hurriedly. "Of course, we'll see each other. Why not? Only . . ."

"What?"

He wanted to say that she should be more careful, but he
182

hesitated. How could she be more careful? There was only the one familiar path along which the wounded could be taken; there was only the one time of day. How could she be more careful? It would be simply stupid to say this to her.

"No, never mind," he said. "Of course, we'll see each other. Without any doubt."

When she had gone, Saburov sat quietly for a moment. Then he stood up and put on his overcoat. He wanted to finish the attack on the warehouse as quickly as he could, not only because this would be good to do anyway, but also because only afterwards could he see Anya again. He thought about this and grew a little frightened at his own thoughts, since he could not hide from himself that they were thoughts of love.

The thoughts had started and they did not disappear. They stayed with him even while he was giving his last instructions before the attack, and after it had begun. They stayed with him while they crawled through the ruins at the start, and later as they were running under fire, and even when, having thrown two grenades in front of him, he broke with the others into the warehouse and plunged into that special chaos of close firing, shouts, and groans which is called hand-to-hand fighting.

This time he recaptured the warehouse at a total cost of one killed and five wounded. And although he had, like many Russian people, a real and sincere habit, not just for display purposes, of neither thinking nor speaking evil about the dead, still he remembered Babchenko again with anger flooding through him.

Vanin, who had returned during the day from Company Two, took part in the attack with him. Although this was unwise, Vanin had insisted on it, and Saburov had not found the strength to refuse him. In general he was in a mood which made it hard for him to refuse any man's request. They were together through the fighting and they returned together to the dugout.

The commissar, sitting on the cot across from him, was cleaning his revolver, which had been covered with mud. With its butt-end in his stomach, he was trying hard to take out the firing hammer. Saburov noticed that the muzzle of the revolver was pointed straight at him.

"When you're cleaning a gun, point it at the floor, or at the ceiling, and not at your neighbor," he said crossly. "You ought to make that a rule."

"But it isn't loaded," Vanin said.

"Just the same."

Vanin shrugged his shoulders, snapped the hammer to show that the revolver was not loaded, and continued cleaning it. He kept it pointed at the floor.

"That warehouse, by the way," Vanin said, "was for scenery. You see, that building standing in front of it was the theater, and the warehouse was built near it to hold the scenery. And did you see in the courtyard? We laid rails there so we could move the scenery directly from the stage on a little truck. Pretty clever, wasn't it?"

"You're right," Saburov said, smiling in spite of himself.

"What are you smiling about?" Vanin asked.

"I was smiling because it looks as if there weren't a single house around here about which you don't know the most intimate details."

"Why not? You see, I helped to build all this. Not only the buildings—I know nearly all the people here. The girl, for instance, the nurse who was visiting you today."

"Yes," Saburov said cautiously. He thought Vanin would now make some kind of wisecrack on this score, and he prepared to ward it off.

"Well," Vanin said, "I know her, too. She used to work at the Tractor Factory, in the tool shop; she was a standardizer. We wanted to make her chief organizer of the Komsomols in her shop. I remember her well." It seemed this was all he wanted to say about the girl.

"Yes, I remember them all," he went on, already forgetting about Anya. "I always imagine the Tractor Factory not the way it is now but as it was before. With all the people at their machines. I can even see their faces. Why are you so sulky today? Tired?"

"No," Saburov said. "I've already rested; I slept in the daytime."

"But you're sulky just the same."

"No, I'm not sulking. Simply thinking."

"What are you thinking about? About Babchenko?"

"Among other things, about Babchenko."

"Yes," Vanin said. "He got it. I wonder who will get his job. Maybe you?"

"No," Saburov said, "probably they'll name Vlassov from the first battalion. He's a major."

"Yes. Babchenko got it," Vanin repeated. "You had a fight with him today?"

"Yes."

"I heard about it."

"Who told you?"

"Maslennikov."

"He ordered a daytime attack, and I didn't like it. It wasn't necessary. We lost eleven men."

"Couldn't you convince him?"

"No. If I could have, I wouldn't have tried the attack."

The telephone rang. It was Protsenko. The sound of his voice made Saburov feel better.

"How are things?" Protsenko asked.

"Good."

"What do you mean by not taking care of your boss?"

"I couldn't," Saburov said. "I wanted to but I couldn't."

"Did you get the warehouse back easily?" Protsenko asked.

185

"Very easily, with small losses."

"That's what you should have done from the start—cut off the approach for any German reinforcements and then re captured it at night. That's the way to handle those things i the future."

It sounded like a rebuke, a mild one it is true, but still . rebuke. Saburov wanted to say that he had not been to blam for the daytime attack, but Babchenko. Then he remembere that Babchenko had been killed, and that whether he had bee good or bad he had fallen for Stalingrad, so he said nothing

Anya kept her word and ran in again late in the evening She was in a great hurry and she dashed in only for a momen but short as their meeting was, Saburov realized that from tha day on they would see each other as much as possible, and tha even when they could meet only for a minute it would stil be good.

When she had run out again, he felt anxious for her. Fo the first time in Stalingrad, he was conscious that the danger surrounding them were endlessly different. Some of them naturally, were his dangers, and others, terrifying and un expected ones, were her dangers. And he realized that now probably, he would always be afraid for Anya.

All his chores for the day and the night were finished. H had only to wait for eleven o'clock, the time he had ordere Vassiliev to come in order to set out on the reconnaissance. Th prospect of exploring tonight, and then tomorrow night try ing to cut off an entire German company, seemed by now s tempting that he thought about what lay ahead with eager ness and confidence. He stretched out on his cot. He wanted t finish with this last business of the day as quickly as he could and then be alone, if only for a half hour, with his own thought He called out to Petya: "Has Vassiliev come yet?"

"Not yet," Petya answered.

"Call him. And tell him to hurry."

Vassiliev appeared five minutes later. He had everything ready. Around his neck hung his rifle, two grenades were tied in a neat linen bag to his belt, and the same flat bayonet hung next to them. He wore no overcoat, but was travelling light in a tightly-buttoned, padded jacket. This was the way he always went out scouting.

"Let's go," Saburov said standing up. "Petya, ask Petrov to go with me."

Petrov was a tommy gunner who accompanied Saburov on those occasions when Petya stayed at headquarters. Saburov took his rifle from the wall, put on a padded jacket like Vassiliev's, pulled his leather belt tight, and put in his pocket two of the lemon grenades which he liked for their small size and powerful action. He leaned over his cot, looking for his cap which had fallen behind it.

Vassiliev looked at his back and pictured in a flash how everything would happen: how they would arrive at the designated spot, how he would take care of Petrov with the bayonet, and how the Germans would throw themselves on Saburov. It was a broad back; he had never noticed before the width of Saburov's shoulders, or the length of his arms. Besides, Saburov was pushing off a little ahead of schedule, and this worried Vassiliev. It was true, the Germans could be counted on. They would probably be sitting in their trap ahead of time. But suppose they weren't? What then? Would everything have to be started all over again tomorrow? He hesitated between a desire to slow up Saburov and a fear that this might make him suspect something. When Saburov finally stood up, having found his cap, Vassiliev said:

"Permit me to report."

"Well?"

"Permit me to report," Vassiliev repeated. "Right now, they are changing guards. Maybe we should hold up a little, Comrade Captain. As you said, let's try it at eleven."

"But you said there weren't any guards there."

"No, there aren't."

"Well, then they won't hear us. Let's go." Saburov hung his rifle around his neck.

They went out, Vassiliev in front, then Saburov, Petrov bringing up the rear. The night was raw and dark, an October night. A drizzling little rain was falling. At first it was so dark that it seemed to them they had walked out not into the open air, but into a kind of vestibule between two closed doors. The contours of the walls merged into the sky and it looked as if high buildings, painted a lighter color, had risen on top of the crumbled walls around them.

As they went out of the dugout, Saburov thought that as a matter of fact it would have been no great sin to have postponed this reconnaissance until the next night. So much had happened that day, and no day was ever the last. But the freshness of the night, the small and quiet rain, and the black low sky which seemed warmer in the rain than the earth itself —all this made him shake himself and feel better.

"It's a nice night," Saburov said, "isn't it?"

"Yes, it is, Comrade Captain," Vassiliev said.

Saburov remembered that the little town near Millerovo where his mother and sisters used to live was just about on the same parallel as Stalingrad. There the night was probably just the same, or almost the same, as here—long, dark, and rainy.

"Where is your family, Vassiliev?" he asked. "Far from here?"

"A long way," Vassiliev said. He instinctively felt the papers in his left pocket, made out in the name of P. D. Vassiliev, resident of the city of Magnitogorsk, married, thirty-two years old, and he added: "In Magnitogorsk."

"Magnitogorsk?" Saburov said. "Where do they live, on what street? Probably in the old town?"

"Yes, in the old town," Vassiliev said quickly. He had never been in Magnitogorsk. "In the old town." He felt he should add something. "On Lenin Street," he said, guessing that here must be a Lenin Street there.

"So," Saburov said, and Vassiliev knew there must in fact be a Lenin Street in Magnitogorsk.

"Are you married?"

"Yes," Vassiliev said. It seemed funny to him to be asked about his life by a man who in exactly half an hour would be answering questions himself to the Germans. "Married, and two children."

"It's a long way from here," Saburov said thoughtfully, and it occurred to him that there, probably, in Magnitogorsk, there was no blackout and lights were shining in the streets. For a second he tried to imagine what it would be like if those lights could suddenly be moved here, to Stalingrad. Right here, where they were walking. On every corner a street light standing, and a full glow over everything. And the windows all lighted. He looked at the luminous face of his watch: it was half-past ten. Yes, all the lights would be on by now. He smiled at his thoughts.

Five minutes later they had clambered through to Company Two where Potapov and Maslennikov met them in the ruins of a building. Maslennikov had known that Saburov was going on this reconnaissance, but he did not approve of it, considering that such an expedition should be carried out not by Saburov but by himself. Since Saburov had made the decision and since it was hard to make him change his mind, Maslennikov had found some kind of pretext to go in advance to Potapov at Company Two, in order in any case to be at the spot from which Saburov would set off. The fact that Maslennikov met him there was a surprise for Saburov, but he did not show it and only smiled to himself in the dark.

"You here already, Misha?"

"Yes, Comrade Captain, I . . . ." Maslennikov began to explain just why he had come over to Company Two, but Saburov interrupted him with a motion of his hand.

"I know," he said. Again his smile could not be seen in the darkness. "I know everything." He felt pleased that Maslennikov was anxious about him and had hurried over here.

When they were ready to start, Maslennikov came up again to Saburov, took his hand, and said quietly: "Alexei Ivanovich."

"Well?"

"Alexei Ivanovich," Maslennikov repeated.

"Well, what?"

Suddenly Saburov understood. Maslennikov had come up to him in order to embrace him. Sensing this, Saburov embraced him first, then quickly turned around and walked away. Maslennikov looked after him. It was no foreboding about what might happen but a kind of unaccountable grief, which comes often at the front, and which had been heavy in Maslennikov's heart since early morning, when he had first learned about this reconnaissance expedition.

At first they walked along openly, the darkness of the night making this possible. Then Petrov carelessly let the muzzle of his gun clatter on a wall. All three froze, holding their breaths, waiting for bullets to be fired at random in the general direction of the noise. But no one fired. Then they went on farther.

The rain kept on falling in tiny drops. It had become colder. The night no longer seemed as soft and quiet as it had earlier. Far beyond the buildings, to their left, there were bright white flashes of artillery fire. When they had gone about a hundred and fifty yards, they had to start crawling between the craters along a little alley which looked as if an earthquake had hit it. Besides the walls themselves, which had tumbled down every which way, turning the alley into a ravine, he ground was covered with bricks and with every kind of bject, strange sometimes to the touch. There were pieces of urniture, splintered dishes, a broken bathtub, a battered amovar. On the jagged edge of the samovar, Saburov cut his and.

They crawled along like this for five minutes or a little more. The distance between the Russian and German lines was not ery great; sometimes it widened to two hundred yards; in places it narrowed to fifty. But in order to get there they had o follow winding paths between the shell holes, and at any particular moment it was difficult to be certain which side hey were closer to—their own or the German.

Vassiliev felt better. There was just a short distance to go now; he had only to be patient a few minutes longer.

Saburov crept along almost by habit, absent-mindedly. He had the distraction of a man who knows everything in advance and who has only to do automatically what is needed. This was to crawl through to his objective, to look around, to make a decision for the next day, and then just as quietly to crawl back again.

So they went on. They crawled until there occurred one of those accidents of war which could be foreseen in advance neither by the Germans nor the Russians nor by Vassiliev nor by Saburov, but which take place anyway. When Vassiliev figured that they had already crawled to within fifty paces of their goal, they suddenly heard over their heads the familiar drone of a U-2 night fighter, sounding like a motorcycle. Like peas poured from a pod in the sky, a handful of little bombs whistled through the air and exploded all around them. In this there was nothing surprising: they were in no man's land and the pilot had obviously missed his target and hit what he thought was only wilderness.

When the bombs exploded around them, Vassiliev was crawl- ing in front with Petrov next to him, and Saburov, ready to fall on his knees as they had done in order to creep forward was standing by a half-destroyed wall. The nearest bomb fell right next to the wall, in a corner. The wall rocked and crumbled to the earth, covering Saburov with bricks. The bricks fell on him from the side like a pyramid of children's blocks. Letting himself fall with them, Saburov closed his eyes. From the blow itself, from the force of the explosion and the air rushing past him, it seemed to him that it was all over, that he was killed. But when he had stopped falling and opened his eyes he felt neither death nor even weakness, but only the tremendous weight of the bricks on top of him, and in his nose and in his mouth the taste of crumbled bricks.

"Vassiliev," he whispered. "Vassiliev."

Vassiliev did not answer.

"Petrov," Saburov called again.

No one answered. Apparently both his companions had been killed. It seemed to him that someone stirred in front of him, but he could not move, literally buried in bricks. He listened hard: no, there was nothing. In his whole body there was an extraordinary and terrifying feeling of constriction, as if he were bound all around with rope, leaving only his left arm and his head free. A piece of brick had fallen on his face, and blood was running into one eye. He got a hand to his face and wiped the blood from the eye, smearing it across his face.

"Vassiliev," he whispered again.

"Here I am," Vassiliev said, just as quietly, somewhere behind him.

"Here?" Saburov said, "where?"

"Here," Vassiliev repeated, and Saburov could hear him crawling somewhere behind him. He could not turn his head to see.

When the flash of the first bomb had lit up everything around him for a second, Vassiliev had seen that they were quite close to the spot where the Germans were expecting them.

The next second, he had been hurled to the ground, and he felt terrible pain in his side and hip. A huge bomb fragment had split his whole hip open. Although some sixth sense told him the wound was not fatal, when he felt the raw flesh under his own hand he barely managed to choke a wild scream of terror in his throat.

He felt himself all over, then stretched out his hand, and all five fingers struck against the bloody head of Petrov. Quietly, through his teeth, he screamed, and he automatically squirmed on the ground, trying to move away from the dead man.

When he heard Saburov's voice, Vassiliev realized he was not alone, and no matter how much he hated Saburov, the feeling of terror was still stronger in him. He began to crawl towards Saburov's voice, conscious of nothing but an overpowering desire to be near another human being.

"Yes," he whispered, "yes, yes." He inched his way until he lay right next to Saburov.

"Wounded?" Saburov asked.

"Yes," Vassiliev answered. "And you?"

"I don't know," Saburov said very low.

Vassiliev could make out in the darkness that only the captain's head, one shoulder, and one arm were not covered by the heavy pile of bricks. It was so curious that he asked, in spite of himself: "Aren't you crushed?"

"I don't know," Saburov said again. "Have you got a first-aid kit?"

"Yes," Vassiliev said. "What do you want? A bandage?"

"No, I don't need it. You do. I've got a kit, but it's under there." Saburov pointed to the pile of bricks on top of him. "You'd better bandage yourself, or you'll bleed to death."

Vassiliev remembered then that it was possible to bleed to death. The thought of dying frightened him so badly now that for a long time he could not get his trembling fingers inside the pocket of his shirt. Finally, he got a bandage, placed it

193

beside him, undid the belt of his jacket, took out his bayonet and felt along the crotch of his trousers. There was so much blood that the trousers were stuck to the flesh. He unrolled the bandage, held it with one hand, and tried to bandage himself.

"Wait," Saburov said. "Move over a little."

Vassiliev moved over. Saburov took the end of the bandage with his free left hand and pulled it down on Vassiliev's wound so that it could not slip.

"Now wrap it around," he said. "With both hands."

Vassiliev wrapped the bandage around the wound. He was thinking not about Saburov, nor about the Germans, nor about what might happen, but only about how to tie the bandage so he would not bleed to death. When he had wrapped it around his leg and fastened the bandage below the wet edge of his jacket, he began to think what he should do now. Everything was quiet around him. He did not know if the Germans had already arrived at their trap or, if they had come, whether the bombs had killed them, too. "No, they probably won't come," Vassiliev thought. Of course they would take those bombs for a betrayal of their trap, and not come. But suppose they did come? He wanted to grab Saburov by the shoulder and ask him: "Will they come or not?" What should he do now? What could he do?

He felt in no condition to crawl to either side. Around him was old iron, stones, tin; he could not manage crawling. If it were open fields, he might make it, but here he would dislodge the bandage and bleed to death. Yell out? But which side would hear him first? The Germans? He knew them well: they never answered cries. They would decide it was a trap, drop a few mortar shells around, and kill them for good. Our side (He still said "our side," by force of habit.) But even if they came, it would mean starting everything again from the beginning. And the Germans might hear them and start shooting. No, he mustn't call, that would never do.

But what could he do? Wait? Maybe the Germans would still show up at their trap. They would not be frightened. Then everything would be all right. Oh, how fine it would be! He would hear them, when they got quite close, and he would tell them where he was. It should be soon, maybe in fifteen minutes, maybe in ten. And if they didn't come? Well, if they didn't come, he would crawl to them himself. He would crawl slowly and very carefully, so as not to bleed to death. That was the main thing, not to bleed to death. Then he remembered Saburov. He would crawl away quietly, without saying anything, and he would tell the Germans where Saburov was. No, that wouldn't work. Saburov would call out as soon as he began to crawl away, and the Germans would open fire on them both. Or maybe not. Still worse, maybe he would crawl away and then die from loss of blood, and the Russians would crawl out and rescue Saburov. He would be dead, and Saburov would live. No, that couldn't be. He would have to wait, patiently, as long as he could. And then, if he couldn't wait it out, he would do something. He would kill Saburov, so he couldn't cry out, so he could do nothing. Then he would rest a minute, and crawl over to the Germans. Yes, that was the way to do it.

"Well, how do you feel?" Saburov asked. "Better?"

"A little better," Vassiliev answered.

"Lie back; take a rest."

Vassiliev saw Saburov lift his free hand to the little fragments of brick covering him and move them, one after another, to the side. One, two, three. He moved fifteen. Then his arm fell back limp, and he sighed heavily.

"Tired," he said. "I can't do it long. You take a rest and then help me, so we can get started crawling back."

Vassiliev said nothing. "No," he was thinking, "he won't tell. He knows, too, that the Germans would shoot. He won't tell. He'll lie there and take each brick off. That'll take a long time. So long that he'll never get it done."

"Lie back, lie back," Saburov said quietly. "Take it easy." He was picking up the bricks again. One of them slipped and made a little noise.

"Quieter," Vassiliev said.

"Yes, yes," Saburov whispered, "I'll be quieter."

When he had fallen, one leg had turned on top of the other and he could feel a tremendous weight resting on the bone.

"Is Petrov killed?" he asked.

"Killed."

Saburov took off a few more bricks, and then rested again. His chest felt as if it were in a vice. Any moment his chest would give way, and then these bricks would be lying not on his chest but on something inside it, crushing it.

"How stupid it is," he whispered, "how stupid!" Then he asked: "How about it? Could you help me, even with just one hand?"

Vassiliev said nothing. Saburov thought he was probably in a bad way, too, and he would have to take the bricks off all by himself. "If I can only do it before dawn," he thought, "and if only there's enough strength left then to crawl back."

"Have you still got your gun?" he asked Vassiliev.

"Yes." Vassiliev softly pulled up his tommy-gun by its strap.

"If the Germans find us," Saburov said, "you must . . you must," he was breathing hard, "shoot me first, understand?"

"No," Vassiliev said.

Saburov thought he had refused because he was afraid of death, his own or anyone else's, and because he could not imagine shooting him.

"Never mind," he said. "That's just in case. But we'll get out of here. You help me unload these bricks, and I'll crawl out."

196

"No," Vassiliev said again, in a strange voice which surprised Saburov.

Vassiliev was lying motionless, pressing his wounded hip to the ground. It seemed to him this would make the blood flow less freely. He was trying to hoard his strength; if the Germans did not come, he would have to crawl. The loss of blood had already made him sleepy; it was hard to hold his head up. He thought he would feel better if he could lie there for another ten or fifteen minutes; the spinning might stop in his head, and his arms might not be so weak. So he waited, and counted as he had when he was a child: one, two, three, up to a hundred; one, two, three, and again to a hundred. He had no watch, and he tried to guess the number of minutes left before eleven, when either the Germans would come, or it would be clear that they were not going to come, and he would have to start crawling. It would have been hard to say which made him hate Saburov more now: the fact that this man he was going to kill in ten minutes could still talk about crawling out of here, or the fact that Saburov's words threw him off his count, so that he had to start again with fifty, fifty-one, fifty-two, fifty-three . . .

"No," he said, "you won't crawl out." He moved away so that Saburov could not reach him with his free arm. "You won't crawl out."

He felt bitter now toward Saburov, from despair, from chagrin over what had happened, from pain, and mostly because deep in his heart he was not at all sure he could crawl through to the Germans. He felt a desire to tell Saburov that the captain wouldn't crawl anywhere, that his hopes were futile, and that he was a fool anyway to have fallen into this trap, and—this he wanted most of all to tell him—that the Germans were coming right away and that they would capture him, which was what Saburov feared most of all. Vassiliev was not sure the Germans were coming, but he wanted to tell

197

Saburov they were coming, coming without fail, so that h[e]
would wait in fear.

"You won't crawl out anywhere," Vassiliev repeated. "Yo[u]
won't crawl out."

"Why not?"

"Because I'll kill you first. I'll kill you." Vassiliev was stil[l]
talking in a calm, quiet whisper. "I'll kill you. That's all."

After his fright he began to feel more calm, because th[is]
man next to him was even more helpless and could not mov[e]
hand or foot while he, Vassiliev, even if he was wounded an[d]
maybe, dying, could still kill him.

"Because you're a fool," he said, still more quietly. "I wa[s]
leading you to the Germans. They're coming here. At eleve[n]
sharp. Look at your watch. You can't? Well, anyway, they'r[e]
coming right away, and then everything will be over, Com[-]
rade Captain."

Saburov remained silent.

"Well, why don't you say something? You think they won['t]
come? They'll come."

Saburov still was silent. This began to anger Vassiliev. B[e-]
fore killing Saburov, he wanted to hit him, to strike him in th[e]
eyes and on the face, to close his fist and smash it in his teet[h,]
to pay for all that he had had to live through in his life fro[m]
its beginning to this dirty night when he was lying he[re]
wounded, his side ripped open, in the mud, under the rain. [He]
would pay off everything he had suffered on account of Sa[-]
burov, and on account of others like him. No, the best of a[ll]
would be to stamp his heel in his face. He was afraid to g[et]
nearer Saburov, he was afraid of his silence, and of his o[ne]
free arm. He moved up his tommy-gun so its muzzle was aime[d]
straight at Saburov's face.

"So I'll kill you. That's all."

Saburov was silent. He had nothing he wanted to say. Aft[er]
Vassiliev's first words, he understood at once what had ha[p]

198

ened today and what had happened before. He remembered
his command posts, knocked out one by one by German artillery, and he remembered the dead Panasyuk, and the gesture
with which Vassiliev had pulled the bayonet out of his boot top.
He remembered all Vassiliev's returns, always with documents, and with captured guns. He remembered everything
his man had done to make the battalion praise him as a man
who could walk behind the German lines as if it were his own
home. Small wonder he had seemed to be at home there! And
then he remembered his conversation with Avdeyev after the
newspaperman had questioned Vassiliev about his scouting
trip, and the contemptuous look on Avdeyev's face when he
had said: "I don't know. No, I don't think I will write about
him." He remembered how two telephone operators had been
killed by the shell which hit his last command post, and how
they had been lying on the ground when he found them. Vassiliev had killed them, too. Now here he was, lying next to
Vassiliev, feeling still strong under the weight of the bricks,
and able to do nothing.

He was silent. He didn't want to talk. If he had often felt
hatred for the Germans, it was nothing compared to what he
was feeling now. All that he had hated in his whole life was
now lying an arm's length from him, and there was nothing he
could do.

Saburov moved his fingers, tightened his hand into a fist,
and quietly, so quietly that the motion could not be heard,
moved his hand up to his body. He tried to stop thinking about
anything. Everything flowed out of his consciousness and only
one thing was left: Vassiliev was almost within arm's length
of him, and if that "almost" could be changed, even for one
second, then . . . He tried to squirm under the bricks. No,
that way he would not gain a centimeter. He needed five centi-
meters, maybe ten. He needed to get Vassiliev to move towards
him, only a little, just barely move towards him.

"Well, why don't you say something?" Vassiliev asked. "Why don't you say something? Are you afraid?"

He wanted Saburov to be afraid, because he himself was afraid of Saburov's silence.

"You son of a bitch," Saburov said suddenly.

"Go on, talk, talk," Vassiliev said. "Talk." It gave him satisfaction that he had forced Saburov to say something.

"Go on and talk. It'll be for the last time anyway. Talk, before you're dead. You hear? Because you're going to die here. Understand?"

Saburov tried once more to squirm under the bricks. He moved his shoulders one centimeter, but no farther. Vassiliev had to move towards him. Move, move, move. He whispered the word over and over. All his desires were now in that one word. He began to swear, at length and with foul language, as he had never sworn in his life, first raising and then lowering his whispering voice. He called Vassiliev every dirty name he could think of. He talked, choking and losing his breath, and all the time he was thinking: if he would only move, if he'd only move, just a little. His eyes stared into the darkness and made for themselves an image of Vassiliev's face.

Now Vassiliev began to grow angry because Saburov gave him no chance to say a word. He was swearing in a steady flow of words which would continue until he died, and Vassiliev would have no chance to say what he wanted to say. Before he had been pleased that he had forced Saburov to talk; now he wanted to make him keep quiet. He wanted to stamp on his face with his heel, or strike his fist against his teeth, to make him keep quiet.

"You're talking," he whispered. "I'll tell you something."

Saburov went on thinking; if he'd only move. With an unconscious, unnatural cunning, he started to lower his whisper little by little so that Vassiliev might move a little bit, only a centimeter, maybe two, nearer to him. Vassiliev could not get

200

used to Saburov's talking now louder, now softer, and he kept moving a little closer to hear him, and then moving back. But each time, and Saburov felt this, the distance was growing smaller by a tiny margin. At last he turned his face towards Vassiliev, and with his mouth full of saliva spat right in his face. Vassiliev raised his hand to wipe his face, and Saburov knew that he had hit him. He spat again. Vassiliev moved closer, raised his arm, and struck Saburov in the mouth with all his strength. He could have used his gun, but he wanted to use his fist, he wanted to feel the teeth break.

This was his mistake. Saburov lunged forward with his arm, grabbed Vassiliev by the shirt, pulled him down on top of him, let go with his hand for a second, and closed it again around his throat. Saburov's whole body, buried under the bricks, had uncoiled itself through his left arm in this one movement. He squeezed so hard that Vassiliev automatically dropped his gun and moved both hands to his throat, trying to break the fingers closed around his neck. But the fingers didn't break. The hand held his throat tighter and tighter. At first, Vassiliev tore at the hand, then he dug at it with his fingernails. Saburov heard him begin to choke and closed his fingers tighter and tighter.

When the rattle ceased in Vassiliev's throat, and the neck began to twitch convulsively, Saburov did not relax his fingers. He continued to squeeze, although he was close to losing consciousness from the pain through his whole body. He squeezed for a minute, or maybe five, until he knew that this was a final quiet, and that what he was holding in his fingers would never move again. Then he loosened his fingers and opened his eyes, which he had kept tightly closed all this time.

The sky above his head was as black as if he had lost his sight. The rain—he noticed this only now—was still falling. His arm was growing numb. He drew it to his body and tried to close his fingers around one of the bricks pressing on him. He closed his eyes, and sometimes losing consciousness, sometimes coming to, he lay there for minutes. Then, biting his lips, he moved his free arm up to the top of the pile of bricks and quietly pushed the top brick to one side. Again he bit his lips with the pain; again he stretched his arm towards his body, again he took another brick, and again he pushed it to the side.

Drops of rain fell endlessly on his face. He wanted to wipe them off, but he did not want to waste an entire movement of his arm for this. He needed his arm for one thing: to drag it up to his body, to take a piece of brick, and quietly to move it to the side; then again to bring up his arm, again take a brick, again move it to one side, and so on until the end. Until he died, until he lost consciousness, until just what he did not know. He only knew that while there was any glimmer of life inside him he would continue this same movement—draw up his arm to his body, take a piece of brick, and move it to the side.

All this took place on the cold and rainy night of October 12, just thirty days after that first night when he had crossed the Volga with his battalion and disembarked on the Stalingrad side.

FOURTEEN

SILENCE was all a-round him. This was the first thing he noticed. Not the low talking of the wounded lying on cots a-round him, nor the broken breathing of some who were dying, nor the tapping of the nurses' boots, nor the clink of hospital glassware, nothing could break his awareness of silence. Maybe it was because this was a hospital and there were many white sheets and dressing gowns, so that the silence itself seemed white to Saburov.

The silence had lasted already for eight days. It seemed to him it would have no end and nothing could break it. Beyond the window fell the first, wet, heavy snow of autumn and it, too, was as white as the silence.

His body still hurt, but it hurt quietly. There was no sharp and grinding pain, as from an open wound, but something quiet, pressing in on him. In the hospital, it was not really so quiet; wounded men were brought in and taken out; sometimes one cried out in pain, but after Stalingrad all this seemed silence to Saburov.

They nursed him, fed him, and washed him, but after all he was only one of many there, and no one showed any special interest in him. He had been brought here from the other side of the river, literally covered with bruises and heavy contusions. Now he was getting better. This was written on his medical chart. But how this had all happened, how they had saved him, how he had remained alive, how he had regained consciousness on this shore of the river, no one knew. Some stretcher bearers had handed him over to others, these others had brought him to the hospital, and when he asked how he had got here, the doctor only threw up his hands.

"Get back to your unit, and you'll find out. How could I tell you?"

In vain Saburov tried to remember how all this had happened. He could remember only how he had strangled Vassiliev, and how he had then begun to move the bricks, but nothing more. The feelings of terror, of helplessness, of physical pain which he had lived through no longer troubled him as he got better. But the thought that this whole incident could have happened at all kept on torturing him. He knew, of course, in theory, that spies exist in war. But although he knew about espionage, he had never consciously believed that it could happen right next to him, before his eyes. And where? Here in Stalingrad, where danger was dealt out to everyone in such severe and equal measure that even the thought of treachery seemed to him incredible.

When he thought of the month he had fought with his battalion and all the people around him—some more and some less brave, some grumbling and some afraid, but all of them with a kind of nobility inside them that made them ready to die for this city most of them did not even know—then the thought that Vassiliev had been with him all that month curdled Saburov's memories of it. Even if he had killed Vassiliev, with this hand now lying quietly on the bed, this did not release him from constant wonder at how a thirty-year-old Russian, a man like himself to all appearances, could have brought himself to such betrayal. He could understand it with his mind, but not

204

with his heart, and he continued to think about Vassiliev even after he had written a long report of all that had happened and sent it off to the proper authorities, bringing the incident, he hoped, to its final conclusion.

The silence standing heavy over the hospital was, perhaps, the best medicine and just what Saburov most needed. Although he felt better and better, he did not want anything to break this silence, in which everything seemed calm and good to him. During the last weeks in Stalingrad he had done so much commanding, yelling, running, quarreling, that it was pleasant for him to say nothing, and he passed for the most taciturn patient in the ward. He lay still and kept silent. He did not want to talk.

Even on the eighth day, in the morning, when Anya ran into the ward with light, quiet steps and slipped between the rows of cots to sit down at his feet, he still did not want to talk. He looked at her nice, tired face, at her arms lying quietly on her knees, at her eyes which were looking at him as if she had been running, running a thousand versts straight to him, and he did not want to talk. For the first minute, she, too, said nothing. Then she exploded with conversation, all at once and about everything. First of all she told him how Maslennikov had grown worried over his long absence, had followed him, and had found him lying unconscious half-way between our positions and the spot where the bodies of Petrov and Vassiliev were still lying. Saburov still could not remember how he had crawled out of there, even when Anya told him about it. It must have been that he somehow took the bricks off his body and crawled out. How strange it was, he thought, that he could remember nothing.

Then Anya told him how they had brought him back to the battalion, and how she had seen him on a stretcher and had come up to him. Telling about this now, she looked at him directly and simply, as people look when they are no longer trying to hide anything and when they are no longer afraid of anything.

"I saw you lying there," she said. "I was terrified that you were dead. I began to kiss you. Then you opened your eyes and closed them right away. I went on kissing you, but you didn't open your eyes any more."

Anya described how she and the stretcher bearers had carried him to the shore and how they had crossed the river in a barge, and how the Germans had fired at them because by this time it had become almost full daylight.

"They fired just the way they did before, do you remember?" she asked.

"I remember."

"And I was terribly afraid," she said. "It was the first time for a long while that I've been afraid. While we were crossing I told the stretcher bearers to bring you without fail to this hospital because I could come here later, and I told them to take care of you. But probably they forgot about it, because they have to take care of everybody."

"Why didn't you come for so long?" Saburov asked.

"You know, I couldn't," she said in a guilty voice. "I went back across the river again and I thought I would be here the next night, but they destroyed the ferry crossing. And then so many wounded had piled up that I had to stay with them there until we could ferry them all across. Six whole days. But you feel better, don't you?"

"Yes," Saburov said. "I sat up today and I even tried to walk."

They were both silent. Then she said: "Do you know mother's here too."

"You told me once before," Saburov said, as if remembering something very long ago. "Here, in this village?"

"Yes. I told her about you. She wanted to come today but I came alone."

"Just what did you tell her about me?"

"Everything." She said this "everything" in such a way hat Saburov felt she had probably told a great deal.

"And do you know," Anya said, "I've got a medal, too, now."

"No!" Saburov said. "Where is it? Have they already given t to you? Show it to me."

She opened her white hospital gown and he saw on her blouse he Order of the Red Banner. It was not dirty, with its enamel hipped, as his was, but new and shining.

Anya, screwing up her eyes, also looked at the decoration. Her face was very happy.

He hitched himself up on the pillow with his elbows.

"Dear," Anya said, putting both her hands on his shoulders out at the same time holding him back. "Dear," she repeated.

He took one of her hands from his shoulder and kissed it for a long time. She blushed, but she did not take her hand away, and went on looking at him closely and happily.

"Anya," he said with a feeling that so much had piled up in his heart that if he did not tell her now about his love, then in several minutes, after she had left, he would not be able to hold out and would talk about it to the nurse, to the doctor, to the first person coming up to him. "Anya, if it weren't for the war . . ." He wanted to say that if it weren't for the war he would take her far away from here at once and never again let her go.

"If it weren't for the war, we would never have met each other, no? Of course, it's so," she repeated firmly, as if she were afraid he might disagree.

"Yes," he said. "I wanted to say that. You guessed my thoughts." For the first time he spoke to her with the intimate pronoun.*

---

* In Russian, as in other European languages, pronouns corresponding to "thee" and "thou" are used inside a family, between intimate friends, and

"I know what I'm going to do," she said, still looking straight at him. "They gave me a leave today for the entire day. I'll take you . . ." she faltered. She had noticed how he had spoken to her with the intimate pronoun and she understood what he had meant by this. In her turn she had wanted to talk to him in the same way, but his unshaved, tired face hollowed out by days of illness, seemed to her so grown-up, almost old, that she did not dare.

"I'm going to take you away from here," she said.

"Take me away? Where?"

"To mother's. You'll get well from now on faster there, with us. It's probably all right for you to be moved by now. Mother will look after you, and I, when I'm home. I'll be leaving every evening, and at night I will move the wounded, but from the morning on I'll look after you."

"And when will you sleep?" Saburov asked with a smile.

"Later, when you have grown well again."

She wanted to ask him if he couldn't understand that she simply could not sleep, with him near her, and in general if he couldn't understand what happiness this would be, to have him near her and in love with her. But she did not say this; she tore herself away from the cot, took a step towards the door, returned to kiss him on the lips with an awkward child's kiss, then ran out.

Saburov expected to hear some kind of comment or to see a smile on the faces of the men lying in the same ward with him. He looked around belligerently. But no one said anything and no one laughed. A middle-aged lieutenant with an amputated leg who was lying next to Saburov turned towards him and met his surly stare with such a good and radiant smile that Saburov smiled back at him before he knew it. Then the lieu-

---

between persons who are in love. They were also used, before 1917, by upper-class persons in talking to peasants or workers. Members of the Communist Party, inside the Soviet Union, now use them in talking to each other.

tenant turned fully towards him and said: "Do you know, it's very hard to lose all you have in the world. To lose more than anyone else, much more than anyone else has lost. It's really tough."

"Yes," Saburov said, and he thought that now his neighbor would probably talk about how they had amputated his leg, and it would be necessary for him to say something warm and comforting in reply, but what could he say?

"No, I'm not thinking about that," the lieutenant said, pointing with his hand to the blanket where the stump of his amputated leg stuck up under the creases. "I'm a translator, so I can go on with my profession anyway, and maybe even still do some fighting, somewhere in a staff job. I was talking about something else. In Minsk, my wife has been killed, and my daughter, too—everyone I have. But that also has happened to many people, to too damned many. I'm not even thinking about that. No, they've taken away from me something else on which I had built my whole life. Do you know what I did for the last fifteen years; what do you think it was?" he said with a little laugh.

Saburov waited quietly for him to go on.

"I've worked all my adult life on a new kind of history of Germany. No, I don't even want to talk about it now, about what I wrote and what I worked on. What parts of it were right and what parts were wrong, God only knows. I know only one thing, that I can't go back to it, not ever. I can't work on their history; I can't do it after all I've seen and all I've lost. I can't. I don't want to. I would sooner go to a home for invalids, after the war, or sell beer behind a bar, than remember that I once worked on their history. To hell with it! Maybe others will work on it, probably they will, but it won't be I. Do you understand?"

"I understand," Saburov said.

"But everything's going to be fine with you," the lieutenant said quietly, after he had sighed and quietly let himself fall back on his pillow. "Very fine. She'll come back right away; and don't you get sore at me for being fresh, for looking at you so closely when she was sitting here. That's legitimate for me now."

He angrily slapped his hand on the blanket at the spot where his leg would have been if it had not been amputated, and swore with unexpected coarseness. Then he closed his eyes, turned away, and continued to lie quietly, with his eyelids closed tightly.

Saburov also closed his eyes. It seemed to him it might be easier that way to wait for Anya's return, with his eyes closed. He lay and thought about this firmly, stubbornly, and endlessly. At the same time he thought about the man lying next to him, and for the first time in the entire war he felt with sharpness the sympathy of one human being for another who is unhappy; and although other people's grief was at this moment more remote from him than it had ever been before, still a kind of constricting sorrow suddenly filled him. What could he say? Nothing. If he should say something sympathetic, this man lying next to him would still not believe him, the look of happiness—he felt this—was written so large on his face.

At the very moment when Saburov was lying with his eyes closed and thinking about Anya, she was standing in front of the head doctor in a little room on the lower floor of the same old school building now being used as a hospital.

The head doctor shared the traditional cynicism which is characteristic of many surgeons. He was a little man, heavy-set and almost fat, with a bright red face, and with eyebrows and moustache so black that they looked as if they had been drawn on his face with a heavy black crayon. He was a good surgeon, and in his time he had saved a great many people, but he still considered it almost his duty to declare on every possible occasion that he regarded the entire science of medicine with deep skepticism. He performed operations with studied coolness, talked about amputated arms and legs with laughter, and loved to make double-edged jokes, even in the presence of women. In actual fact, he was a sensitive man, with a somewhat shy nature. But Anya did not know this, and the head doctor, with whom she had been acquainted around the hospital for a long time, and whose jokes she had often listened to, seemed to her the man least capable of listening to and understanding what she now wanted to say to him.

So when she walked in to him boldly, she clenched her fists in her determination to blurt out what she wanted to say. She was determined not to let him insult her, or Saburov, or, most of all, this new happiness which had entered and filled her life.

"Nikolai Petrovich," she said, before she had crossed the threshold, "I have a favor to ask of you."

"I hope you don't have to have anything amputated," he said with the smile she was used to. "To my great regret, that's what all the favors I'm asked for usually amount to. Is that it?"

"No," she said. "There is here . . . a certain captain, Captain Saburov . . ."

"Saburov? Ah, yes, I remember him. With contusions. Well?"

"He is getting better."

"Quite possible. Very glad to hear it. Well, so what?"

"My mother is living here in the village . . ."

"I'm glad to hear that, too. But what has that got to do with it?"

"I am asking you," Anya said, raising her eyes to him, "I want to take him home with us while he is getting well."

Her eyes were now so bright, and they demanded consideration so eloquently, that the chief doctor, although he already had one of his usual jokes on the tip of his tongue, restrained himself.

"I want to take him home with us. I beg of you . . ."

"Why?" he asked her in a serious voice.

"It will be better for him there."

"Why?"

"It will be better for him there," Anya repeated stubbornly. "I know that it will be better for him. I beg it of you."

"What is he, your relative?"

"No, but . . . this is very important to me. I can't get along without it. I want to be with him," she said desperately, ready by now to use any words he might force her to, and any confession, even a false one.

The head doctor considered it quite in the order of things that there should be a little romance between his nurses and the orderlies and the wounded and convalescent patients, and he made no attempt to check up on it beyond reserving to himself the right to joke about these little secrets, not in any mean way but with plenty of coarseness. But this was the first time that anyone had approached him with such a direct and frank request.

He suddenly remembered something far away in space and time, something left behind him in Irkutsk. There were his home, his children, and the wife he had loved with great tenderness from the days when he had been a student. These were subjects he preferred never to talk about, with anyone at all. The tone of this conversation, its unexpectedness, and most of all the way Anya looked at him with a kind of fierce hopefulness, disturbed him, so that he felt almost as if he were behind his operating table doing a difficult operation.

He had to decide the fate of two human beings. This much was clear. So it would be impossible to say, "Let's wait and see how he feels," or "You know it's against the rules," or "I'll have to think about this," and to his credit, not one of these sentences even entered his head. He knew he could say only "yes" or "no" and he said: "Yes, that will be all right."

The conversation had turned out to be unexpectedly short. Neither he nor Anya, as a matter of fact, had anything else to say, especially Anya, who had been steeling herself for a rebuff. She stood in complete silence, confused, for half a minute, and then without thanking him quietly walked out.

An hour later they moved Saburov to the other end of the village in the head doctor's small car. It was in a settlement of little houses standing at the edge of the water. Below one house ran the water, quiet, slow, and green, of one of the many streams of the Volga watershed. From the stream to the house ran two rows of willow trees, and the water, the bare branches of the trees, and the little peasant hut growing out of the ground seemed to Saburov almost as quiet as the hospital itself.

In the hut, which had been partitioned into two halves, it was also quiet. The last flies of summer buzzed quietly, the little boy who met them at the door stepped quietly out of their way, and at the table were sitting two quiet women who were no longer young, each wearing a black shawl over her head— the woman of the house and Anya's mother. This feeling of silence which had begun in the hospital stayed with Saburov without a break through all the ten days which he was to live here.

When he walked into the room, following Anya, the woman who lived there bowed gravely to him and said, "You are welcome." Anya's mother at first threw up her arms, then said "Good Lord," then said, "Oh, how you have changed!" and only after all this did she say, "How do you do?"

The stretcher bearers lowered him onto a broad peasant bench behind the table and stood by doubtfully.

"Never mind," Saburov said, "I can get to the bed myself. You can go on."

They went out. The woman of the house went into her half.

213

For the first time in many years it seemed to Saburov that he had landed in a family which he had known for a long time and in which he felt very good indeed. He sat on a bench by the open window. Beyond the window were only the freshness of the stream and the fusty smell of autumn leaves.

"You won't catch cold?" Anya asked. "Can I close the window?"

"No, I won't catch cold; what do you mean?" he said. He continued deliberately to call her by the intimate pronoun.

Anya walked over to the big bed standing beside an enormous Russian stove which divided the little house into two halves. She spread out the blankets and began to fluff the pillows. She was doing what the nurses had done every day in the hospital. But to Saburov it seemed that she did it all with some special skill. He kept his eyes on her and he was sorry when she said: "There, now it's all finished."

"I'll move over in a minute—wait," he said.

The mother was sitting behind the table, nearly opposite him, and from the way she looked at him he understoood there had already been talk about him between her and the daughter. Anya's mother looked quite different now from the way she had looked in Eltonskaya. She sat silent; it was clear that some great sorrow weighed her down, but at the same time her eyes were clear and calm. She had seen everything, everything had been fathomed in her heart, and now she was only waiting for it all to end.

"Well, it's better here than in Eltonskaya," Saburov said after a short silence.

"Better," she agreed. "We were out of our minds then. I had all but forgotten my own daughter. That was why I wandered all the way to Eltonskaya. And, do you know, my sister-in-law was here all the time. Of course, this is good here. There's no comparison. If we only had the whole family under this roof! You've grown so thin!" she added, looking into Saburov's face.

214

(He had a feeling that she had wanted to say, "You've grown so old!") "You've grown so thin!" she repeated, and then she shifted her glance to Anya, who was sitting quietly across the table from her.

Saburov understood the mother's look: she was trying to figure out how they would be together, he—so old, and Anya—so young. For the second time that day he wanted to say that he was not really old after all. But he remained silent.

"She's always on the move," the mother said, pointing at Anya. "Always moving, always moving, up to five times a day, and when will it all be over with?" She stood up, tied the corners of her shawl beneath her chin, and walked to the door.

"Mother, mother, wait a minute," Anya turned to her. "Wait a minute. Help me to move Alexei Ivanovich over to the bed."

"I can do it myself," Saburov protested, trying to muster his strength.

He tried to stand, but Anya had already come up to him on one side, her mother on the other. Leaning on their shoulders, he hobbled over to the bed. His legs still hurt terribly; on one he could almost rest his weight, but the other buckled under him with pain. When he had stretched out on the bed he had to wipe the sweat from his forehead.

The mother went out. Anya drew over a little bench and sat down beside him.

"Well?" he said.

"Do you feel all right?" Anya answered his question with another.

Saburov held out his hands to Anya; she took them in hers and sat for a long time looking at him, rocking a little on her bench, first towards him, then away from him. Suddenly she stopped, frightened.

"Doesn't your arm hurt at all?"

"No, not at all."

She began again to teeter gently on her bench, looking searchingly into his face, examining every line in it. This was her man, entirely hers. Here he was, in her house, and even if the house wasn't really hers, and even if tomorrow she would have to go back to Stalingrad, and probably he, too, after several days, still she was holding him now by the hands and looking him in the eyes, and this was so unexpected and at the same time had been waited for so long, and was so unbearably wonderful, that tears welled up in her eyes.

"What's wrong?" he asked.

"Nothing." Without letting go his hands, she dried her eyes on his shoulder. "Nothing. It's just that I'm terribly happy."

She moved the little bench away, sat on the bed next to him, buried her face on his chest, and cried. She cried for a long time, and then raised her face, smiled, and again buried her head against his chest. She was crying because she remembered how they had first crossed the Volga together, and how she had been wounded, and how much it had hurt, and how he had kissed her then, and how excited she had been by this, and how long she had not seen him, and how terrifying he had been when they had found him, and how finally she had been unable for eight whole days to get to him.

He looked at her hair and slowly ran his fingers over it. Then he pressed her close to him with both arms, without saying a word. Hearing steps, he barely turned his head and saw that the mother had come in. Automatically he made a movement to release her, but Anya, on the contrary, only pressed more tightly to him. Then she lifted her head, looked at her mother, smiled, and drew herself even closer. It was at this moment that the feeling went through his heart which would not later leave him—that this was for good, something permanent.

The whole day went by as if in a dream. Anya's mother came in and went out, preparing dinner. She bustled about, trying with every look to show that the children need not be embarrassed by her presence. Saburov thought he could see the word "children" on her lips, and it seemed strange to him that any woman except his own mother could use the word for him.

In spite of his efforts to keep her near him, Anya ran off to the hospital for some vodka. She was determined that he should have a drink before dinner, even if only a very little one. She wanted everything to be as it should be. She brought back a small medicine bottle of alcohol and, screwing up her eyes, carefully diluted it with water. All these details—how she ran out and in, how she mixed the vodka, how she screwed up her eyes—filled Saburov with tenderness for her. When they had moved the table up to his bed, Anya ran out for the woman of the house and dragged her in. Without sitting down, the old woman touched glasses ceremoniously with Saburov and downed her drink with great decorum, without a grimace, just as all village women drink who have lived a long time. Then she went out.

After dinner Anya sat beside her mother and told Saburov at breakneck speed all the little things about herself, about her father, about her brothers, about their children, about how they had lived before—in a word, about everything that one tells once in one's life, suddenly, all at once, and only to the person one loves. He leaned back on his good arm and let her chatter pour over him. He was thinking how a time would come when she would no longer walk around in squeaky boots and no longer carry stretchers and escort the wounded across the Volga. They would go away together. Where? How should he know? He knew only that it would probably be very good. About what would happen within a few days, when he would be returning to Stalingrad, Saburov thought only casually. It seemed to him that everything would somehow arrange itself. Maybe he could even fix things so that Anya could be with him in his battalion; he would only have to talk to Protsenko

217

about it. He remembered Protsenko's shrewd, good-natured face, and he thought that if the times had been different Protsenko himself probably would have come to the wedding. "Wedding . . ." Saburov smiled.

"What are you smiling about?" Anya asked, using and hardly faltering over the intimate personal pronoun. "Why?"

"Just a thought I had," he said.

"What kind of thought?"

"I'll tell you later. Don't get angry. All right?"

"Good."

He thought again "wedding," and he remembered his dugout, and for a moment it was as if he could see himself returning, sitting there at his own table with Anya, and beside them those whom he would summon on such a day. Maslennikov, Vanin, maybe Potapov . . . He imagined their faces, and then he found himself wondering whether the dugout was still intact and how they were doing there without him.

When they had finished eating and the mother had begun to clear the table, Anya sat down on Saburov's bed next to him. The woman of the house brought in a big apple, and they did what tens of thousands of others had done before them: they began to eat the apple together, taking bites in turn, each trying to take the smaller bite in order to leave more for the other. Suddenly Anya jumped up and cried:

"Mother, tell us our fortunes."

The mother refused at first.

"No, come on, tell us our fortunes."

They brought the table back again next to the bed and the mother said, as people usually say in such circumstances, that she had not told fortunes for a long time, and what was the use of trying anyway, since they were unbelieving people, but she finally began to deal out the cards.

Saburov had never been able to understand just why a black six meant a long journey, or the ace of clubs meant a government office, or why, if the queen of spades fell on a black ten it boded no good, but if four jacks came out in succession that meant happiness. But he liked the confidence and the gravity with which fortune tellers explained the meaning of the cards they dealt.

Anya, too, watched her mother's hands closely as they dealt the cards. Since on this day her future seemed crystal clear, they managed to find an explanation for everything her mother told them. The long journey they explained as the crossing of the Volga, and the government office was Saburov's dugout. When the mother turned up the queen of clubs, which together with the king of diamonds signified that Saburov was interested in a Lady of the Red Cross, then this meant Anya, absolutely and positively Anya, in spite of the fact that she was not dark but fair, and simply because she was a medical student, and therefore, perhaps, a Lady of the Red Cross. This explanation amused them, and they laughed for a long time until the mother was offended, or perhaps simply grew bored with telling fortunes, and stopped dealing out the cards. She hung sacks on the windows, as had already become the custom in villages during the war, and went out.

Saburov, exhausted from long sitting and long talking, leaned back on his pillow and relaxed. Anya took out a short sheepskin coat and a pillow, and began to make a bed for herself on the bench by the wall. Saburov watched her quietly. The mother came in again two or three times on household errands and then went out for good. Then Anya came over to Saburov, knelt on her knees beside the bed, embraced him, and listened to his heart. In a whisper she said, "It's beating," as if there were something wonderful and extraordinary in this. But what was wonderful was the silence standing around them, and the mother being gone, and the two of them there alone, and most of all that they would be together now for a long time, for today and tomorrow, for always.

Anya remained on her knees, kissing him. Without any shyness she came closer, and he felt that she had fallen in love for the first time and that all her love was now for him, and that this love was so great that everything else was drowned in it— all feelings of fear, of shyness, or of confusion. She moved closer and sat down beside him, then embraced him again, and lay close to him. He pressed her to him until he could feel his arms and his chest hurting from the close embrace, but this only made him glad. The pain itself made him feel closer to her.

"Do you know," Anya said, "my heart is beating just as strongly as yours is. See, listen."

She stretched herself out towards him so that he could hear how her heart was beating. Only a girl as simple and strong in frankness and innocence, not thinking about anything else, could say: "Listen, how my heart is beating." And after all that followed had taken place, she whispered honest and simple words into his ear, and he knew again how much he loved her, and that he would rather cut off his hand than hurt her. But now he was not hurting her nor offending her, he knew, neither by the way he kissed her, nor by his holding her still closer and tighter to him.

FIFTEEN

T H E sound of the samovar woke him the next morning. It was strange to look around and see this room, with the mother bustling around the table, just as if nothing had changed at all. Anya ran in from the entrance passage where he had heard the splashing of water.

"Have you waked up?" she said. "I'll be with you right away." She squeezed her long wet hair, twisting it on her fists, as she had on the little steamer when he had seen her for the first time.

Then she went out again. Saburov closed his eyes and let memories flow over him. He remembered everything in order, minute by minute, from yesterday morning; he remembered the morning and the day and the night. Besides the words of love which had been said to him, besides the things that had happened which were evidence of that love, there was something else which made him believe without limit in her love for him. This was the way she had touched his broken, hurting body. No one could have told her, not even a doctor, but she knew by some instinct where he hurt and where he did not hurt, how you could embrace him and how you could not. In her caressing hands there had been so much love and tenderness that when he remembered about them he felt warm and good.

221

At four o'clock Anya was supposed to go. She pulled on her boots, put on an overcoat, neatly darned in three places where shell fragments had pierced it, and clapped a cap on her head. Then with quick, decisive steps she walked over to the bed, pressing her lips severely together, kissed Saburov, and walked out of the hut.

From now until tomorrow he would know nothing about her. During the war he had become used, it would seem, to the most terrible things, to the fact that healthy people could be joking with him one minute, and killed the next. But he was not used to the kind of feeling he had now. For the first time in his life he experienced that day and that night the physical torment of waiting—the anxiety, the supersititous fear that right now, when everything seemed to be so good, something would happen to her. He remembered thousands of dangers which ordinarily he had not even noticed. He remembered the crossing and the shore on which the shells exploded, and the little trench so shallow that your head could be seen if you did not crouch down, and Anya probably did not crouch down. He figured on his watch when, approximately, she would be on the shore, when the barge would leave, how long it would take to cross, how much time the unloading would take, how much time she would need to get up to the battalion, how many minutes would be required to place the wounded on the stretchers, and how long the trip back would take. But these futile calculations—futile because he knew better than anyone else how impossible it is in war to guess how much time anything will require—did not quiet him.

Stalingrad was about eighteen kilometers away. All night he listened to artillery fire, sometimes fading away, sometimes rumbling closer. It was like the unchangeable striking of a clock; it measured time. And although he knew that the cannon fire sounded first louder and then softer simply because of the wind, this did not help to release him from his fear. When it grew louder, he grew more anxious, as if its roar were actually a kind of measure of Anya's danger.

In the evening Anya's mother sewed for a long time on a sewing machine in the other half of the little house. Then she came in with the stub of a candle, placed it on the table, and looked at Saburov.

"You're not sleeping?" she asked.

"No, I'm not asleep."

"At first I couldn't sleep either, when she used to go, but now I sleep. After all, I have three of them at the front, and if I didn't sleep for all of them, I'd be dead in a week. Have you got relatives?"

"Yes, my mother."

"Where?"

"There."

Saburov made the gesture with his hand which many people made and which everyone always understood at once. It meant that "there" was behind the German lines.

"But whom have you got on this side?"

"No one. Only her . . . What have you been sewing?"

"This? My sister-in-law gave me some cloth, so now I'm sewing a dress for Anya. After all, she is a young girl. Even if she wears a dress only once a month—well, I'll still make one for her. But she'll have to go barefoot in it; she hasn't any shoes. Maybe I could give her these?"

She sat on the chair, put one leg over the other, and thoughtfully looked at her old, patched, low-heeled slippers. Then she raised her head to Saburov, and suddenly remembering their first meeting, said:

"These aren't mine either. Some good people gave them to me. Before, my feet were smaller than hers, but now, ever since they were burned, they've been swollen. Probably these slippers would fit her. What do you think?"

She asked this as if Saburov knew more about her daughter than she, her own mother. In this trivial, almost absurd question was a recognition of all he was now thinking about.

Without answering directly, Saburov said: "I'll be getting up soon and we'll be having a wedding." He smiled himself at the word. "You won't be angry, will you, if we have a wedding over there?"

"On the other side of the river?" she asked simply.

"Yes."

"Wherever you live is the place to do it," she said accommodatingly. The idea did not surprise her, because "the other side" was for her Stalingrad, the city in which she lived, and the full truth about which, no matter what rumors came now from the city, she still could not picture to herself over her memories of what it had been.

"What's most important is that she shouldn't have to make the crossing every day, sometimes three times in a day," she said. "Maybe it would be better if she were there with you."

For a long time she sat by Saburov and talked to him about the things mothers like to talk about with the husbands of their daughters: how Anya had grown up, how she had had scarletina and measles, how she had cut off her braids and then let her hair grow out again, how her mother had looked after her all her life because, after all, she was an only daughter, and about many other little things which it was very pleasant for her to tell.

Saburov listened to her and found in what she said a kind of delight and a kind of sorrow——delight to be learning about these details, and sorrow because he had not seen them all himself. Like all people in love, he wanted passionately to have a share in everything she had done, in everything that had happened in her life before him.

The mother went on talking with him, and he realized that he was not stronger but weaker than this old woman at the

224

business of waiting. She knew better than he did how to wait and how to stay calm. Maybe, it occurred to him, she was comforting him on purpose with this conversation.

At last she went out. Saburov did not sleep the whole night, and only at eleven in the morning, when the sun came in the window and threw a yellow band across the bed, dozed off without knowing it. He woke up again, just as he had once in the dugout, from being stared at. Anya was sitting on the bed at his feet and looking at him. He opened his eyes, sat up in the bed, and reached his hands toward her. She hugged him and then pushed him back by force.

"Lie down, my dear, lie down. How did you sleep?" she asked.

He felt ashamed of having dozed off for these fifteen minutes, without having waited for her, but he did not tell her that he had not slept all night. He knew this would disappoint her rather than please her.

"All right. I slept," he said. "How is it over there?"

"Good," Anya said. "Very good."

She spoke cheerfully, but on her animated face he noticed signs of complete fatigue. Her eyelids were barely opened, like those of a person who has not slept for a long time, and not thinking about sleep at all, could fall asleep at any moment. He looked at his watch: it was about eleven, and at four she would have to go back again.

"Lie down now and go to sleep," he said. "Right away."

"But how about talking?" she said with a smile. "I want so much to talk to you. While I was coming on the little ferryboat I kept remembering things I haven't told you. There is so much I haven't told you yet."

She quickly drank a cup of tea, lay down next to him, and one minute later was fast asleep, almost in the middle of a word. He lay on his back, with his elbow curved under her head, and thought. From time to time he turned his eyes so that he could see her, and it seemed to him the impossible had happened: time itself had stopped.

This sensation of time having stopped remained with him through all the ten days which he lived here before his return to Stalingrad. He made no effort to imagine himself sicker or weaker than he actually was in order to remain longer in this state of happiness, but at the same time he did not try to get up before it was time. Like any man used to controlling a kind of natural violence, he tried to force himself not to think about what was now happening in his battalion. He remembered it, but he did not want to worry about it. In any case he could not be there now, so what use was it to think about it every minute? There was only one thing to think of, and about this he could do nothing at all. This was the growing feeling, somewhere below the level of consciousness, of the enormous dimensions of the fighting now going on there. The longer he stayed away, the greater and the more exciting grew this awareness. He began to understand the excitement with which the word "Stalingrad" sounded in men's hearts.

News still came to him through Anya, through the old woman who owned the house, through wounded men who wandered over sometimes from the hospital, and this news was not cheering. Almost every day he learned about new streets which had been taken by the Germans. Every day the distance from the Russian line to the Volga was measured in fewer hundreds of meters. More and more often he restrained himself from cross-questioning Anya in detail. From this distance he did not want to learn the details, and he postponed them all for that day when he himself would go back. But whenever Anya appeared—from her eyes, from her walk, from her tiredness—he quietly drew his own conclusions, and he knew they were correct conclusions, about what had gone on that day.

Once—this was on the sixth or seventh day, and about three hours after Anya had left—he heard someone on the porch call

ut his name, then he heard quick steps outside the room, and
n walked Maslennikov.

"Alexei Ivanovich, my friend," Maslennikov blurted out
rom the threshold, and ran rather than walked over to him.
Ie stopped short, embraced him firmly, kissed him, took
ff his overcoat, pulled up a little bench, sat on it facing him,
gitatedly took out a cigarette, offered one to Saburov, struck
match, and began to smoke—all this with incredible speed—
t seemed in half a minute; then he finally sat and looked at him
vith his black eyes full of curiosity and friendliness.

"So you've left the battalion in the lurch?" Saburov asked
vith a smile.

"On Protsenko's orders," Maslennikov said. "He came over
o the regiment, then to the battalion, and ordered me to come
nd see you. How are you, Alexei Ivanovich?"

"All right," Saburov said. Noticing Maslennikov's close ex-
mination of him, he asked: "What's the matter, have I grown
very thin?"

"You're thin, all right."

Maslennikov jumped up, dug into the pocket of his overcoat, and pulled out a package of biscuits, another package of
ugar, and three tins of American canned meat. He piled this
ll hurriedly on the table and sat down again.

"You trying to butter up your commanding officer?"

"We have lots of everything now. Supplies are good."

"Are many sunk on the way?"

"A good many. Just as it was before you went away, Alexei
Ivanovich."

"Well, what heroic deeds have you been performing over
there without me?"

"What have we been doing? Just what we did when you were
there," Maslennikov said. He wanted to tell how he and everyone else missed Saburov and were waiting for him, but he looked
at the captain's thin, tired face, and said nothing.

227

"Aren't you expecting me back?" Saburov asked.

"We're waiting for you."

"I'll come in three days."

"Won't that be early?"

"No, just right," Saburov said calmly. "Where are you now? The same place?"

"Exactly the same," Maslennikov said, "except that to the left of us they've broken all the way through to the bank of the river so that our communications with the regiment are squeezed pretty tight now. We can get through only at night."

"Well, so that means I'll have to come back at night. I'll come some night and inspect everything. How is Vanin getting along?"

"Very well. He and I have appointed Konyukov commander of a platoon."

"Can he handle it?"

"Pretty well."

"Who's alive, and who isn't?"

"We're almost all alive. But we've had a lot of wounded. Gordienko's wounded."

"Have they brought him over here?"

"No, he stayed there. His wounds aren't much, but still they punctured him in four places at one time. And I go right on without ever getting touched," Maslennikov said. "Do you know, I sometimes think that either they'll never manage to wound me, or they'll kill me all at once."

"Don't think about that," Saburov said. "Once and for all think to yourself that it's entirely possible, but then don't go on thinking about it every day."

"That's what I try to do."

They talked the whole day about the battalion, about who was stationed where, about what had changed and what had stayed the same.

"How is the dugout?" Saburov asked. "Is it still where it was?"

"Exactly the same place," Maslennikov said.

Saburov felt good to know that his dugout was still there, in its old place. There was in this a kind of stability and besides, he thought of Anya and his plan to get married in the dugout.

"Listen, Misha," he turned suddenly to Maslennikov. "Aren't you surprised that I'm not in the hospital but here?"

"No. They told me."

"What did they tell you?"

"Everything."

"Yes . . . I'm very happy . . ." Saburov said after a moment's silence. "Very, very. Do you remember how she sat on the barge with us and wrung out her hair and I told you to put an overcoat around her. Remember?"

"I remember."

"And then when we got off she was already gone."

"No, that I don't remember."

"Well, I remember it. I remember everything . . . I was thinking of asking," he added after a pause, "that she be taken as a nurse into our battalion, but then somehow my heart turned over."

"Why?"

"I don't know. I guess I'm afraid of tempting fate. Here she is travelling back and forth every day and she's still whole, but there . . . I don't know. Somehow it's frightening to change anything."

Saburov would have liked to go on and on talking about Anya, but he checked himself, shifted the conversation, and asked: "How does Protsenko look?"

"All right," Maslennikov said. "He laughs a lot, as he always did, even more now."

"That's bad," Saburov said. "That means he's nervous."

"Why nervous?"

"When things bother him, he laughs more often than usual. Yes, I haven't asked you the most important thing of all. Who's commander of the regiment?"

"A new man, Major Popov."

"Well, what's he like?"

"He's all right, I guess, maybe even very good. Better than Babchenko anyway."

"Is he brave, too?"

"He's brave, too. Yes, and he's calm, and not irritable—a cheerful fellow, a little like the general. They served together, by the way, somewhere else, it seems."

"That's very likely. The general never forgets his old fellow officers. And that's a good thing. Sometimes we haven't got enough of that."

"Of what?"

"Remembering the men you fought with."

They went on talking this way for another ten minutes, and then Maslennikov was suddenly in a hurry, and Saburov saw on his face a new expression of grown-up responsibility. Maslennikov didn't feel right; he had been away from the battalion a long time. Now he was hurrying, and it was as if he were no longer there, as if he were already back on the other side of the river.

"In the evening," Saburov said, "and three days from now. Have the tea hot for me. I've been trying to liberate a samovar here," he pointed to a samovar standing in the corner. "I wanted to bring it to you as a present to the dugout. But they won't give it away. Well, on your way, get going. Give my greetings to everyone. She went to division headquarters to-day. Maybe she'll be at the battalion too."

"Well? What message for her?"

"What message? Pour her some tea, and she'll guess it her-self. On your way. I won't say good-by."

A day after Maslennikov's visit, Saburov stood up and tried to walk for the first time. His legs ached and sagged under him. He felt unbelievably weak and dizzy, and he went out on the street and stood a little while at the gate listening to the distant artillery rumble.

Every day Anya came back later than the day before and left earlier. In her tired face he could see how hard it was for her, but they did not talk about this. What was the use?

The doctor ran over to Saburov for a minute from the hospital, at Anya's request, but he did not examine him and only bent his legs at the knees and ankles with a professional twist, looking in his face and asking if it hurt. Although it actually hurt a lot, Saburov had set himself for the pain and he answered that he felt nothing. Then he asked when the truck drivers would be going to the river crossing the next day. The doctor said it would be as usual, at five o'clock in the evening.

"So, you're already preparing to decamp?"

"Yes," Saburov said.

The doctor expressed no surprise and did not begin to argue or protest. He was used to this here, near Stalingrad; it was in the normal order of things.

"The truck drivers leave at five. But you remember just the same that you're not entirely well."

"I'll remember."

"Well, that's fine, it's good-by then," the doctor said, standing up and pressing Saburov's hand. Saburov felt a sudden malicious impulse. Holding the doctor's hand in his own for a second, he squeezed it, not with all his strength, but fairly hard.

"You can go to the devil," the doctor said. "I already said you could go back. What are you trying to do to me?" and rubbing his fingers he turned and went out the door.

When Anya came, Saburov told her he was going back to Stalingrad the next day. Anya was silent. She did not even argue that it was too soon, and she did not ask him to stay for just one more day. This kind of talk would have been out of place between them.

"Only let's go together," she said. "All right?"

"That's what I was thinking, too."

All that day she was quiet and thoughtful and although she was very tired, for once she was not sleepy. She sat next to him, quietly moving her hand over his hair and looking closely at his face as if trying to remember it better.

She did not fall asleep, but he dozed off for half an hour, and she woke him when she had to leave. Once more she stroked his hair gravely and said: "It's time for me to go." He stood up and walked with her to the gate, and then watched her for a long time as she hurried down the street.

In the morning Saburov packed away his few belongings in his knapsack. Anya was a long time in coming. Several times he walked out to the road but still she did not come. It was two o'clock and she was not there; then three; then four. At half-past-four he had to leave himself, if he was not to miss the hospital truck along the road. He went out once more on the road and stood there for a long time. Then he went back to the little house, sat down at the table, and wrote a short note to say he was leaving without her. At first he wanted to sign it "Saburov," but this seemed formal; then "Alyosha," but this was strange and unfamiliar; so he finally signed it with the letter "A" and put a dot after it.

He said good-by to Anya's mother. She did not wring her hands, did not grieve, and took his departure quietly. Probably this calmness was a family trait, he thought.

"You're not going to wait for her?"

"No, I've got to go."

"Well then, go." She came close to him for a second and kissed him on the cheek. This was the only sign she gave of her fear and anxiety for him and for her daughter.

At ten minutes to five he set off in the direction of the hospital, looking at everyone he met. The night before some little boys had cut him a strong cherry stick, and he limped along leaning heavily on it.

The trucks began to move just after five. They tried to seat him in the cab with the driver, but he sat in back hoping he would be able to see Anya from there if they should pass her on the road. He lay on the bottom of the truck and looked out the left side at every car they passed. But Anya was not in any of them. The evening had grown quite cool; he pulled his cap tighter on his head and buttoned up the collar of his coat.

After three kilometers they turned on to the main highway leading from Eltonskaya to the river crossing. The road had been destroyed many times, and just as many times repaired. It was lined with ruts and the truck bounced and shook. His legs hurt when they hit the bottom of the truck. In the air above them at a great height the last dogfights of the evening were going on. There were a lot of German planes. Ours appeared only seldom, in pairs or singly. In the air, it was clear, the situation was just as tough as on the ground. The Germans bombed the string of trucks twice on its way to the crossing. The trucks were piled high with boxes of ammunition, sides of beef, and sacks of something white, probably sugar.

At the edge of the suburb where the river crossing was, he saw the remains of a Messerschmitt still smoking on the road. The truck drove around it and up to the ferry crossing. The Germans held the crossing under regular but fairly infrequent fire from heavy mortars. It looked at first as if everything, on the surface at least, was just as it had been when Saburov had crossed the river here the first time, except that it had grown colder. The Volga was hurrying its waters along as before, but now the water seemed somehow chained and heavy, and he felt that maybe today, or tomorrow, or soon, the first thin skin of ice would cover the river.

When they had left the trucks and gone on foot to the crossing, to which a little ferry with a barge was coming, Saburov realized there would be no meeting with Anya on that side of the river. He sat on the sand and gave up his search. He smoked, and it tasted good to him. It always seemed warmer when he was smoking.

The little ferry approached the dock. A hundred meters behind him several shells exploded on the shore. Wounded men on stretchers were being carried off the ferry and its barge. Saburov sat and waited. Men were hurrying with the unloading and the loading, but around him he thought he heard less noise than when he had crossed the first time. "They've grown used to it," he thought. Everything was being done quickly and with skill. The city on the other side, when he looked at it, seemed familiar to him, and he marvelled that he had been so long away from it—eighteen whole days.

He showed his papers to the officer in charge of loading and was already on the gangway leading to the half-crippled barge which served as a dock when Anya hailed him.

"I knew I would see you here," she said. "I knew you wouldn't wait for me and that you would start at five in any case. I was right, wasn't I?"

"You were right."

"I came over with the barge before this one and got rid of my wounded, and then I waited for you. We'll go back together now."

"Good. Look," Saburov said taking her by the elbow and pointing at the other shore, "there is less smoke now, don't you think?"

"You're right, less."

"But more noise."

"Yes, more racket," she agreed. "But you're not so used to it now."

"Never mind, I'll get used to it again."

They walked along the shaky gangway onto the barge and

from it climbed over onto the ferry. Anya jumped down to the deck of the boat first and gave her hand to Saburov to help him jump. He took her arm and jumped down with an agility he had not expected. Yes, he had been right in coming, he was well again, or very nearly.

The little boat shoved off. They sat on the deck, dangling their legs and holding on to the handrail. Below them the Volga rocked and swung with a kind of autumn anger, in places glistening with its first crystals of ice.

"It's grown colder," Anya said.

"Yes."

Neither of them wanted to talk. They sat pressed close to each other and were silent.

The little ferry came close to the shore. Outwardly everything seemed as before, and the city from here looked almost the same. It seemed as if nothing had changed in the landscape, and in general nothing had changed if you did not take into account what had come into their lives. They were both conscious of this, and were silent.

"It's good," he said quietly.

She answered, also in a low voice: "Yes, it's good."

The shore came closer and closer. "Get the mooring ready," shouted the same hoarse, Volga bass they had heard a month and a half before.

The little ferry was tied up to a dock even more battered than the one they had left on the other side of the river. Saburov and Anya were among the last to get off. Although they had quite a way to go together, as far as regiment headquarters, it still seemed to Saburov that he would not be able to do for a long time what he now wanted to do. So he held Anya close to him, stroked her hair, and kissed her. Then they walked on side by side. They had to clamber up along the dark slope of the shore pitted with shell holes. Sometimes he stumbled, but he walked quickly, almost never leaving her side. Under their feet they felt again the soil of Stalingrad, the same cold, hard ground which had not changed during the last month, and which had still not been surrendered to the Germans.

SIXTEEN

HESE were the first days of November. Only a little snow had fallen and the snowless wind whistling through the ruins of the buildings was cold as ice. To a flier from the air the earth looked spotted, black on white.

The first thin ice was floating on the Volga. The crossing had become almost impossible. Everyone waited impatiently for the Volga to freeze and hold. Although the army had laid up some reserves of provisions, shells, and bullets, the Germans kept on attacking without a break, fiercely, and the reserves were melting with every hour.

Still another division besides Protsenko's had now been cut off from army headquarters. The Germans had broken out to the Volga not only to the north of Stalingrad but at three places within the city itself. To say that the fighting was going on inside Stalingrad would have been to understate it: almost everywhere the fighting was going on at the very shore of the river. In only a few places were the Germans a kilometer-and-a-half from the river, and on some sectors the distance separating them from it was measured in hundreds of meters. The idea that any place in the city might be relatively safe had

237

simply disappeared. The entire area, without any exceptions, was under heavy fire.

In many places you could now look right through what had been whole blocks of buildings. They had been completely leveled by air bombardment and methodical artillery fire from both sides. No one knew which was strewn more thickly on this ground, stone or metal, and only someone who knew what insignificant damage is usually done to any big building by even the heaviest artillery shell could understand what a quantity of steel had been poured onto this city.

Distance was no longer measured in kilometers on staff maps, and no longer by streets, but by buildings. Fighting was going on for individual houses. These houses figured not only in the reports of regiments and divisions, but in those of all the armies lined up along this front.

Telephone communications between the army staff and the divisions which had been cut off ran from the west shore to the east shore, and again from the east to the west shore. Several divisions were now supplying themselves separately, with their own docking facilities on the east side of the river, across from them. Officers at army headquarters had already had to defend themselves two or three times with guns in their hands. At division headquarters, this had become an everyday affair, part of ordinary life.

On the evening when Saburov returned from the hospital, Protsenko was summoned to army headquarters. In spite of the fact that Protsenko had a realistic picture of the situation, he was still surprised by the nearness of headquarters to the Germans; the distance by now was not more than four hundred meters.

When Protsenko answered a question as to how many men he still had by reporting fifteen hundred and then asking in an entreating tone if he could not wangle a few more, the army commander did not even let him finish his request. He told him that he, Protsenko, was probably the richest man in Stalingrad, and that if it became necessary to scrape up a few men for reinforcements somewhere, they would take them away from him. Protsenko had cheated a little on his figures and had not reported that in recent days he had added a hundred fighting soldiers recruited from his own supply services on the other bank of the river. So he shut up and did not return to the question.

After the official part of the conversation, Matveyev turned on the radio and for a long time they listened to a German broadcast. To Protsenko's surprise, Matveyev understood German fairly well, even though he never mentioned it—well enough in any case to be able to translate almost everything in the broadcast.

"Can't you feel it, Alexander Ivanovich," Matveyev said, "how cagey they have become in the words they use? You know, before when they were fighting somewhere on the outskirts of a city—I remember how it was at Dnepropetrovsk— they used to shout to the whole world: we've captured it. Sometimes it was even worse. When they were approaching Moscow, and they were still thirty kilometers away, they were already announcing: Tomorrow will be the parade. But now they're actually in this city, and they've taken more than half of it—after all, the truth is the truth—and still they're not saying that they've captured Stalingrad. And they don't give any date when they will take it. What do you think? What's the reason for this?"

"We are the reason," Protsenko said.

"That's just it, it's us. And it's you, in particular, and your division, even though you have only sixteen hundred soldiers at the moment."

Protsenko was unpleasantly surprised at this accurate figure. He assumed an expression of amazement.

"Sixteen hundred," Matveyev repeated. "While the commander was here I didn't want to show you up by letting him know that you had hidden away a hundred men. He might have made a row. But in actual fact you have sixteen hundred, so don't argue about it," and he laughed, happy that he had caught the shrewd Protsenko. Protsenko also laughed.

"That's how it is," Matveyev continued, "they're afraid now to set any time limits. That's a good thing . . . Senya," he called to his adjutant, "give us some cognac. When will Protsenko come to see me again? When the first ice has come and gone on the Volga. No?"

"Yes, it's beginning to freeze, little by little," Protsenko said. "Pieces of ice already scratch the oars. Tomorrow, probably, the ferry crossing will be entirely out."

"Well, we foresaw that," Matveyev said. "But I wish the Volga would freeze quicker. There is just one prayer to her from all of Russia—that she should freeze and hold, and quickly."

"Maybe she isn't listening," Protsenko said.

"Maybe," Matveyev agreed. "Then it will be bad. But . . ." he raised his finger. "Let's drink to that 'but.'"

He poured cognac for himself and Protsenko and after touching glasses with him, drank it at one gulp. Protsenko followed his example.

"That 'but,'" Matveyev said, "means that you and I are up against it again together. Whether the Volga listens or not, we've got to stand."

Protsenko returned to division headquarters in a good and even uplifted mood. The fact that he had been refused any reinforcements produced in his heart a curious sort of calm. Until now he had been counting his losses every day with anxiety, and waiting impatiently for reinforcements to come. Now there was nothing to wait for; he would have to fight with what he had and build his hopes on this. Well, at any rate, everything was now clear: those men who had already crossed the Volga and were stationed here with him on this shore of the river might have to die, but they would not give back the five city blocks which had fallen to their lot. Protsenko knew quite clearly that he and most of those he knew in the division might die here, on the Stalingrad shore. But he thought about this now without trepidation and without distress. Well, so be it. And why not, even if he and many others should be killed? Just the same, the Germans would not win. "They can't win," he repeated again, and so loudly that his adjutant walking behind him overheard him.

"What did you order, Comrade General?"

"They can't win," Protsenko repeated. "They can't win, do you understand?"

"Yes, exactly," the adjutant said.

They seated themselves in a rowboat. When the rowers dipped their oars in the water, from time to time little pieces of ice clung to the blades of the oars.

"It's beginning to freeze," Protsenko said.

"Yes, it's slowing up," said the Red Army soldier sitting at the oars.

"Will it take long? What do you think?" Protsenko asked.

"Who knows?" the soldier answered coolly. Protsenko felt that the indifference in these words was sincere; whether it took long or not, just the same they had to stand.

When he got back to his headquarters, among the reports he found of what had gone on in his absence was one that a fugitive had crossed the lines.

"A soldier?" he asked.

"No, one of us, a Russian," Vostrikov said, "a citizen."

"A citizen?" Protsenko raised his eyebrows in surprise. The very thought of a citizen had vanished a long time ago in Stalingrad. "Bring him in."

"He's wounded."

"Where?"

"He's lying in the adjutant's dugout."

"Well, all right, let's go to him then."

When Protsenko bent down to get through the low door leading into the adjutant's quarters, he saw an old man lying on the bed, or rather half-sitting, half-lying, with his eyes closed. The division's surgeon was sitting next to him on a stool.

"Hello, granddad," Protsenko said as he went in. The old man said nothing, and lay there with his eyes still closed.

"Badly wounded," the doctor said. "Unconscious now."

"Did they cross-examine him?" Protsenko asked Vostrikov.

"Yes, they did."

"Where's the record of it?"

"I'll bring it right away."

While Vostrikov ran off to get the written report of the cross-examination, Protsenko sat on the other cot in the room and looked carefully at the old man. He was obviously very old, at least seventy. His face was lined with countless deep wrinkles. His tangled gray beard stretched almost half way down his chest. He was dressed in a ragged Red Army jacket, under which there was an old-fashioned black waistcoat and a relatively clean, homemade shirt.

"Where is he wounded?" Protsenko asked the doctor.

"In the back, three bullets."

"Is he going to die?"

The doctor nodded his head.

"Will he regain consciousness?"

The doctor shrugged his shoulders.

"Here is the report," Vostrikov said, coming back into the room.

Protsenko took several handwritten sheets of paper and moved over towards the light to read them better. The report stated that the old man had crossed the front three hours before, at 2:30 in the morning, on Remizov's sector, and had

242

been found half-conscious about fifteen minutes after several bursts of tommy-gun firing had been heard from the German sides. When he had come to, he had said his name was Yarkov, Timofei Petrovich, that he was a citizen of the suburb of Gorodisha, and that he had crossed the front in order to bring a report to the Red Army. It was clear the old man had been in bad shape during the cross-examination. He reported that some kind of German staff was located in the former building of the village soviet in Gorodisha and in two houses across from it, and that the whole ravine beyond the village was filled with boxes of shells. Besides this, he reported that a month ago a man he knew, accompanied by Germans, had appeared at the building where he lived, and that this man had been one Ivan Nikolaievich Benediktov, the son of the former priest of the village church, Father Nikolai, and that he had been wearing Red Army uniform, had asked about his father, and had then gone off with the Germans for whom he was obviously working.

Whether this report was the old man's only reason for crossing the front remained unclear. The report of the cross-examination broke off with this account of Benediktov.

"Why didn't they go on with this?" Protsenko asked.

"He lost consciousness," the doctor answered. "They were questioning him while I was here."

"Who was questioning him?"

"Yushenko," Vostrikov replied.

"Call him," Protsenko ordered, "and then," he looked again at the report he was holding, and added, "then call Saburov for me, quickly. I'll sit here. Let them both come straight here."

He looked again at the report, then at the old man. "Of course, it was right to summon Saburov," he thought. He was comparing this report with the one Saburov had sent through from the hospital, after the incident with Vassiliev, and it

243

seemed to him there was more than coincidence between the two. Like Saburov, he found it almost impossible in his heart to accept the idea of espionage here, under Stalingrad conditions, and so the idea that the spy figuring in both reports might be the same man seemed logical to him.

At this same hour of the early morning, Saburov had just walked out of his dugout into the open for a breath of fresh air. Only ten hours had gone by since he had come back to the battalion, but his return had not worked out at all as he had expected. He had arrived at seven in the evening and had not found either Vanin or Maslennikov, who were out with the companies, and a half hour later when he was ready to go and find them, the evening artillery barrage had started. Then in the darkness the Germans had mounted two attacks, and he had been plunged into the routine alarm and confusion of defense, just as if he had never been away. He gave orders by telephone, had mortars dragged from one flank to the other, sent reinforcements to Company One, managed to say two words to Maslennikov as he passed him in a trench but never saw Vanin, and only got back to his dugout to rest at four o'clock in the morning. He had grown so unaccustomed to such fighting and he was so weak that his head ached. He wanted neither to eat nor to sleep, and after a quarter of an hour spent sitting in the dugout he threw his coat over his shoulders and walked out into the open air.

Petya was sitting at the entrance to the dugout. There were so few men left by now in the battalion that in the last few days he had been carrying out the duties of an orderly, of a cook, and of a sentinel. Petya made a sudden motion, about to jump to his feet at the appearance of the captain.

"Sit down," Saburov said. He leaned against the logs which lined the entrance to the dugout and stood quietly for a few minutes, listening. There was not much firing. Only occasionally a single German shell would whistle over their heads to

244

strike somewhere far off on the shore itself or to plummet into the water.

"Was I gone long, Petya?"

"A long time, Comrade Captain." Petya shivered.

"What's the matter, are you cold?"

"I am, a little bit."

"Go into the dugout, and get warm. I'll stand watch for you meanwhile."

Left alone, Saburov turned first to the left and then to the right. In the hurly-burly which had at once engulfed him, he had had no chance really to look around him, and now the view of Stalingrad at night astonished him. During the time he had been away, Stalingrad had changed beyond recognition. Before, the entire field of vision had been filled with buildings, half-destroyed but still buildings. Now in places what one saw was almost wasteland. The three buildings which Saburov's battalion had been defending no longer really existed; they were only foundations on which the remains of walls and the lower parts of windows still stood in a few places. They all looked like children's toys, smashed and broken. To the left and to the right of the buildings ran unbroken lines of ruins. In some places the chimneys were still standing. Now, at night, the rest dissolved into the darkness and looked like an uneven rocky valley. It looked as if the houses had disappeared into the ground and as if burial mounds of brick had been raised over them.

Astonishment filled Saburov; was it possible that all this had happened in the eighteen days he had been away? For the first time he felt how enormous was the scale of what was going on around him.

"Comrade Captain," Petya said, coming out of the dugout, "the general wants to see you."

"Right away?"

"Yes, immediately."

When Saburov walked into the adjutant's dugout, Protsenko was still sitting on the bed. With him was Yushenko, who worked in the special division in charge of counterespionage. The old man was still sitting up on the bed, his eyes open, frowning with pain.

"What sort of a man was he?" Saburov heard Protsenko ask, continuing the cross-examination.

"What sort?" the old man said. Then, groaning through his teeth, he asked: "Lift me higher, can't you?"

Vostrikov leaned over and began to raise the old man.

"The higher he is, the worse it is for him," Protsenko said.

"No, the higher the better," the old man said, "otherwise the blood runs into my throat. Why, he was a tall man, broad-shouldered, dressed like you. His hair was light . . ."

Protsenko leaned over to Saburov and explained to him what had gone before. "Well, go on, granddad, go on," he said to the old man.

"That's all there was to it," the old man said. "What else could there be? I lived next to his father for forty years, and he was a good man. But his good-for-nothing son, he was always worthless. When he came up with the soldier, I could see right away that he was no prisoner; I didn't believe it for a moment."

"Well, Alexei Ivanovich," Protsenko said, "ask him if it was your bird or not."

Saburov was a little at a loss, both because the conversation was so unexpected and because of the strange appearance of the dying man. But he asked a few hurried questions about the appearance of the soldier the old man had seen, about his insignia, and whether or not he wore a medal on his uniform. The old man answered slowly, with difficulty, and almost indifferently. He had already done and said everything he wanted to, and now, in his final minutes, he was more interested in his own pain and in thinking about approaching death. He knew

246

nothing about insignia, and about the soldier's appearance he only repeated that he had been tall and light-haired. About the medal, he said there had been one on the soldier's uniform. Then he thought for a moment, as if trying to remember, and he repeated: "There was one." Then he closed his eyes.

A long silence followed in the dugout. The old man finally opened his eyes again and stated with surprising strength what was obviously the most important thing for him—what had brought him, an old, sick, helpless man through two front lines, through danger and shooting, into this dugout.

"He wanted to be the judge," the old man said angrily. "Then to his shame he brought foreign judges; he wanted to show that he was right. The fact that people died all around him because of this didn't bother him, damn him!" *

The old man sighed, grew quiet, and closed his eyes. He never opened them again. His chest heaved a couple of times, he tried to raise his head as if to speak, then he relaxed against the wall.

"That's all," said the doctor, lifting back the sleeve of the old man's big, ill-fitting jacket and feeling for the pulse in the wrinkled wrist. "That's all."

Protsenko stood up. Saburov saw on his face an expression he had never seen before, of some sadness he could not hide.

"Well, there's the end of your story," he said, turning to Saburov. Then he looked again at the old man. "You could

* Many of the "enemies of the people" liquidated in Russia between 1936 and 1939 were accused only of opposition to the regime or of "diversionist" activities not involving direct contact with foreign powers or their agents. Others, including nearly all the defendants in the major public trials, were convicted of actual treason. Both in law and in politics, the Soviets have always held that their capitalist encirclement tended to blur any distinction between the two. This old man's summary of Vassiliev's development from disgruntled failure to oppositionist, then to enemy agent and war criminal, is a condensation of the newest version of the Communist party line in Russia which has frozen harder and harder, under pressure of the war, the earlier Bolshevik thesis that political opposition to the regime in any form leads inexorably to outright betrayal of the Soviet Union.

247

have met him before the war and thought nothing of him, nothing good and nothing bad. For forty years he lived next to his priest, locked the church doors, climbed up in the belfry to ring the bells on holidays. But there's something in a Russian just the same, Alexei Ivanovich, when he's without weapons and without everything you and I have got; he's still strong, he's got some special strength that can't be broken . . . Well, Vostrikov," he turned to his adjutant, "let's dig him a grave before the sun comes up, and let's bury him under the bluff, close to the Volga. Take along ten soldiers, with rifles to fire a salute. Tell me when you're ready, and I'll come along . . . Let's go back to the dugout, Alexei Ivanovich, and sit and talk."

An hour later a short volley from a few guns sounded crisp in the cold early morning air over the Volga. Saburov was standing next to Protsenko beside a fresh grave on the side of the bluff.

"Yes, that's the end of that story," he repeated Protsenko's words to himself. And the heavy feeling that had been born in him that night with Vassiliev grew softer and almost disappeared. In the long run the evil Vassiliev stood for, and which had worried him for so long, was as nothing compared to this old man and the manner of his dying.

SEVENTEEN

FOUR days went by. It was late in the morning. Saburov woke up, sat on his cot, and noticed with surprise that light was pouring through the door of the dugout. Judging by the light, he must have slept a good eight hours. Apparently Vanin and Maslennikov, who considered him still an invalid, had gone out without waking him. He listened: everything seemed quiet; there was almost no shooting. Well, he thought, that was only natural. After all these days of continuous attack some kind of silence had to follow. He listened again. Yes, strange as it was, everything was quiet.

The door opened and Vanin came running down the steps.

"You're awake?"

"But I asked you to wake me up."

"Why? Especially when it's quiet for once."

"Have you been visiting the companies?"

"Yes, I went over to Company Two."

"Well, how is it up there? Anything special happening?"

"Nothing special so far," Vanin answered. "It's just the way the papers say: 'Fighting continues in the Stalingrad region.'"

While Saburov had been in the hospital, Vanin had sud-

249

denly acquired a capacity for good-natured irony which h
had lacked before.

"How many casualties today?" Saburov asked.

"So far, one killed and five wounded."

"That's a lot."

"Yes. By our former standards it's only a little, but nowa
days it's a lot. Of the five wounded we're sending only one back
to the rear. Four are staying."

"But can they stay?"

"How should I know? In general, they shouldn't, but unde
our present circumstances they can. How about you, are you
feeling better?"

"Better. Where's Maslennikov?"

"He went out to Company One." Vanin laughed. "We can'
get used to the idea, Captain, that our battalion is no longer
a battalion. We still say: companies, platoons, units. The
whole battalion became just a company a long time ago, bu
we never admit it."

"And we shouldn't," Saburov said. "When we admit, my
friend, that we're not a battalion but a company, then we'l
have to give up two of these three buildings, because a com
pany can't defend all three. That takes a whole battalion. I
would cost us plenty to admit that we're only a company, and
that we haven't enough forces left."

"But sometimes we just don't have any men."

"You know, I think you've become pessimistic."

"A little. I look at this place that used to be a city, and my
heart hurts. Shouldn't it?"

"No, it shouldn't."

"Well then, if it shouldn't, it shouldn't. Maslennikov told
me something about you getting ready to get married," Vanin
added after a pause. He had known about this before, but
until now he had not allowed a single word to slip out about it.

"Yes," Saburov said.

"And the wedding?"

"There'll be a wedding sometime."

"When?"

"After the war."

"No," Vanin said smiling, "that won't do."

"Why not?"

"Because after the war you won't invite me to the wedding."

"I'll invite you."

"No. That's what we always say in wartime: 'after the war we'll meet again.' We won't meet again. You'll be in one place, I in another. And I want to have a good time at your wedding. Do you know, without you here—the devil with it, I was lonely. I wonder why. We've really talked together not more than five times in our lives, but still I grew bored without you. So don't put it off too long."

On Vanin's face was an expression of suppressed emotion. His profession made him think of others, watch over them, and sympathize with them. But it rarely occurred to anyone else that he himself needed watching over, and sympathy, and that he could have, and did have, the same worries and misfortunes other people had.

"All right," Saburov said. "It shall be as you command, Commissar. If the wedding should be here, here it will be. Can we choose the day together?"

"You choose it together."

"Hadn't we better ask the Germans?"

"No," Vanin shook his head. "Why ask them? If you ask them, you won't live to see your own wedding."

"By the way, where are your people?" Saburov asked, reproaching himself inwardly for having grown like Babchenko, and for never having found the time or the occasion to ask a man who was fighting by his side whether or not he had a family and where they were.

"What do you mean, my family?" Vanin asked, and his face suddenly went cold and hard.

"Yes, your family; where are they, and how are they?"

"We won't talk about that," Vanin said.

"Why not?"

"We just won't. I know nothing about them and there is nothing to be said."

He turned away and began to busy himself with his papers. Saburov was silent. He seated himself more comfortably on the cot, leaned up against the wall, rolled himself a cigarette, and lit it.

Vanin's words about the wedding had made him think again about Anya, who had never been far from his thoughts during the last few days. Since they had parted on the shore of the river, he had seen her only once. Three or four hours after his arrival, Saburov had realized how tense the fighting had become, and that all he and Anya had been planning would work out quite differently, and that their decision to be together had no relation to what was going on around them. What had seemed to him so simple back at the medical base station—to ask Protsenko to make Anya a nurse in his battalion—now seemed so inappropriate, here, that he could not have opened his mouth about it to the general.

Anya had not appeared until the third day, the day before yesterday, towards evening. Although they had only fifteen minutes to talk together, neither said a word about the decision they had made on the other side of the river. He was grateful to Anya for not reopening the subject here. Like all men, he disliked more than anything else in the world being made aware of his own helplessness. No matter what he had said to her on the other shore, he was not in a position here to change anything. Everything had to take its course.

Anya had come in when he had just returned after the repulse of a routine German attack, and was sitting in his dug-ut with Maslennikov. She had walked quickly up to Saburov and before he could even stand up, had thrown her arms round him and kissed him several times. She had then gone up to Maslennikov and shaken hands with him. From all her movements, from the way she looked, Saburov had understood at once that she would not reopen the old conversation, but that she was still his wife, and simply by coming she was letting him know that nothing had been forgotten and that nothing had changed.

Maslennikov had gone out. Neither Saburov nor Anya made any effort to hold him. Saburov knew that in Maslennikov's place he would have done the same. For ten minutes they sat side by side on the little cot, their arms around each other, leaning against the wall. There was nothing they wanted to talk about, probably because no matter what they said it would have been unimportant compared to the fact that they were sitting here together, in spite of what was going on around them. These were ten minutes of happiness, undisturbed by thoughts about the future. He did not ask her where she was going (he knew it was to get the wounded) ; nor did he tell her how many wounded there were in his battalion that day (she knew this, too, herself) ; he did not even ask whether she had eaten. He had a feeling that these ten minutes were theirs to sit here and to be quiet. When Anya got up to go, he did not try to hold her.

She had not come again. Yesterday another nurse had come for the wounded and had brought Saburov a little note, written in pencil on a torn piece of paper. It said: "I am with Remizov's regiment. Anya." Saburov was not hurt that the note was so short. He knew that no words could express the size of what there was between them. Anya was simply telling him that she was alive and where she was. Probably she was there at this minute, he thought, at Remizov's, no further from him, maybe, than five hundred short but impossible steps.

A whole string of shells crashed somewhere right over the dugout, and then a second, and a third, shaking the ground. Saburov looked at his watch and thought with a smile that the Germans were still as addicted as ever to precise timing. It was seldom they started anything between hours; it was nearly always exactly on the hour. So it was now. Salvos followed one after another.

Without putting on his overcoat, Saburov climbed out of the dugout into the communication trench. Everything around was roaring from the cannon fire.

"Vanin, it looks as if something's starting. Telephone the regiment," he shouted, leaning towards the entrance to the dugout.

"I'm trying to telephone; the line is broken," Vanin's voice carried to him.

"Petya, send some messengers."

Petya climbed out of the trench, ran across the ten meters which separated him from the messengers' dugout, disappeared for half a minute, and came back followed by two signal corps soldiers who ran off quickly between the piles of ruins in the direction of regiment headquarters. Saburov watched them. One minute they were running quickly, not trying to hide themselves. Then a series of explosions would go off not far from them, and they would lie down. They would get up again, lie down, and again get up. He followed their little figures for a few minutes until they disappeared from sight behind a pile of masonry.

"The telephone line is working again," Vanin yelled from the dugout.

"What do they say?" Saburov asked, walking back into the dugout.

"They say that along the entire front of the division there is a barrage attack. Probably they're going to start a push along the whole line."

254

"Is Maslennikov over at Company One?" Saburov asked.

"Yes."

"You stay here," he said to Vanin. "I'm going over to Company Two."

Vanin tried to protest but Saburov, wincing with pain, had already pulled on his overcoat and walked out.

All that followed in the next four hours was difficult for Saburov to remember later in any detail. Fortunately, the battalion's position was so close to the Germans that they had decided not to use aircraft. But they poured everything else on the battalion in quantities it had never seen before.

The Germans had piled up in the streets such heaps of shattered steel and brick that there was nowhere for their own tanks to pass. Still the tanks did come up as far as they could, almost to the buildings where Saburov's men were waiting. From behind the cover of broken walls, they hammered the buildings from 37mm. guns with short, slapping explosions which merged into the uninterrupted chatter of machine-gun and rifle fire.

Several times during these four hours Saburov was covered with earth from close explosions. The feeling of danger which usually stayed with him, as with all men, even in the roughest moments of fighting, seemed for once to disappear, so uninterrupted and boundless was the danger now. Obviously something of the sort had happened to the soldiers under his command. To say that he commanded them during these minutes was something more than the truth. He was side by side with them, but they did what had to be done without any command. What had to be done was simply to stay where you were and with every slightest possibility raise your head and fire—fire without end on the Germans creeping, running, hopping, from one heap of wreckage to another.

At first Saburov had a feeling that all the fighting was aimed directly at him and that everything that moved, fell,

255

walked, or ran was coming directly at where he was standing
Gradually he began to feel, rather than to understand, tha
the blow was really aimed to his right, and that the Germans
obviously, were determined today to cut his regiment off from
its neighbors and get through to the Volga. At the end of th
fourth hour of fighting, this aim had become completely clear

Going over from Company Two to his right flank, wher
Company One stood at the hottest spot of all, at the junction
point with the neighboring regiment, Saburov ordered hi
battalion's battery of mortars to be dragged over behind him

"Comrade Captain . . ." the commander of Company Two
Potapov, protested unhappily.

"What?"

"You are taking my last mortars," Potapov threw up hi
hands and his voice shook with anger.

"Wherever it's toughest, that's where I'm taking them."

"It's rougher there now, but an hour from now I'll be getting it."

"You must not think only of yourself, Comrade Potapov."
At any other time he would probably have shouted rudely at
him, but now he had a feeling that Potapov really felt mad,
not for himself, but for his company, at being left without
these mortars.

"Don't you see, Ivan Ilyich," he said, "the way I see it,
they're squeezing Remizov's regiment over there. They may
get through to the Volga. We've got to hit them on their flank.
Give an order for them to drag those mortars quicker. Well?"

He looked at Potapov's face, made certain that he had been
understood, and then held out his hand to him: "Hold on
tight. You'll hold without your mortars; I know you."

At Company One, when he arrived, hell itself had broken
loose. Maslennikov was there, sweating, red with excitement,
without an overcoat, and with the collar of his tunic unbut-

256

oned. He was sitting with his back against a piece of wall
nd hurriedly spooning out of a can cold meat covered with
ongealed fat. Next to him on the ground were two soldiers
nd a machine-gun.

"A spoon for the captain," he said when he saw Saburov.
'Sit down, Alexei Ivanovich. Have something to eat." Sa-
urov sat down, dipped several times into the tin, and gulped
down some bread.

"What's this machine-gun doing? Why have you got it
ere?"

"Over there—look," Maslennikov pointed in front of them
where, about fifty meters away, a piece of wall was standing
with a fragment of staircase still attached to it, and with two
windows opening out toward the Germans. "I had this
machine-gun taken away from its position. The three of us
are going to crawl up there with it. We'll fire at them from
the window. From there you can see everything like the palm
of your hand."

"They'll knock you down," Saburov said.

"They won't get us."

"They'll get you with the first shot, as soon as they spot
you."

"They won't get us," Maslennikov repeated stubbornly.
He knew as well as Saburov that the Germans ought to get
them, but just because they ought to he was determined to
crawl there anyway. He had an instinctive feeling that in spite
of all probabilities they would not get him and that his plan
might work out very well.

"To the right they've captured the whole of No. 7," he said.
"They're putting the squeeze on Remizov."

"Aren't they still shooting from No. 7?" Saburov asked.

"No, probably they're all killed there. They may cut us off
today, if it goes on like this." Maslennikov pointed to the
machine-gun. "But we'll put this in the window and from

257

there we'll pin their ears back. That ought to help a little
no?"

"All right," Saburov said.

"May I go?" Maslennikov asked.

"You may go."

Maslennikov turned to the two soldiers waiting for him
beckoned to them, and all three walked out from behind thei
cover and moved along the foundation of a building, running
lying down, and then running again. Saburov could see clearl
how they got safely up to the building, how they climbe
through the shattered masonry, and passing the machine-gu
from hand to hand, began to scramble up along the remains o
the staircase. At this moment several shells exploded next t
the trench in which Saburov was standing, and he dove fo
cover.

When he got up again he saw that Maslennikov and the tw
soldiers had established themselves at the window and ha
already opened fire. Several minutes later German shells began to drop around the remains of the wall. Maslennikov continued to fire. Then the entire wall was wrapped in smoke and
dust. When the smoke cleared, Saburov could see that all three
were still firing, but that below them in the wall a German
shell had torn an enormous hole. Still another shell hit the wall,
a little lower. Maslennikov continued to fire. Then a shell
exploded higher and Saburov watched one of the machine
gunners throw back his arms, as if making a back dive, and fall
from the third floor window to the stones below. Even if he
had only been wounded, it was all the same now, Saburov
thought; he had certainly been crushed to death.

Saburov watched Maslennikov lie flat on the embrasure of
the window, shape his hands like a megaphone, and yell something down below once, and a second time, and then return to
the machine-gun and begin to fire again. Although the Germans had seen Maslennikov and were only a short distance

om him, they had not yet succeeded in hitting the window.

One more shell bit into the wall below Maslennikov, between
e second and third floors. Ten minutes later, whether from
hell splinter or from a bullet, the second soldier spun around
om the machine-gun, teetered, and almost fell, but managed
balance himself and sit down on the edge of the window.
aslennikov left the gun, crept over to the wounded man, and
id him flat along the wall in such a way that he could not fall.
e stayed there a little while, bending over the wounded man,
d then returned to the machine-gun. Now he was firing
one.

By this time they had dragged up three of Potapov's mor-
rs, the fourth having been destroyed on the way. Saburov
awled out with the mortar squad and arranged them on the
ins of an old garden wall. They opened fire at once on the
erman battery which had been firing at Maslennikov. Hardly
d the mortars begun to fire when the Germans discovered
eir position and sprinkled dozens of shells around them.

The officer in charge of the mortars was hit by a shell splin-
r. Saburov took his place. He had stopped watching Maslenikov and now looked in his direction only occasionally, be-
ween firing orders. The Germans shifted their fire to the mor-
rs, and this made it easier for Maslennikov. He lay there and
ent on firing. A little later, when Saburov looked in his direc-
on, he could see only the machine-gun. There was no Maslenikov. "Did they really get him?" he thought. But after a few
inutes Maslennikov appeared again on the wall: he had ex-
austed his ammunition and crawled off for more.

It was already evening, just before dark, when Saburov was
lmost buried under dirt thrown up by a shell. He got up with
ifficulty. Little gold sparks were flashing before his eyes. He
t down, holding his head in his hands. The sparks grew fewer,
nd he began to see what was around him as if he were looking
hrough fog.

Petya crawled up to him and asked him something.

"What?" Saburov interrupted him.

Petya again whispered something he could not hear. Sab rov turned the other side of his head toward him.

"They didn't hit you?" Petya asked, and his voice was loud that Saburov understood he must have gone suddenly a completely deaf in one ear.

"They didn't hit me," he said, and raising his head notic that his overcoat was ripped all along his chest, and that und it his blouse was cut. A shell splinter had flown by, hardly gra ing him; the mortar standing beside him was demolished, muzzle torn completely off.

The Germans continued to fire, but not so steadily. Judgin by their fire they had managed to cut off Remizov's regiment because the firing now came from Saburov's right, and fro much lower, nearer to the Volga. He tried to get through b telephone to Vanin, but this was hopeless. All telephone lin had been cut in dozens of places. But the fighting, it seeme had begun to subside.

"Where is Maslennikov?" Saburov asked.

"Here."

Saburov saw Maslennikov, even more sweaty, excited, an tired than he had been two hours before.

"I guess I stitched them back there," he said.

Saburov saw an enormous blue bruise running across Mas lennikov's forehead and down the entire length of his cheek.

"Are you hurt?" he asked.

"No, they just knocked me down. You know what? It brok the machine-gun, but didn't hurt me at all."

"I'll recommend him," Saburov thought . . . "Without an doubt, I'll recommend him. Best of all, for Hero of the Sovie Union.* Let them decide. But he really is a hero." Aloud h only said: "And your soldiers?"

* The Red Army's highest decoration for personal bravery.

"One of them was smashed to death by the fall, the other I dragged out."

"Good for you," Saburov said. "It's getting quieter, isn't it?"

"It's getting quieter," Maslennikov agreed. "Only it looks as if they'd got through to the Volga anyway."

"Yes, it looks that way," Saburov said.

Both were silent for a little.

A plump, snubbed-nose nurse crawled up to them, breathing hard, and asked if they had any wounded.

"Only out there in front of us," Saburov said. "Wait until it gets dark, then drag them back." It occurred to him that Anya might now be crawling up to someone over there in Remizov's regiment, from which they had now been cut off.

"I'll drag them out right away," the nurse said.

"Don't crawl out there," Saburov said roughly. "Don't crawl out there." He hoped that right now some other officer was holding Anya back in the same way. "In ten minutes it will be dark and then you can make it."

The nurse and two stretcher-bearers lay back on the stones. If Saburov had not said "Don't crawl out there," they would have gone out, but once he had forbidden it, they were glad to rest for ten minutes.

Behind them, one after another but close together, fifteen or twenty shells exploded.

"They're making their last attack before night," Maslennikov said. "Don't you think so, Alexei Ivanovich?"

"Yes," Saburov agreed.

"They say the first ice has covered the Volga."

"So they say." Saburov leaned back on the stones, turning his face upward, and he noticed for the first time that the snow had never stopped falling. The big wet flakes chilled his flushed face pleasantly.

"Turn over like this," he said to Maslennikov.

"How?"

"Like me. It's wonderful."

Maslennikov also turned over. Saburov watched the snowflakes fall on his face. "Nice?"

"Very," Maslennikov said. "What do you think, will it take long for the river to freeze?"

"I don't know," Saburov said. "Can we get through yet to Vanin?"

"No, the lines are still broken."

"Well, you stay here for a while. I'm going over."

"Wait a little," Maslennikov said. "It will be dark right away."

"Shut up. I'm not a nurse. Keep an eye on her. See that she doesn't crawl out there before it gets really dark."

Saburov climbed out of the trench, squirmed his way over the ruins, and taking cover along the wall of a building, went back to the command post of the battalion.

"Communications are working again with regiment headquarters," Vanin said to Saburov as he walked into the dugout.

"Well, what do they say there?"

"We've been cut off from Remizov."

"It looks like it," Saburov agreed. "What are they thinking of doing?"

"They didn't say. Probably they're waiting for orders from Protsenko."

Both were silent.

"Maybe you'd like some tea?" Vanin asked.

"Is there any, really?" Saburov felt that after everything he had just lived through there could be nothing as commonplace as tea left on the face of the earth.

"Of course there is," Vanin said. "Except it's probably cold by now."

"That doesn't matter."

Vanin lifted a teapot from the floor and poured out cups for both of them. "But don't you want some vodka?"

"Vodka? Pour out some vodka!"

Vanin poured the tea back into the teapot and poured out for each of them a half-cup of vodka. Saburov drank his at one gulp, almost without tasting it. Vodka no longer had any flavor for him, but had become a kind of medicine against fatigue. Then Vanin reached for the teapot again. They slowly drank the cold strong tea. Neither wanted to talk. They knew there had taken place today what would later be described in reports from the front: "On such-and-such a date the situation grew materially worse."

Drinking the tea, they remained silent. It was still too early to make arrangements for tomorrow, and about today, about what had already come and gone, neither wanted to speak.

"Would you like to listen to the radio?" Vanin asked.

"That's a good idea."

Vanin sat down in the corner and began to fiddle with an old receiving set. At first there was music, as if from very far away, but in a few minutes it stopped. Vanin began to twist the dial. There was only silence in the ether. Then they heard some snatches of a broadcast which sounded familiar—a little like Russian, perhaps Bulgarian or Yugoslav. They could not understand the words. Then there was silence again.

"Nothing comes out of it," Vanin said. "It's as quiet as if it were dead."

"Try turning it to Moscow," Saburov said.

Vanin turned the dial to the line over which the word "Moscow" was written. Both listened hard.

"Moscow's also silent as the grave," Vanin said.

"It can't be."

"Not a sound."

Then suddenly from the loudspeaker came the voice of a man speaking obviously in great excitement.

263

"The meeting of the Moscow Soviet of Deputies of the Working People, together with Party and public organizations of Moscow, I hereby declare open. Comrade Stalin will make a report."*

For two minutes there could be heard long and loud applause.

"Is today really the sixth?" Saburov asked in surprise.

"As you see."

"How in the devil would I know? Everything's been mixed up for me today. Since morning it's seemed to me as if it were the fifth."

"What made you think the fifth?" Vanin said. "It's the sixth all right, and everything is just as it always was. They haven't passed it up a single year. Even last year they had the celebration."

"Last year I didn't hear it. I was in the trenches."

"I heard it," Vanin said. "Then it was nice and peaceful here. We were frightened for Moscow. We stood here at the loud speaker and listened."

"Yes—then you worried about Moscow, now they're worrying about us," Saburov said thoughtfully. He remembered the first speech Stalin made during the war; it was the one he had heard in his little room in Moscow on the last day before he had gone off to the front.

"I am addressing you, my friends," Stalin had said then, in July of 1941, in a voice which had strangely excited Saburov. Besides its usual firmness, there had been in the voice a kind of intonation which had made him feel that the heart of the man speaking was pumping blood hard. This had been the speech he was to remember later during the war, almost always in moments of the most extreme and mortal danger. He always

---

* Every year, on November 6, the Russians celebrate the eve of the anniversary of the 1917 Revolution with a meeting in the Moscow Opera House. Some prominent Soviet leader always makes a political or military report at this meeting; in recent years the report has been made by Stalin himself.

remembered it not by its words, nor its phrases, but by the voice in which it had been given—even by the sound of water gurgling into a glass in the long pauses between sentences. Although on that morning he had been all alone at his own receiver, it seemed to him that it had been precisely then, listening to that speech, that he had given his oath to do everything in this war that was in his strength to do. He thought the situation had been extremely hard for Stalin at that time, and that Stalin had determined to win at any price. This was exactly what Saburov himself had felt, because it had been tough for him, and he also had decided to win at any price.

Saburov remembered now, with a clarity which surprised him and in minute detail, just what he had lived through at that moment and had never later been able to forget.

Meanwhile the applause continued. Saburov moved up right in front of the radio. He was interested now not only in what Stalin would say, but in how he would say it. The applause was so loud that for a second it seemed to Saburov as if people were cheering here, in the dugout. Then from the loud-speaker came the sound of someone clearing his throat, and the voice of Stalin, unhurrying and precise, said: "Comrades . . ."

Stalin spoke about the progress of the war, about the reasons for our failures, about the number of German divisions hurled upon us, about many other things which were extremely interesting in themselves. But Saburov at this moment was not thinking about the meaning of the words but listening to the intonation of the voice. He wanted suddenly and very much to know what was in Stalin's heart at this moment, what mood he was in, almost how he looked. He sought in the voice the same intonation he had found in the other speech to which he had listened in July of 1941. But the intonation was quite different. Stalin was speaking now more slowly, and in a lower, more quiet voice.

Before the end of the speech, Saburov already felt easier at heart. He felt that both what Stalin said and the voice in which he said it, for reasons which he could not yet understand, inspired some special and unusual kind of calm. With particular precision he listened to one of the closing sentences: "Our task is, in fact, to destroy Hitler's army and its leaders," Stalin said slowly and evenly. After this had come a long pause, which had seemed endless, and then had come applause.

Vanin and Saburov sat for a long time in silence by the radio.

What Saburov had just heard seemed to him extraordinarily important. For a moment he tried imagining that this voice had been speaking not now, when everything had grown quiet, but an hour earlier, when he had been with Maslennikov in the hellish racket of the attack. When he thought about this, the quiet voice he had heard from the loud-speaker seemed even more surprising. The man who had been talking must have known what was going on here, and still his voice was calm. If Saburov or Maslennikov or Vanin, at the toughest minute of the fighting, had suddenly said: "To hell with it, we'll beat them back," they would have been talking about their battalion, and in the final analysis their responsibility for these words would have consisted of only five hundred square meters of desolation and two hundred human lives. But this man had spoken about victory, thinking of millions of square kilometers and millions of human lives, and still he had spoken calmly and firmly, like a man who does not doubt victory for a moment.

"And it's true, we will beat them in the end."

Saburov said this out loud without meaning to. Seeing that Vanin had heard it and was looking at him, he repeated:

"Just so shall it be. No, Vanin?"

"So shall it be," Vanin said.

"When I left the hospital, one of the doctors who had just come from Eltonskaya told me that there, and in general along

266

the entire railroad, there are masses of troops, and cannon, and tanks, and everything. I didn't believe him then, but now I think maybe it was the truth."

"It's possible," Vanin said. "It's possible. Maybe it's true."

"And still they don't give us anything," Saburov said. "I was away from here eighteen days, and they didn't give you anything while I was gone, did they?"

"Protsenko gave us thirty men."

"But they were from his own rear services."

"Yes, they were our own supply troops."

"They don't count. Except for them, did you get anything?"

"Nothing at all."

"That's what I mean. I remember Moscow," Saburov said. "I remember how at the end of November people came to us and told us, in secret, how troops stood behind Moscow and around Moscow, as far as you could see. But we went on fighting with whatever we had. They didn't give us any of those troops before the time came; before December 5th, they didn't give us any reinforcements at all."

It was nine o'clock and the loud-speaker was full of sound. From different cities men shouted in foreign languages. Some kind of music was played, very emotional music—not quite a hymn and not quite a march—something neither Vanin nor Saburov recognized. The enormous size of the world was caught up in this simple little apparatus and seemed to fill the dugout. They had the feeling that it had grown crowded, and a kind of sadness filled Saburov.

"They are playing music," he said. "It's strange to think there are still so many things in the world. Different cities, countries, music, theaters."

"What's strange about it?" Vanin asked.

"Well, it's just strange. Although, of course, it really isn't strange at all. But it seems strange . . ."

Maslennikov came into the dugout, dirty, wet, and half-frozen. He seemed thin and dark after the day's fighting. His cheeks were sunken but his eyes shone, and there was something ineradicably youthful in them, something even the war could not put out. Before he had taken off his cap he asked for a cigarette, inhaled deeply a couple of times, then sat down, turned towards the wall, and without taking the cigarette out of his mouth, fell fast asleep.

"He's tired," Saburov said. He took off Maslennikov's cap, carefully lifted his legs from the floor, and placed them on the cot. Maslennikov did not wake up. Without thinking about it, Saburov ran his hand over the sleeping man's hair.

"What are you doing, sleeping?"

Maslennikov did not answer.

"He's asleep," Saburov said, stroking his hair again. "I think I'll recommend him for Hero of the Soviet Union. What do you think, Vanin?"

"I don't know," Vanin shrugged his shoulders. "He's a good boy, all right, but for hero . . ."

"Yes, hero," Saburov said. "I'm going to recommend him for a hero's star. After all, do you have to knock down an airplane to be a hero? Nothing of the sort. This fellow is a hero. I most certainly am going to recommend him, and you're going to countersign it. You will, won't you?"

"Of course I'll countersign it," Vanin said. "Once you are convinced, that means I'll countersign."

"We'll sign it," Saburov said, "and the sooner the better. You need medals while you're still alive. They're very good to get while you're still alive. After you're dead, they're all right, too, but mainly, you know, for your folks. For you yourself it's all the same then."

"Yes, for the dead man, of course," Vanin agreed.

"He's only twenty years old," Saburov said. "If it had not been for the war he'd be studying now in the first, maybe in the second class at some institute. You know, it's strange even to think about that now."

The telephone rang.

"Yes, Comrade Popov," Saburov said. "What am I doing? Getting ready to go to sleep. All right, I'll come at once."

"Popov says that Protsenko has summoned me. What in hell that's for, I don't know. In any case, you take over command for a while. All right?"

"Yes," Vanin said.

"You take over. I'll probably be back quickly. But anyway, in case something happens."

He shook Vanin's hand and walked out.

EIGHTEEN

IT WAS already dark. Not far away, white signal rockets hung in a semicircle over the front lines. Saburov walked along with a tommy gunner, stumbling occasionally, tired to the marrow of his bones.

"Wait a second," he said in the middle of the path. "Let's sit down."

He sat down on a pile of dirt and thought bitterly that he must be growing old, or that he was beginning to experience, instead of the fatigue which comes at the end of every day, the chronic and continuing exhaustion from which most men suffer who are fighting for the second year. They sat for several minutes and then walked on.

They did not find Protsenko quickly. No one had told them, but he had moved in the four days since Saburov had last gone to see him. His command post was now, like Saburov's, in an underground sewage tunnel, in one of the enormous, four-meter-wide sewers of the chief municipal system leading to the Volga.

"Well, how do you like my new quarters, Alexei Ivanovich?" Protsenko asked. "It's all right, isn't it?"

"Not bad, Comrade General. And the best thing about it is that you've got five meters over your head."

"When a bomb falls, only the dishes rattle, nothing else. Sit down." Saburov sat down.

"Tea," Protsenko said. The orderly quickly served them. "Drink."

Saburov drank a cup of very hot tea, scalding his mouth. He hoped his sleepiness would leave him, but it didn't. It was hard to keep himself from dozing off in front of the general.

"Are you still at your same old place?" Protsenko asked. "They haven't bombed you out yet?"

"Not yet, Comrade General."

Saburov noticed that Protsenko was looking at him closely, almost as if he had just met him for the first time.

"How do you feel?" Protsenko asked.

"All right."

"I'm not asking about your battalion but about you. How do you feel? Are you really well again?"

"I've recovered entirely," Saburov said.

Protsenko was silent for a little but he continued to look at Saburov.

"I want to give you an assignment, Alexei Ivanovich," he said suddenly and severely, as if to make it perfectly clear both that he had the right to give the assignment and Saburov the strength to carry it out. "They've cut off Remizov."

"I know, Comrade General," Saburov said.

"I know you know. That doesn't make me feel any better. I know they've cut him off, but what I don't know is how things are with him there; who's alive and who's dead, how many men are left, what they can do and what they can't do—I don't know anything. And I've got to know—today—you understand?"

"I understand."

"Later, maybe, it will be easier. When the Volga has frozen we'll be able to go around on the ice. But today we'll have to get there along the shore. I've checked it. In theory, it's pos-

271

sible to get there, because the Germans have gone right up to the edge of the bluff above the river, but they haven't gone down to the water's edge. From here we haven't been firing at them, just to keep them from doing so, and it looks as if Remizov has been doing the same. In general they don't often go right down under the slope itself. So you will have to pass below the bluff, underneath. And you'll have to do it . . ." Protsenko paused, looked at Saburov's tired face, and added roughly, "tonight and no later."

"I need someone to go not simply as a messenger, but someone who can help me learn everything exactly, and if everyone has been killed, take over the command himself. So, depending on the situation, I'll either expect you back tonight, or if you stay there, I'll expect someone whom you'll send. How do you want to go, alone or with a soldier?"

Saburov was thoughtful for a second. "There are no Germans right on the shore itself?" he asked.

"It's very unlikely."

"If I bump into the Germans, then even two men with rifles wouldn't help me." Saburov shrugged his shoulders. "And if they simply shoot at me, then I'd be less noticeable alone. That's the way I see it."

"Well, it's as you wish."

Saburov wanted desperately to sit five minutes longer in warmth and safety, but he noticed Protsenko getting ready to stand up, which would mean the end of the conversation, and he hurried to stand up first.

"May I go?"

"Go, Alexei Ivanovich."

Protsenko stood up and shook his hand, no more strongly and no longer than was his custom, as if he wanted to show by this that everything would work out all right, and that there was no reason to make any special farewell.

Saburov walked behind the partition into the outside section of the dugout where Protsenko's adjutant, Vostrikov, was sitting. Vostrikov was a short-witted fellow who was always getting everything mixed up, but he was rated highly by the general for his unlimited courage.

"Are you going, Comrade Captain?" Vostrikov asked.

"Yes. Listen, Vostrikov, I'm going to leave my rifle with you."

"All right, it will be safe here."

Saburov placed his rifle in the corner. "Now here's something else. Give me two lemon grenades, or better yet, three or four. Have you got them?"

"We certainly have."

Vostrikov dug around in the corner and, a little reluctantly, gave Saburov four small F-1 grenades; they were already neatly tied with strings to be fastened to a belt. Saburov carefully hung them in pairs on each side of his belt, after having checked them.

"Gently, gently," Vostrikov said, "you'll set them off."

"Never mind."

Having fixed the grenades, Saburov took off his clumsy triangular German holster, placed it by the side of his rifle, and thrust his automatic under his windbreaker, next to his chest.

"Did he give you a drink for the road?" Vostrikov gestured in the direction of the door behind which Protsenko was sitting.

"No."

"What's the matter with him?"

"I don't know."

Saburov shook Vostrikov's hand and went out.

"Vostrikov!" Protsenko shouted.

"Yes, Comrade General."

"What are you messing about with there?"

"Nothing. Captain Saburov was getting ready to go."

"What was he getting ready?"

"He left his rifle and took some grenades from me."

"Well, all right."

Protsenko was thinking. To tell the truth, he had sent Saburov not because he had no one else to send, but because Saburov had already served him once as courier to army headquarters, and he felt Saburov could do this job, too. Although it was clear that the assignment was almost impossible, still this feeling of confidence did not leave Protsenko. He sat at his table and slowly and meticulously thought the situation over. Whether Saburov returned or whether he stayed there in command of the regiment and sent someone else back really made no difference. One way or another, they still had to take back these four hundred meters of ravine into which the Germans had driven. Protsenko called his chief of staff, and with pencils in their hands they figured up how many men were left to them for operations that night. Only two weeks ago the figure would have frightened Protsenko, but now he had grown so used to poverty that the results of his calculation seemed to him not so bad after all. He did not know how things stood with Remizov, but here in his other two regiments losses today had been smaller than he had a right to expect.

Still, with what forces was he to take the shore back again? There could be no thought of taking even one battalion from its regular position; he would have to scrape up several dozens of men along the entire sector, from every battalion, and transform them before tomorrow night into an assault brigade. This was the only way; there was no alternative.

"Well, how have you decided, Comrade General?" asked the chief of staff. Protsenko took the piece of paper and counted the make-up of the new unit. "There you are," he said. "Here is written out how many men to take and from what units. During the night bring these men here into the ravine. During the day we'll get them ready, and tomorrow night, if we're on our toes, we'll take that shore back again."

Protsenko looked gloomy. His usual sly smile did not once light up his face.

"Will you please sign the report to army headquarters?" said the chief of staff, taking the paper out of his briefcase.

"A report about what?"

"As usual, about operations."

"About what operations?"

"About today's."

"What operations today?"

"What do you mean, what operations?" the chief of staff asked in confusion, and a little irritated. "Naturally, how the Germans broke through to the Volga, and how they cut off Remizov."

"I won't sign it," Protsenko said without turning his head.

"Why not?"

"Because they didn't come out on the shore and they didn't cut us off. Hold up the report."

"Then what should we report?"

"Today—nothing."

The chief of staff gestured with his hands to show he did not understand.

"I know," Protsenko said. "I accept full responsibility for holding up the report one day. We will take back the shore and report it all in one dispatch. If we take it back, they will forgive us our silence."

"And if we don't take it back?"

"If we don't take it back," Protsenko said with a gravity unusual for him, "then there will be no one to forgive or not to forgive. I'm going to lead the attack myself. You understand? What are you looking at, Yegor Semyonovich?" he said to the chief of staff in a different tone. "What are you staring at me for? You think I'm afraid to take responsibility for what's happened? I'm not afraid. I haven't been afraid and I'm not afraid now. But I simply don't want it to be known that the

Germans have come out on the shore here, too. No, I won't have it. I report to army headquarters. From army headquarters it goes to front headquarters, and from front headquarters to the High Command. I don't want it. It would discourage all Russia. Do you understand? I don't want to discourage all Russia. It's all the same anyway; if I report it they'll say: 'Drive them out, Protsenko, get it back.' But they won't give me a single soldier to do it with. So it's better if I win it back myself without any orders. And the worry I'll keep for myself alone. You understand?"

The chief of staff was silent.

"Well, if you understand," Protsenko said, "that's fine. And if you don't understand, as you know, it's all the same. You will do as I have ordered. That's all. Go on, carry out the order."

Protsenko climbed out of the dugout. The night was dark, the wind whistled past him, and a heavy snow was falling. Protsenko looked below. There, framed between two mounds of ruins, could be seen the freezing Volga. From here, well above it, it seemed to be motionless and entirely white. Spots of white lay on the ground around him. In other places, shell holes were filling fast with the snow which had been falling all day. To the right, along the shore, could be heard the slapping of mortar fire and occasional bursts of rifle shooting.

Protsenko thought about Saburov, who by now had probably crawled to where he was going, and instinctively shivered. The ground was cold and wet; to crawl along it would be tough tonight. And to die in this slippery, cold mud would be still tougher.

Saburov had taken a rifleman from the company stationed on the shore of the river, and the two of them together had clambered through to the ruined building where the last machine-guns were stationed, and from which he would have to go down to the river in order to crawl past the Germans. The commander of the company had offered him a soldier to go with him to Remizov, but he had refused again.

Hanging on to bricks sticking out of the ground and to frozen clods of earth, he quietly let himself down the steep slope of the river bank and soon stood at the water's edge. He knew this place well; once when they had crossed the river they had landed right here. The narrow belt of shore sloped upwards steeply, and immediately above it rose the clay terraces of the bluff above the river. In places there were the remains of a dock, and on the ground were scattered its charred beams and planks. A cold wind was blowing from the Volga. As soon as Saburov had let himself down to the river he felt the wind blowing right through him.

The river was white. If he tried to walk close to the water, his silhouette would be noticeable from above against the white background. For this reason he decided to move along a little higher up and closer to the bluff itself. Before he set off, he arranged with the company commander to open fire with machine-guns along the entire bluff as soon as the Germans started shooting at him. This would be, in truth, pretty dubious help. But it might help on the first half of the trip. Farther on would come the harder part. He could not warn Remizov in any way, and as soon as he could be seen from that side, they would probably open fire on him. Then he could bank only on his luck.

He walked the first hundred meters without lying down, trying to move as soundlessly as he could, and at the same time as quickly. No one fired. Along the shore everything seemed empty and quiet. Once he stumbled against something and fell forward on his arms. Getting up again, he felt carefully for what had tripped him. It was the already stiff body of a dead soldier, and in the darkness he could not tell if it was a Russian or a German. Saburov stepped over the body.

But hardly had he taken two steps more when a slanting burst of tracer bullets cut across in front of him from the top of the bluff. That meant, he thought, that he must have made some noise after all when he had fallen. He crawled quickly to one side and huddled behind some charred beams. The Germans fired a few more bursts and for one short moment lighted up a piece of the shore behind Saburov where the dead soldier was lying. The Germans took him for living. The bursts of fire crept closer, until finally one of them plugged directly into the dead body. Lying behind his beams, Saburov continued to wait. Finally, apparently considering that they had killed whoever had broken the silence, the Germans ceased firing.

Saburov crept on farther. Now he was crawling, never lifting himself from the earth, and trying not to make the slightest sound. Two or three times more he bumped into dead bodies. Once he hit himself hard against some stones and swore quietly to himself. It seemed to him that something was stirring in front of him. He stopped and listened. Only the lapping of the water could be heard. He crawled quietly on another few steps. The lapping was now stronger. Slowly it began to sound like the noise a bucket makes against water. He remembered how once in his childhood, challenged by other little boys, he had walked at night right through the cemetery in his town, and as proof that he had done so had brought back with him a little porcelain flower from a wreath hanging on a gravestone at the very end of the cemetery. Right now he felt almost as uneasy as he had then.

Quiet, darkness, being alone, and that curious noise.

He crawled on a little farther and then he saw a crouching figure appear from behind the wreckage of a boat. The man made as if to go by him and then, rounding a pile of beams, moved directly towards him.

Saburov waited. There was no thinking in him, only waitng. Let this man move once more, then another time, and it would be possible to reach out his hand and touch him. When the man had moved still another step, Saburov stretched out his arm, grabbed him by the leg, and pulled with all his strength.

The man fell and yelled in terror, and at that second something hit Saburov on the head, and cold water drenched him completely. The man had yelled not in Russian and not in German, but simply in despair: "A-a-a . . ." Saburov hit him full in the face with his fist and with all the strength there was in him. Then the man yelled out something in German, grabbed his arm, and buried his teeth in it. Saburov knew it was all the same now whether he was quiet or not. He pulled out his automatic with his free hand and fired several times in a row at the German, holding the muzzle of the revolver directly against his body. The body quivered and grew still.

From above bursts of rifle fire broke out and the bullets flicked up dirt around him. Several bullets struck metal with a little clink. Saburov fumbled and found a pail lying next to him. A rope was tied to it, and he realized that the German had gone down to the Volga for water. The firing grew heavier from above.

"Will they come down or not?" Saburov thought. "No, they won't come down, they'd be afraid to." He decided this because the firing came from all along the top of the bluff, without any order, and obviously at random. So he lay there, propping up with his shoulder the corpse which was lying half over him and giving him cover from the bullets.

"When will they stop?" Saburov thought. He felt he was freezing stiff all over because the German, in falling, had poured the water from the bucket on top of him. They were going right on shooting from above, and they could go on shooting all night long. Saburov threw the dead man from him and crawled on. Bullets were hitting the ground in front of him and behind him, and when he had crawled about thirty paces and the shooting was still continuing along the entire shore, the feeling came back to him, precisely because they were shooting so much, that they would not hit him.

He crawled fifty, then a hundred paces. They went on firing at the shore line. Fifty paces more . . . His arms grew so stiff and numb that he could no longer feel the ground. The flashes of the shooting were easy to see on the top of the bluff. Now he could see tracer bullets also coming from behind him, where he had started, and from in front of him—from Remizov —both firing in the direction of the Germans. As the shooting grew heavier, the Germans began to fire less often in his direction and more often to the left and to the right. Then Saburov stood up and ran; he could crawl no longer. He ran stumbling, jumping, and falling over the planks. The thought entered his head: in front of him, Remizov's men must see now that the Germans are firing at one of us. In spite of the mud and the darkness he ran desperately fast. He stopped, or rather fell, only when someone grabbed him by the leg. He fell with his face in the mud, twisting his shoulder; at the same moment someone sat on his back and began to twist his arm.

"Who are you?" asked a hoarse voice.

"Russian, the devil take you," Saburov said, for some strange reason in a whisper. He felt someone still twisting his arm, and he struck with his free hand at one of the men swarming over him, so hard that the man rocked on his heels.

"Who are you hitting?" he heard a voice.

"I tell you I'm a Russian. Lead me to Remizov."

The Germans must have heard the racket and they fired several bursts. Someone sobbed.

"What's the matter, did they wound you?" asked a voice.

"In the leg; it hurts."

"This way," said someone who grabbed Saburov by the arm
280

nd pulled him forward. They ran a few steps and took cover
behind a foundation wall.

"Where are you from?" asked the same voice.

"From the general."

"Who are you? It's so dark I can't see."

"Captain Saburov."

"Ah, Saburov. Well, I'm Grigorovich," and the voice at
once sounded familiar to Saburov. "So it was you who gave me
that crack on the ear? Well, I guess I'll have to take it, from
an old friend."

Grigorovich was one of the staff officers whom Protsenko had
sent out a month before at his own request to take command
of a company.

"Let's go to Remizov," Grigorovich said.

"Is Remizov still alive?"

"Alive, but laid up."

"Why, is he badly wounded?"

"Well, you couldn't say badly," Grigorovich said with a
short laugh, "but certainly uncomfortably. All day today he
has been swearing at everyone's mother, without drawing
breath. To tell you scientifically, they got him with a bullet in
his buttock, so he has to lie on his stomach or else walk around;
he's in no condition to sit down."

Saburov laughed in spite of himself.

"What are you laughing at?" Grigorovich asked.

"Nothing, but it's funny."

"It may be funny to you," Grigorovich said, "but we've had
nothing but a bawling out from him all day on account of his
bad disposition. It's not funny to us."

Saburov found Remizov in a tight little dugout, lying flat
on his face on a cot, with pillows placed under his head and
chest.

"You come from the general, no?" Remizov said slowly.

281

"From the general," Saburov said. "How do you do, Comrade Colonel?"

"How do you do, Saburov. I guessed you were someone from the general and so I ordered the soldiers not to open fire. Well, how is it there with you?"

"Everything in order," Saburov said, "except for the fact that the only way to get from General Protsenko to Colonel Remizov is to crawl here on your stomach."

"It's worse when you have to lie on your stomach," said Remizov, and he swore at length and with imagination. Then he screwed up his eyes slyly, looked at Saburov from under his heavy gray eyebrows, and asked: "They've already told you, probably, about my wound?"

"They've told me," Saburov said.

"Well, of course, they're glad to have a chance to laugh at me. The commander of their regiment has been wounded in an interesting place. Wait," he suddenly interrupted himself, "you're all covered with blood. Are you wounded, or what?"

"No," Saburov said, "I killed a German."

"Well, take off your jacket, take it off. Do you know, you look like a butcher. Hey, Sharapov, give the captain a chance to wash and give him my jacket. Yes, take it off, take it off."

Saburov began to unbutton it.

"Well, what are your orders from the general?"

"To investigate the situation and report back," said Saburov, keeping silent about the fact that Protsenko had anticipated the worst and had also told him to take over command of the regiment.

"Well, as for the situation," Remizov said, "it is not so bad as it is mortifying. We gave up a piece of the shore. The commissar of the regiment has been killed. Two commanders of battalions have been killed. I, as you see, am still alive. We must restore the situation. How does the general feel? Does he feel like restoring the situation?"

282

"I think it was in preparation for it that he sent me," said Saburov.

"I think so, too. Well, we shall have to restore it from both sides, that's understood," Remizov said. "That means, get yourself warm; it means you'll have to go back again."

"I'll have to," Saburov said.

"Or you can stay here with me, and I'll send an officer back. What were your orders?"

"No, I'll go back," Saburov said.

"Semyon Semyonovich," Remizov yelled out. A major, his chief of staff, walked in.

"Is the outline of our dispositions ready?"

"We're finishing it now," the chief of staff said. "We're checking it."

"Well, give it to me quickly, as quickly as you can, brother. Stir yourself a little . . . You beat me to it," Remizov turned to Saburov. "I wanted to send an officer to the general. But they were fixing up the plan here, so that everything would be exact, and we were delayed because of that. They'll have it ready right away and I'll send an officer back with you. Do you know Filipchuk?"

"No, I don't know him," Saburov said.

"He's from my regiment. He's a good, brave officer. He'll go with you. As soon as they get the outline ready, you can be off." Remizov tried to lift himself up and began to swear again at length.

"Just imagine yourself getting hit here. I've got a bad habit anyway of running around all the time. I can't think unless I'm running, and I can't command—I can't do anything. I don't know where I got the habit. But I'm nearly sixty now, and it's time for me to get rid of it. Sharapov!" he shouted again. His orderly appeared.

"Sharapov, help me get off this bed."

283

Sharapov took him by the shoulders and helped him stand. Remizov groaned, moaned, and swore, and somehow managed to do all three at the same time. Grimacing with pain, he trotted several times back and forth across the dugout.

"Is the outline ready?"

"It's ready," the major said, handing him a piece of paper.

"Here everything's written down on the outline," Remizov said, taking, or rather snatching, the paper from the major and continuing to trot up and down. "It's all written down: what I have, and where it is, and what can be done from my side. You know, it all happened at once somehow. They killed both battalion commanders, they killed my commissar, and they wounded me, all of it in half an hour. It was while all this was happening that we got into this mess."

"Did you have many losses?" Saburov asked.

"One battalion practically gone. The one which was holding the bank. But the two others are almost as they were. In general, we can still fight. No doubt about it."

"How do you stand on moving out your wounded?" Saburov asked with a little hesitation. He had been getting ready for this question for a long time. He knew that Anya was here, with Remizov's regiment, but at first he could not make up his mind to open the subject for fear of bad news.

"Well, how can we move them? There's still only thin ice on the Volga. So we're keeping them in the ravine. We've dug into the ground, and we're keeping them in caves."

"Far from here?" Saburov asked.

"Yes, pretty far. It's quieter on the right flank, so we've put them there . . . How is Filipchuk? Is he ready?" Remizov called out.

"He's ready," came the answer from the other half of the dugout.

"Well, on your way now. My God, how is it I didn't offer you anything to drink? Sharapov!"

284

Sharapov ran up to the colonel.

"Something to drink. I forgot about it. I'm getting old, but what's the matter with you?"

"Yes, Comrade Colonel," Sharapov said. Without moving a step, he unhooked a German canteen from his belt, unscrewed a little cup from its top, poured it full, and handed it to Saburov.

Saburov drank it at one gulp. It stopped halfway down his throat, and he coughed and sputtered. It was pure alcohol.

"Ah, I forgot to warn you. I don't drink vodka unless I have to," Remizov said. "In the Finnish war I was on the Petsamo sector. I got used to alcohol up there. There's a wonderful warmth in it. It drops right into your stomach. Just notice, your throat may tickle a little, but doesn't your stomach feel fine?"

"Pretty good," Saburov said, breathing with difficulty.

Remizov turned to Sharapov: "You should always say 'Allow me to report, Comrade Officer, that this is alcohol.' Understand?"

"I understand," Sharapov said.

"Help me again."

Sharapov went over to Remizov and they repeated the operation they had performed before, in reverse, with the same moaning, groaning, and profanity.

"I guess I just can't walk," Remizov said, stretching out and breathing hard. "But my character just won't let me lie still. I've been wounded several times, but such an idiotic wound as this, if you don't mind my saying so . . . word of honor, if I could catch the German who did this to me, in spite of all the Articles of War I'd grab him and thrash him. What a swine! Well, to whom should I give the order, you or Filipchuk? Filipchuk!"

"Here." A tall man in a jacket walked into the dugout, carrying his rifle.

285

"Give it to me," Saburov said. "I managed to get here Somehow I'll get back."

"All right, take it. Report to the general that Colonel Remizov will do everything to get the shore back; he'll make up for his own mistake. And he'll make others do it, too," he added angrily, and he pointed at the staff officers around him. "Report that our spirits here are good, that we're ready for fighting. About my wound I would tell you not to report at all, but I know you couldn't restrain yourself anyway. To you, Filipchuk," Remizov said, turning to the waiting officer. "I have only one request and command: get through to headquarters and come back here alive and well."

"Yes, Comrade Colonel," Filipchuk said.

"Well, I guess that's all. Yes, one more thing . . ." Stopping short, Remizov closed his eyes and bit his lips. He lay quietly for several seconds and Saburov realized that the old man was talking on his nerve, fighting down his pain.

"There's this, too," Remizov said in his former tone of voice and opening his eyes again. "It seems to me we don't need to restore the situation at dawn or during the day. The Germans will be expecting a counterattack then. Today we should hold where we are, and get ready, and tomorrow night when they'll be thinking that we're reconciled to the situation, then we should strike. Report that to the general as my opinion. Are you ready, Filipchuk?"

"Yes, I am, quite ready."

"Well, come over here." Filipchuk walked up to his cot. Remizov shook first his hand, then Saburov's. At the same time he turned toward them his blue eyes set in a network of old man's wrinkles. In this glance there was both anxiety and an unspoken wish for a good trip. Saburov felt that this wild little colonel, in spite of his angry way of talking, was probably a good man and a kind one.

286

"Go on, go on," Remizov said after them. "I'll be waiting here impatiently."

When the two of them had clambered along the slippery path and had begun to descend to the shore of the river, Saburov again asked, this time of Filipchuk: "How are your wounded fixed? Are you managing to move them?"

"Where could we move them? The ice is still thin," Filipchuk answered with the same words the colonel had used. "Why?"

"No reason. I was just interested," Saburov said. Suddenly he remembered how openly Anya had come up to him the last time and embraced him in front of Maslennikov. He felt ashamed of his own embarrassment, which might keep him from finding out what he wanted to know now more than anything else in the world, and he said: "The reason is, my wife is here with your regiment."

"Your wife?" Filipchuk asked in surprise. "Where?"

"She's a nurse, at the medical base. But I know that she's somewhere here with you, with your regiment."

"What does she look like?" Filipchuk asked.

"How should I say?" Saburov smiled in the darkness and thought how hard it would be for him to describe Anya. "She's about average height, and sort of thin. Well, what else . . . well, she wears her hair combed back. Her name is Klimenko."

"Klimenko," Filipchuk repeated. "Klimenko . . . I don't know her."

"Anya," Saburov said.

"Anya—why didn't you say so right away? Anya . . . of course I know her."

"Is she all right?" Saburov asked.

"As far as I know, yes," Filipchuk said. "I saw her today, about six o'clock. I happened to be over on the right flank when they were taking out the battalion commander. As far as I know, everything's all right with her," he said with a certain

doubt in his voice, because seven or eight hours had gone by
since he had seen Anya, and seven or eight hours in Stalingrad
was a very long time.

"If you see her when you come back," Saburov said, "tell
her that everything's all right with Saburov. And . . . and
that I sent her my greeting. No, that's not necessary, simply
say that everything's all right with me." ·

"Good," Filipchuk said. "Anya . . . I saw her yesterday
with Remizov. The old man was swearing at her terribly. You
know how he can."

"For what?" Saburov asked, already guessing why.

"For what? Because she crawled out where she had no business crawling. And the old man still can't stand it when a
woman gets wounded or killed. He had tears in his eyes. So he
bawled her out. How he did swear! He even stamped his foot,
and kicked her out. And then he called Sharapov over and ordered him to write out a recommendation of a medal for her. He
always does everything at once."

Saburov smiled and felt a kind of tenderness for Remizov,
not so much for the medal he had recommended as because he
had sworn at Anya and stamped his foot.

They went on to the ruins of the building beside which Saburov had arrived a half an hour before. There sat Grigorovich.

"Saburov?" he asked in a low voice.

"Yes."

"You going back?"

"Yes, I'm going back."

"Well, I wish you luck."

Grigorovich moved nearer and shook hands with Saburov
and Filipchuk. A bandage showed white around his head.

"What's the matter with you?" Saburov asked.

"You're not the one to ask. You've got a fist like a mallet.
You broke my ear."

"Forgive it."

"All right. By the way, the Germans are all excited again. Can you see? They're searching along the entire bank. You'll have a hard time getting back."

Saburov looked in front of him. Along the slope bursts of rifle fire were hitting first in one spot, then in another.

"We'll have to crawl the whole way," he said quietly to Filipchuk.

"Good."

"Just in case, I'm putting the dispatch inside my shirt. I'm sticking it in here," Saburov said. He took Filipchuk's hand and made him feel where the envelope was placed. "Can you feel where it is?"

"Yes," Filipchuk said.

"Well, fine then, let's be moving."

Saburov had an exceptionally good memory. By now the shore was almost mapped in his mind. He remembered one by one each beam, plank, and pile of stones behind which it would be possible to take cover.

Filipchuk crawled after him. From time to time, when bullets struck especially close, Saburov would turn around and whisper: "Are you here?" And Filipchuk would answer, just as quietly: "Here." In the middle of the trip Saburov asked him nearly every minute: "Are you here?" And each time, Filipchuk answered: "Here."

By Saburov's reckoning they were already approaching their own advanced positions on the other side, when suddenly several bursts of fire struck around them.

"Are you here?" Saburov asked.

Filipchuk was quiet. Without raising himself from the ground, Saburov crawled a couple of yards backwards and fumbled at Filipchuk's body.

"Are you here?"

"Here," Filipchuk's voice was barely audible.

"What's the matter?"

But Filipchuk did not answer again. Saburov groped over him. In two places, on the neck and on his side, his jacket was wet with blood. He leaned over Filipchuk's lips. Filipchuk was breathing. Saburov hooked one arm under his shoulder, and pulling himself with his other arm and pushing with his legs, began to crawl on farther. This went on for about thirty paces. Saburov felt his strength slipping away from him. He let go of Filipchuk and lay next to him.

"Filipchuk, Filipchuk," he whispered.

Filipchuk did not answer.

Saburov bent over to his lips again, and it seemed to him that Filipchuk was no longer breathing. He placed his hands under the jacket and under the shirt and touched Filipchuk's bare body. It had already grown noticeably cold. Saburov pulled out the blouse pockets and took out a small packet of papers, then slipped the revolver from its holster, placed it in his own trousers pocket, and crawled on. He did not like to leave Filipchuk's body here. But the envelope lying inside his own jacket gave him no alternative.

When he had crawled another fifty paces and was at the extreme limit of his strength, he heard a whisper from in front of him: "Who goes there?"

"Russian," Saburov answered, also in a whisper. He stood up on legs that barely held him, and seeing nothing in front of him moved forward. It turned out that he had been only three steps from the projection of the wall where they were waiting for him.

"Where is your company commander?"

"Here."

"About fifty paces back there's an officer. He came with me."

"Wounded?" asked the company commander.

"No, killed," Saburov said angrily, feeling behind those words a doubt about whether to drag him out or not. "Killed, but just the same you've got to bring him out. Do you understand?"

"Naturally, Comrade Captain," said the company commander. "Did you take his documents?"

"I took them," Saburov said.

"Well then, what about it, Comrade Captain? It's all the same to him . . . He won't feel any better. But I'd have to send two men, and I might lose them."

"I already ordered you to bring him out," Saburov said.

"Yes, Comrade Captain," the company commander said, "but . . ."

"But what?"

"Any other time I wouldn't say this, but right now every man I have has to be accounted for."

"This is how it is," Saburov said with a fury which surprised himself: "Unless you drag him out, I will take my report to the general, then I'll come back here. I'll drag him out myself, and then I'll shoot you on the spot for failure to carry out a command. Give me a guard so I can get to headquarters fast."

He turned and walked with uncertain gait behind a soldier to Protsenko's dugout. He felt that in one second more he would have hit the company commander. Maybe, in his way, the officer had been right, and had to hoard his men, but somehow bringing back the body of a killed officer was so important and sacred for the army that in Saburov's eyes it justified even losses, if they could not be avoided.

When Saburov staggered into the dugout everything went black in front of him and he collapsed on the bench. Then he opened his eyes and tried to stand. But Protsenko, who was already beside him, put his hand on his shoulder and pushed him back.

"Could you drink a little vodka?"

"No, Comrade General, I couldn't. I'm so tired, it woul[d] knock me out. If there's any tea . . ."

"Give him some tea, as quickly as you can," Protsenk[o] shouted. "Is Remizov still alive?"

"Alive, only wounded. Here is a message from him," Sa[-] burov pulled the envelope from under his jacket.

"Good," Protsenko said as he put on his glasses.

Saburov saw that Protsenko was reading the report, an[d] he thought this was the minute for him to rest. Almost befor[e] the thought had formed itself, he had collapsed in his corne[r] by the wall. Only when Protsenko—how much later he did no[t] know—shook him by the shoulder, did he realize that he ha[d] fallen asleep. "Are you awake?" Protsenko was asking. Sa[-] burov tried to stand up.

"Sit down, sit down."

"Have I been asleep long?"

"A long time. Ten minutes. Remizov is wounded, you say?"

"Wounded."

"Where?"

Saburov explained where Remizov had been wounded an[d] how it angered him.

"I bet the old man is cursing?"

"He certainly is."

"How is their mood in general?"

"As far as I could see, fine," Saburov said.

"He writes me he can pull his forces together and hit th[e] Germans from his side. He also doesn't want to put up wit[h] the situation," and Protsenko poked with his finger at th[e] paper he was holding in his hand. "Did you come alone from there?"

"Alone."

"Why didn't he give you an officer to go with you, so we could have sent him back. He's getting older and older, and I guess he's beginning to slip."

"He gave me an officer," Saburov said. "They killed him on he way." He remembered suddenly that he still had Filip-chuk's documents and weapon, and he put them all on the table.

"So," Protsenko said, frowning. "Did they shoot you up badly?"

"It was pretty heavy."

"In daytime there's no way of getting there?"

"In daytime it would be impossible," Saburov said.

"Yes . . ." Protsenko again hesitated. He evidently wanted to say something but could not make up his mind. "But by tomorrow night we've got to try to storm it. How did they kill him?"

"Whom?"

"The officer," Protsenko pointed to Filipchuk's documents lying in front of him.

"They wounded him badly, then I dragged him for a while, and he died in my arms."

"Yes . . ." Protsenko grunted again.

Saburov's eyes were closing with fatigue. He had an uneasy feeling that Protsenko wanted to send him back again to Remizov but had not yet made up his mind to say so.

"Listen, Yegor Petrovich," Protsenko said to his chief of staff sitting beside him. "Be a good fellow, sit down and write out an order to Remizov. Get everything in it the way we decided; the exact time for the attack, and the rocket—every-thing."

"I'm already writing it," the chief of staff said, looking up from the paper.

Protsenko turned to Saburov, looked at his tired face, and for about the fifth time said again: "Yes . . . Well, what are you sitting there for? You should lie down for a little." He spoke the words "for a little" carefully, almost shyly. "Lie down for a little, go on, lie down and rest. That's a command."

Saburov used the last strength that was in him to lift his legs on to the bench and just as he was, lying in his boots with his face to the cold, wet wall of the dugout, fell asleep immediately. The last thought that flickered in his head was that probably they would send him back anyway. Well, let them send him, only now give him a half hour's sleep, and then it would make no difference.

Protsenko paced slowly up and down the dugout dictating the text of his order to the chief of staff. Sometimes he turned around and stared at Saburov. The latter slept. Protsenko went on with his dictating and then turned again and stared at Saburov.

"Listen, Yegor Petrovich," he said, suddenly interrupting the dictation. "What if we should send Vostrikov?"

"We could send Vostrikov," the chief of staff said. "Are you going to send any verbal message, or only the order?"

"It's a bad order if you have to add something to it verbally."

"Well then, if there's nothing to be passed on verbally we could send Vostrikov."

"I would send him," Protsenko pointed to Saburov, "but it's hard to ask him to make that trip for a third time in one night."

"It's harder to send him, but easier for him to get there," the chief of staff said. "He has crawled it twice on his belly now; he probably knows every little mound and every hole."

"Yes . . ." Protsenko grunted again. "We've got to. The order must get there." He looked at the sleeping Saburov and grew thoughtful.

"Yes, here's what we'll do," he said, "I've thought of it."

"What have you thought of?" the chief of staff asked.

"I've thought how we can know for certain that he got through and delivered the order . . . Alexei Ivanovich," he pushed Saburov.

"Yes." Saburov stood up with the air of being ready for

anything, which people sometimes have when they have been awakened suddenly.

"Here is the order. Take it," Protsenko said. "When you get through to Remizov, then do this: as soon as you get there, let them give us at the same time one green rocket and one red rocket over the Volga. And if they haven't any rockets, then let them fire three volleys into the air in the same direction with tommy-guns and at the same time, and make some of them tracer bullets. Will we be able to see it from here?"

"Yes," Saburov said.

"Fine, then I shall know that you have gotten through and delivered the message. You won't go to sleep on me on the way, will you?" Protsenko asked, clapping Saburov on the shoulder. "If you fall asleep, when you wake up it will be daytime."

"I won't fall asleep," Saburov said. "The Germans won't let me."

"Won't they really?" Protsenko said with a smile. "On your word of honor, aren't you badly tired?"

"Never mind, I won't fall asleep," Saburov repeated.

"Well, that's fine. Sit down at the table."

Saburov sat at the table. Protsenko half opened the door and shouted out: "How about tea for us?"

Then Protsenko went out beyond the door and quietly gave some kind of order. Two minutes later while Protsenko, Saburov, and the chief of staff were sitting at the table, Vostrikov brought in a copper tray on which were three cups of tea, a handful of biscuits, and a freshly opened can with cherry jam, secured from God-knows-where.

"Look," Protsenko said, "I can't give you little cheese dumplings, but if you like Ukrainian cherries, help yourself!" He took up the can in his hand and underlined with his fingernail the words on its label: "Ukrainian State Canning Trust, Kiev." "Do you understand? I've brought it from Kiev."

"You mean you've been carrying this around since Kiev?" Saburov asked.

"Well, as a matter of fact, I was exaggerating. They were issued to us somewhere near Voronezh, I guess. I love cherries . . . Well, come on, let's drink."

Protsenko's doubts as to whether to send Saburov back did not return. He felt instinctively that to express any unusual warmth or sympathy would only be to underline the fact that he was thinking about the possible death of the man he was sending. Instead of this Protsenko abruptly shifted the conversation to the Ukrainian school for cavalry officers where he had studied.

"They didn't teach badly," he said. "Everything looked fine, especially the uniforms and the riding breeches. Do you know, although at that time it wasn't usually done, they even tried to teach us dancing and good manners."

"How did it work out—did they teach you?" the chief of staff asked with a smile.

"That's for you to judge, Yegor Petrovich, whether I ever learned manners or not."

"To tell you the truth, the answer depends on when you're talking about," the chief of staff said.

"Right. When people on my staff do things my way, then I keep my good manners, but when they do something not my way, then I forget I was ever taught good manners. I've got a strange character—forgetful."

Saburov drank a cup of the steaming tea, and again he wanted desperately to sleep. After his second cup he roused himself a little. The jam tasted wonderfully good, the cherries were the kind he had loved from childhood—without stones. Protsenko ordered a third cup for each of them. At this point Saburov felt it was time to go. He swallowed several gulps and stood up.

"Why don't you finish drinking?" Protsenko asked.

"It's time, Comrade General. May I go?"

"Go. We're agreed, then, that if there are no rockets, then three volleys of rifle fire."

"It's clear," Saburov said.

"In the direction of the Volga."

"Exactly."

Saburov saluted, turned, and walked out. Protsenko and the chief of staff were silent for a moment.

"Well, how about it?" Protsenko turned to a staff officer who had entered the room. "Have you assembled the men from the battalions here?"

"We are just finishing."

"Hurry it up, it will soon be dawn. If we don't move them before then, we'll lose men unnecessarily. What do you think, will he get through?" Protsenko said to the chief of staff, remembering Saburov.

"In my opinion, yes."

"I think so, too. Do you know, there was one minute, just before I sent him off, when I wanted to tell him straight: get through for the third time and I'll get you the Order of Lenin, on my word as a general. If they don't give it to you, I'll take off my own and give it to you and let them raise a fuss about it later."

While they were talking, Saburov was crawling along the ground which by now had frozen hard. Either because sunrise was approaching and the Germans figured that no one would try to make the trip again, or simply because they had become bored with shooting all night along the shore, he managed to crawl half the distance without a single shot having been fired from above. This began to make him a little nervous. He took out his revolver and released the safety catch. Then he untied one grenade from his belt and held it in his right hand. Although it was harder for him to crawl like this, he did not put the grenade down but held it so he could throw it at the first dangerous movement. Then he remembered the dispatch he was carrying. Well, if worst came to worst, he could always throw a second grenade at his own feet. After another fifty paces he began to dismiss these thoughts. He had a curious feeling that he would get through this time, too. So it worked out; he clambered to the ruins on the other side, and not a single shot had been fired along the entire route.

"You here again, Saburov?" Grigorovich said.

"Here again."

"Where's Filipchuk?"

"Killed."

"Where was he killed?"

"Over there, near the other side."

"What do you mean—is he lying on the bank?"

"On the shore, but inside our lines."

He remembered the dead face of Filipchuk. On his way back here, Saburov had asked the company commander if the body had been dragged in. Learning that it had, he went to where the body was lying and turned his flashlight on Filipchuk's face. The face was white and cold. One of the soldiers had wiped the blood and mud from it. And for the hundredth time in his life it had seemed strange to Saburov that only about an hour before he had been talking with this man. "Are you here?" he had whispered; "I am here," Filipchuk had answered.

Saburov went into Remizov's dugout and handed him the dispatch. Remizov read it and then asked about Filipchuk. The same short conversation he had had with Grigorovich was repeated.

"Didn't you bring his documents?" Remizov asked.

"No, I gave them to the general."

"Good," Remizov said.

"Oh, yes," Saburov suddenly remembered, "we must give a signal that I got through. Have you got any green and red rockets?"

"We should have. Take a look, Sharapov, are there any rockets?"

"No, Comrade Colonel, they are all gone."

"There are no rockets," Remizov said.

"Then we shall have to give three bursts of fire with tracer bullets over the Volga."

"That we can do," Remizov said, and again he shouted out: "Sharapov!" Sharapov appeared.

"Help me get up."

Sharapov helped him stand. He walked around the dugout and groaned with pain.

"Give me a gun. Have you got a clip with tracer bullets in it?"

"It's already inserted."

"Give it to me. Let's go, Saburov. Out of happiness that you got here, I'll give the signal myself. It's seldom a poor colonel ever gets a chance to fire a weapon. Things were different when I was a lieutenant in the first German war. I wandered around then like a hunter, and I got some Germans. I was only a little fellow, but I was pretty shifty. That was the way. But now I can't; it's supposed to be beneath my dignity. Well," he added, lifting his gun, "where should I shoot? Anywhere? Was that the arrangement?"

"Yes," Saburov said. "Wait a minute, wait a minute, I've got it all mixed up. I'm so damned tired. Not three bursts, but from three guns at the same time."

"That means we need a whole volley? Sharapov!" Remizov shouted back into the dugout.

"Yes?" Sharapov emerged from the dugout.

"Bring your tommy-gun and get someone else, too, and with tracer bullets. Come on out."

Sharapov and another soldier came up to them.

"Stand next to me here, and at the command 'one, two, three,' fire a long burst, all together. I'll fire lowest, you a little

299

higher, and let him fire straight at the moon. We'll consider this a salute to Filipchuk. Is that all right with you, Saburov?"

"Of course," Saburov said.

"He was a good officer; I'll miss him," Remizov said, and he turned to the soldier: "Well then, give your rifle to the captain here. Take it, Saburov, in memory of our comrade."

The sky had already begun to grow gray when, at the word "three," they fired into the sky. The shining tracer bullets flew high into the dark gray air over the Volga and arched downward somewhere at the end of their course. Remizov and Saburov looked at each other.

"Well," Saburov said, and he was on the point of adding that it was time for him to go back. But Remizov guessed his meaning and said, in a special kind of way—firmly, like a father: "No, I won't let you go, it's already getting light. And in general I won't let you. Up to three times it's all right to try your luck, but no more. We'll break through tomorrow night, and then you'll be back again."

"But my battalion is there without a commanding officer," Saburov said.

"I've got two battalions here without commanding officers," Remizov answered. "Go along now and sleep. Sharapov, fix the captain up on the commissar's cot. My commissar got himself killed. He was a very good man, an excellent fellow. They just sent him up here, only a month ago, from the district committee of the party. He didn't know how to fight, but he had a good heart. It was so good that he made even an old wolf like me cheerful. I miss him badly. It's surprising how I miss him," and he wiped the corners of his eyes roughly. "Let's go into the dugout."

NINETEEN

HEN Saburov woke up, it was three o'clock in the afternoon; he had slept exactly eight hours. In the corner of the dugout someone was bustling around.

"Who's that?" Saburov asked.

"It's me."

In front of him stood a heavy-set girl. Her sleeves were rolled up, and she wore an apron over her military blouse.

"Where is the colonel?" Saburov asked.

"Up at the front line."

"And where is your front line?"

"Right next to us here."

Saburov swung his legs down to the floor and noticed that during his sleep someone had taken off his boots and the cotton cloth he wore around his feet.

"Sit still," the girl said. "Your things are still drying. I'll bring them to you in a moment."

"Who took my boots off?"

"It must have been Sharapov. Do you like to sleep in your boots?"

The girl walked out into another room and returned almost immediately, holding in one hand his dry and slightly warped boots, and in the other the cotton foot bindings.

"There you are, put them on."

"What's your name?" Saburov asked.

"Pasha."

"Did all the others go out and leave you here alone?"

"I'm all alone," Pasha said. "The others went out to the front line. The telephone's there, too."

Saburov looked at her carefully. She was a big girl, not exactly fat but built on a large scale. She had a red face and a small turned-up nose.

"That means the entire defense of headquarters here has been entrusted to you?" Saburov asked while he wound the cotton cloth around his feet.

"That's what it must mean," Pasha answered dryly, not liking the question. "Would you like to eat?"

"I'd like to."

"The colonel ordered me to take good care of you, and to see that you got enough sleep and enough to eat."

"Didn't he give you any other orders?" Saburov asked with a smile.

"No," Pasha answered, and it was clear she did not want to joke about her responsibilities. "He just said that you should go and find him after you had had something to eat. A soldier is waiting to take you to him."

"And what are you going to feed me?"

Pasha shrugged her shoulders with regret; this question really made her feel unhappy. "Porridge, made out of concentrate. It's buckwheat. Have you ever eaten it?"

"I certainly have."

"But I've added some fat. What I'll be able to serve tomorrow, I just don't know."

"Has the Volga frozen yet?" Saburov asked.

"God only knows. Some say it's frozen, others that it's still running. All I know is they're not bringing us any supplies. That's what makes it hard."

302

She went out and brought back a frying pan full of buckwheat porridge.

"There you are. Eat." Pasha walked over to the corner, picked up a canteen of vodka, shook it up in a professional way, and without asking Saburov, poured him a glass half full.

"Where is Sharapov?" Saburov asked.

"With the colonel. He is always with the colonel; he never leaves him."

Pasha, without waiting for an invitation, sat down on a stool across from Saburov, rested her chin on her hands, and began to examine him with close attention and without the slightest embarrassment. She had already looked over everyone in the regiment; she had satisfied her curiosity about each of them, and the appearance of someone new clearly gave her enormous pleasure.

"Well, what are you looking at?" Saburov asked.

"Nothing, just looking. How about you, are you to stay with us now?"

"No, not with you."

"Then what are you going to do?"

"With your permission," Saburov said with a smile, "I've come here on a temporary mission, and tomorrow I'll be leaving. How about it, may I?"

"Why not?" she said, again disregarding his joking tone. "Maybe you'd like something more to eat, except that there isn't anything more. Maybe you'd like some tea; there is more of that."

"No, I don't want any tea," Saburov said.

"But Sergei Vassilievich always drinks tea," Pasha said with reproach in her voice.

"And who is Sergei Vassilievich?"

"Why, he's the colonel."

"Well, I still don't want any."

"Just as you wish. Could I give you some chocolate?"

"No."

"Sergei Vassilievich said to give you anything we have. So don't you want some chocolate?"

"No, I really don't."

"Well, all right then," Pasha said, a little relieved, "because we have only one bar left."

When Saburov had eaten some of the buckwheat, he looked questioningly at Pasha. "Where is the soldier you were talking about?"

"Outside, in the trench. Sergei Vassilievich told him to take you up to him."

Saburov got up. "Thank you," he said.

"May your health stay with you," Pasha said. "Somehow you eat very little. You're like Sergei Vassilievich, but we used to have a commissar here—he was killed yesterday—who really liked to eat. He was a good man, a nice man. Platon Ivanovich. Didn't you know him?"

"No, I didn't."

"He was a very good man," Pasha said with great conviction. "No matter what you gave him, he always ate it and praised it, and then asked for a second helping. He was a friendly sort."

Saburov went out. In the trench outside the dugout he found the soldier waiting for him.

"Well, let's go to the colonel," Saburov said.

"You won't have to go far, Comrade Captain," the soldier said. "He's not far away."

You could sense neatness and accuracy in Remizov's affairs. In front of the dugout, through the ruined buildings, communication trenches had been dug in all the places where it was not possible to dodge between piles of masonry with clear safety from shell splinters. In five minutes Saburov had reached a well-constructed observation post. At the very edge of the sloping ravine which divided Remizov's position from the Germans stood a shattered building, under constant German artillery fire. Remizov had burrowed under its foundations and made a fairly spacious dugout with two camouflaged openings in the direction of the Germans. During the night the ground had frozen for good. At the bottom of the ravine lay a tank, upside down, which had fallen down the slope, and bodies were strewn on the ground around it.

"How did you breakfast?" Remizov greeted Saburov.

"Very well, thank you, Comrade Colonel."

"That's good. It means Pasha didn't let you down. She's a tightfisted sort. She saves everything for me, both when she has to and when she doesn't have to. I can't seem to teach her how to be hospitable."

"No, on the contrary," Saburov said. "She even offered me chocolate."

"Really? Well, that's progress, real progress . . . I've got it quiet here today. Even suspiciously quiet."

"Why suspiciously?"

"They're pushing me too gently. To tell you the truth, ever since yesterday I've been expecting they would push me harder. On the other hand, it looks as though they were giving the works to the general over there. Can you hear it?"

To the left, it was true, heavy firing could be heard.

"Judging by the racket, it's already come to fighting with grenades there for the fourth time today. Did you sleep yourself out? You fell asleep last night like a baby. You haven't slept much, you know. In your place, after what you went through, I'd have slept twenty-four hours. I gave an order for you not to be wakened. Of course, we would've wakened you if it had been necessary, but so far there's been no emergency. They're fidgety over there, that's true. Here, take the field glasses if you'd like to."

Saburov took the field glasses from Remizov and looked for a long time at the other side of the ravine. Here and there people were running around. In the empty spaces between the buildings he saw first one, then another tank.

"Have they been bombing you?" Saburov asked.

"Not us. They've been bombing over there, on the left bank of the river. They're trying to get the Katyushas.* Just before sunrise, just as always, the Katyushas were singing. In my opinion, they disturb the Germans quite a lot . . . Did you get really rested?"

"Entirely."

"At first, today, I wish you would stay as a general staff officer attached to me. You'll get a chance to watch how the fighting goes. Then later . . ." Remizov led Saburov to one side. They walked out of the dugout and sat on the edge of the trench. "Then later," Remizov repeated, "it would be a good idea if you would go over to the right flank. I have a feeling that they have piled up today chiefly against the general, and they already consider me a kind of branch cut off from the tree, which they can clean up any time they like. But anyway, just on the chance, go on over there. I'm a little weak on my right flank. Lieutenant Galishev, who's commanding the battalion there, is really just a boy. They killed nearly everyone yesterday, so what else can I do? I'd like you to watch what he does until evening. If you have to, you can take over command. And tonight we'll spend together. Then I won't let you leave me . . . Good?"

"Good," Saburov said, marveling at the light and gentle tone in which Remizov had spoken, although it had been entirely clear that he was giving commands.

"All right, all right, let's go back to the dugout," Remizov said quickly when a heavy shell exploded above them, about

---

* "Katyushas" were possibly the first rocket guns used in this war. The Red Army kept the weapon secret for a long time. It was invented by Andrei Kostinov and sometimes called, by Russians, "Kostinov's gun." Many Russians believe it was the "Katyushas" which saved Moscow in the 1941 German offensive.

a hundred paces away. "Let's go, let's go." He grabbed Saburov by the arm. "It looks to me as if they knew very well where my observation post is. But, do you see, they can't hit me from above, and in order to get a direct hit on these openings they would have to drag a cannon straight up onto that side of the ravine, across from me. From there they could do it. They've dragged one up twice already, but we smashed it each time. And they're afraid to try a third time. They've tried to do it at night, it's true, but in the dark they can't get there. You know they're really terrible artillerymen. Look, listen to it—they're firing everything at us . . ." They sat talking like this for five minutes in the dugout.

"Now, probably, there'll be a little quiet for a quarter of an hour. Go. The rifleman will lead you."

The battalion commander's dugout had been excavated exactly like Remizov's observation post, under the foundation of a shattered building, and back from it ran exactly the same kind of deep communication trench. Lieutenant Galishev, just as Remizov had said, turned out to be a very young fellow, only recently graduated from a military academy. But during the week he had passed here, he had already learned the ways of the front. When he had greeted Saburov and they had sat down in the entrance to the dugout, Galishev pulled a pouch out of the top of his boot and rolled himself a cigarette of such incredible size that Saburov could not help smiling.

"Give me some," he said, remembering suddenly that he had not smoked since the night before.

"Where is the battalion commander?" a familiar voice said behind them.

"Here," Galishev said, and he smiled happily. "Here, Anichka, I'm now commanding the battalion."

Saburov turned and his eyes fell on Anya.

She had been rummaging in her first-aid kit as she approached them. She dropped her hand in sudden surprise and as if with weariness, and stood looking silently at Saburov.

"Anya," he said, and he moved towards her. She continued to stand without moving.

He took another step towards her, reached out his hand, and drew her to him.

"Anya, is it really you?"

She remained silent, and without moving her head, simply raised her eyes to his. Large tears were standing in them.

"Are you really here?" she said finally. "When did you come?"

"Last night."

"That means it was you who came from Protsenko, yes?"

"It was I," said Saburov.

"And we were all wondering who would come. But I never thought it would be you." She was so surprised, happy, and deeply moved that for the first time in a long while she was speaking to him with the formal pronoun. "Tell me, how are you?"

"I'm fine. Tomorrow we'll all be together again; we'll join up with Protsenko."

"I know," she said. "I heard. Have you any wounded men?" she turned to Galishev.

"Yes, two."

"All right," she said. "We will carry them back to the ravine right away. It's really true that you're here?" she looked at Saburov curiously.

"I'm here all right."

Without changing her expression, she stretched herself up, took his face in both hands, kissed him quickly on the lips, and let her hands fall.

"How good it is!" she said in the same tone of voice. "I have been very much afraid."

"I, too," Saburov said.

308

Galishev was watching this scene in silence.

"I'm going now for the wounded men," Anya repeated, turning to him. Then she moved again towards Saburov.

"Are you here for good?" Now that she had kissed him it was as if she had recovered from an illness during which her memory had left her, and she began again to speak to him intimately.

"No," Saburov said. "I must go back tonight."

"Walk with me a minute," Anya said. "Come with me a little along the trench. The stretcher bearers are waiting for me there."

"I'll be back right away, Comrade Lieutenant," Saburov said to Galishev as he walked away behind Anya.

At a bend in the trench, where they could no longer be seen by Galishev, Anya held Saburov by his leather belt and asked him: "Have you spoken about it yet?"

"About what?"

"About our being together. I want terribly to be with you. I didn't tell you so, but I want it so much . . ."

"So far I haven't talked about it," Saburov said.

"It seemed to me when we came over together, when we crossed the river to this side, that this wasn't the place to talk about it. Didn't it seem that way to you?"

"Yes," Saburov said.

"But you know, it'll always be like this from now on. Maybe it will be worse. On our sector the fighting is really heavier than it is here, isn't it?" she said, listening to the noises around them.

"Yes."

"Well then, that means there is really no reason to be ashamed of asking. Why are you ashamed to ask?"

"I'm not ashamed," Saburov said, "I'll ask about it tonight."

"Do ask . . . It was really frightening," Anya said,

"when they cut us off entirely yesterday evening. I thought maybe I would never see you again. I really want us to be together. No, no, don't listen then; do just as you like. But I still want us to be together. You know, if a bomb should fall right here, right now, I wouldn't be frightened at all, because we are together. I'll be braver if we're together, don't you understand? And you, too, probably, won't you?"

"Probably," Saburov said with a little hesitation. He could imagine that if Anya were next to him, maybe he would be less afraid for himself, but he would be even more frightened for her.

"Probably," Anya said. "I know it's the same with you as it is with me. And it's that way with me. Well, I must go and take care of the wounded. You can't leave here, can you?"

"No, I mustn't."

"I know. I'll go and move the wounded. Do you know, we have an awful lot of them now in the ravine. We never had so many before. That's because we can't move them across the Volga. I'm going," she added quickly, stretching out her hand to Saburov.

He noticed that she had on a different overcoat, not the one in which he had seen her before.

"Where did you get this coat?" he asked.

"This isn't mine. They gave it to me from a soldier who had been killed. Look"—and she pointed to a small hole on the left side of the coat. "Except for that it's in fine shape. A shell landed on my old one and ripped it to ribbons."

"What do you mean, a shell?"

"I was hot, one evening, when I was moving out wounded, so I took it off and folded it up very neatly—you know, the way you fold a coat in a bunk on a ship. And then a shell had to land right on top of it."

Saburov held her hand in his. He noticed the new coat did not fit her, so the ends of the sleeves had been turned back. The rough cloth had rubbed her wrist and had left red marks right at the end of the sleeve.

"Give me your other hand," he said. On the other wrist were the same marks.

"Look how it's rubbing you," Saburov said. "You tell them to give you a new coat."

"Good."

"Don't forget to tell them." He held her hands tightly in his own, lifted them to his lips, and kissed each one several times where the red welts ran across them.

"All right. Go," he said. "I'll see Protsenko and I'll ask him if we can't be together."

"He won't refuse," Anya said. "There isn't a chance of his refusing." She stuffed her hands deep into her pockets, probably so that Saburov would no longer be sorry for her, and strode off along the communications trench.

Saburov passed an almost quiet day with Galishev. When it grew dark, he returned to Remizov's command post. Remizov was smoking, half lying on his cot. Across from him sat his chief of staff. In the dugout there was that special quiet which comes when everything has been decided and prepared, when no more arrangements need to be made, and when there is nothing more to do but to wait for the appointed minute.

"Major Annenski," Remizov said, "I am leaving you in command of all the rest of the sector. I am going myself with the assault group."

The chief of staff, behind Remizov's back, made a kind of entreating gesture to Saburov, trying to tell him that the one to go with the assault group should be he, Annenski, and that the colonel should stay behind because he had been wounded and there was no sense in his going. This, at any rate, was how Saburov understood the gesture.

"What are you gesticulating about?" Remizov said without turning around. "Don't argue—don't argue with me. I know you're making signs. I don't see them, but I can feel them. You won't talk me around. It's useless for you to make signs to the captain—he won't talk me around either. And what's nicest of all, he won't even try to. Isn't that so, Captain?"

"Whatever you consider necessary," Saburov said, knowing that it was useless to argue in situations like this.

"So you see," Remizov said with relief, since he had been getting ready to oppose Saburov, too. "And as for you, I think you would like to go along with me. If you go with me, you'll get back to your own men sooner. In any case, it depends mostly on what you want to do."

"If you will allow me to go with you, I'll be very pleased," Saburov said.

"You, Semyon Semyonovich," Remizov said to Annenski, "are a good officer, and it's already high time for you to have your own regiment. I mean that, seriously. I'm going to say so to the general when I get a chance. You've got too much temperament for a chief of staff. A chief of staff should have a taste for solitude—for a dugout with five layers over it. Yes, yes, I'm telling you this without any sarcasm. But you—if they shoot up the commander of your regiment three times in a day and you only twice, you convince yourself that you've been skulking shamefully at the bottom of a trench, and that it's somehow essential for you to jump out into some attack as quickly as you can in order to restore your spiritual equilibrium. No, don't argue with me, it's high time for you to have the responsibilities of command. And if you draw the same kind of chief of staff I've got now, and if you have to hold him all the time by the flap of his coat to keep him from tearing out to the front line, then maybe you'll understand me and sympathize with me," and Remizov laughed.

Annenski stood there in silence. He was a little dejected by the unexpected turn of the conversation, but there was nothing to which he could take offense. The old man had spoken out of a good heart, with something like a fatherly interest in him. Remizov summoned Sharapov and with his help put on a jacket over his blouse, tightened up his leather belt, and pulled a peaked cap down to his eyes.

"I don't like forage caps," he said, catching Saburov watching him. "Maybe they're more comfortable, but they haven't any style." Then he fumbled with his cap until he made sure that it was sitting at the right angle. He tied two grenades to his belt and took his automatic rifle. When he had made all these preparations, Remizov looked at his watch. Saburov also looked at his; he knew from Protsenko's order that the attack was supposed to begin exactly at ten, and it was now ten minutes before ten.

"Well, good-by, Semyon Semyonovich," Remizov said. He shook hands with his chief of staff. "Don't get lonesome. Come on, Captain, let's go. Sharapov, come along."

Five minutes later they were sitting in a narrow little ravine leading down to the Volga with many trenches dug along its sides. It was here that Remizov had ordered the assault group to assemble.

Men were sitting in trenches among the ruins, holding their weapons in their hands, leaning as best they could against the earth walls, against stones, against each other. Talking went on in whispers. At one end of the ravine, the distance to the Germans was fairly great—two hundred meters; at the other end, as far as could be judged by estimates made in daylight, it was less than fifty meters. The men talked to each other out loud only when a U-2 droned loudly over their heads to drop a white circle of illuminating rockets some five hundred meters beyond them over the German positions, and after the rockets, bombs. During these minutes it was possible to talk out loud.

"There goes the King's Aviation again," someone said when another U-2 droned over the ravine.

"It's a cornhusker."

"Up on the northwestern front we called them lumberjacks."

"Well, it all depends where you are. It depends on nature," a third voice said judiciously. "Where corn grows, they call them cornhuskers. Where there are lots of vegetables, they call them gardeners. Where there's woods, they call them lumberjacks. It's the same reason—they fly low; they love the earth."

"One minute more, if there's no delay, and the artillery barrage ought to start," Remizov said. "Did you take a lot of grenades?" he turned to a soldier sitting by his side in the trench.

"Eight of them, Comrade Colonel," a young sergeant replied.

"Softly, softly, don't shout," Remizov said. "Eight of them? That's nothing. What if there's a wall, and Germans behind the wall, and no way to go around it?"

"Then we'll blow it up, Comrade Colonel," the sergeant said.

"You took dynamite with you?"

"Of course, Comrade Colonel."

"How much?"

"We took six kilograms."

"What are you doing without a bayonet on your rifle?" Remizov turned to one of the soldiers.

"I've got its sister," the soldier answered, and he clapped his hand on a saber hanging at his side.

"What do you mean—are you a Cossack?"

"From the Cavalry Corps of the Hero of the Soviet Union, Major General Dovator." *

* Major General Lev Dovator was one of the greatest heroes of the Russian war against the Nazis. At the age of thirty-eight he organized the 2nd Guards Cavalry Corps, made up largely of Cossacks, which played an important part in the defeat of the Germans just outside Moscow in December, 1941. He was

"If you're a Cossack, where's your horse?" Remizov asked with a laugh.

"I've forgotten about horses. It's a month and a half since I've seen a horse."

"Don't you miss them?" Remizov asked.

"Here there's no chance to feel lonely," the soldier said, but there was a kind of sadness in the way he rubbed his hand along his saber.

"It's time," Remizov said. He called the officer who was to lead the attack and asked him if everything was ready.

"Everything," was the answer.

"Then we move on the first artillery volley from the left bank. Is that understood?"

"Yes."

"But don't count too much on the left bank," Remizov said. "The left bank is after all the left bank; you've got to count on your own mortars."

"Your orders will be carried out, Comrade Colonel."

"All right. Well, what's the matter, it's time," Remizov repeated a second time, turning his face toward the Volga.

Saburov also turned around. Just at that moment something far in the distance, on the left bank of the river roared, flashed in the sky, and flew over their heads, whining, rumbling, and screaming.

"Now the Katyushas have started to sing," Saburov said. Remizov gave no sign that he had heard, and Saburov realized that in the racket made by the Katyushas his words could not be heard.

Both below and above them on the left bank there was again a deep and heavy rumbling, and after the quick flashes in the sky flaming belts of shells arched over them. They were falling not far beyond them, half a kilometer away.

killed in action at that time. He was a Hero of the Soviet Union, twice awarded the Order of Lenin.

"I have a feeling they're landing beautifully," Remizov said when the roar of the barrage ceased. "It's very good. To tell you the truth, I'm a little afraid of those Katyushas myself. Let them make a mistake of one point on their chart, and there'll be nothing left of us but our names. It's a powerful weapon."

Immediately after the Katyushas, artillery began to speak from the left bank. First here, then there, flashes could be seen far in the distance before the heavy shells flew over their heads. In front of them the sky over the Germans was aflame with red light. When the shells fell close, these flashes carved out of the smoke first the corner of a building, then the base of a wall, then the metal skeleton of a smashed gasoline tank. The assault group began to crawl out of the ravine and to inch its way forward. One very heavy shell exploded quite close to the ravine.

"They aimed that one short," Remizov said. "Well, Captain, let's go."

Remizov climbed out of the trench with surprising agility and moved forward without looking around him. Saburov was right behind him. Beside them went Sharapov and three or four soldiers with automatic rifles.

Our artillery attack continued. The German positions and the area deep behind them rumbled from the explosions of the heavy shells. Ignited by the Katyushas, pools of gasoline or crude oil caught fire and red tongues of flame lifted themselves towards the sky. Besides the explosions in front of them, others now began around them. The Germans were firing back. Several times heavy shells passed over Saburov's head and exploded somewhere behind him. Then the cannon began to fire and finally, in front of them, could be heard the quick firing of tommy-guns.

The attacking group quickly covered the distance from the ravine to its old trenches in which the Germans were now sitting. This area, which had been captured the day before by the Germans, was familiar to Saburov. It was a square about four hundred meters on each side. It was covered with trenches and communications ditches, and only in a few places on the almost bare ground were there some ruins and piles of masonry. This was because a petroleum base had once stood here. There was nothing left of it now but its foundations and an enormous quantity of torn sheet metal scattered all around. Saburov ran after Remizov across the space separating him from the first trenches on the other side. Several times he clattered across burned sheets of metal which rattled under his feet with a strange metallic noise. In front of him were the remains of a stone sentry box. Remizov was trying to get to it, and Saburov with him.

When they had run up, machine-gun fire started on their left, and at the edge of the ruin one of the men running behind Saburov fell to the ground with a heavy thud. Several men had already set up two machine-guns in the ruins.

"That's the way to do it," Remizov said. "Gavrilov!"

"Yes, Comrade Colonel."

"Well, how is it? Have you taken it?"

"It looks as though we've taken it, Comrade Colonel."

"And are they moving on farther?"

"They're going forward."

"Go on with them. Pass the word along that I'll be here all the time."

Single bullets whistled and slapped against the sentry box. Sometimes a burst of machine-gun fire cut the air next to it. Different colored tracer bullets crossed each other's paths against the sky. To the left and quite near could be heard a lot of grenades going off. To the right shooting continued but there were no explosions: it had not yet reached the stage of grenade fighting there.

"Ah, they're no good; ah, they're no good," Remizov said

angrily. "They're all lying down. Their officers must have been killed. Saburov, go on over there. Since we can't hear grenades it must mean they're all lying down. Go over as fast as you can. Take any measures you want to."

Saburov crept out of the sentry box and crawled to the right, through the darkness. It turned out that the officer on that flank actually had been killed. A German heavy machine-gun standing in the middle of the ruins made it impossible to go forward, but the delay had occurred not because the officer had been killed, but because three sappers were crawling along a detour to place a charge under the ruins of the building on the second floor of which the machine-gun was standing. The others were waiting for the blast before moving farther. A sergeant was running everything, and when Saburov crawled up to him he explained quietly and efficiently what was going on. "If they don't crawl through they won't blow it up, and then we'll have to go forward anyway, Comrade Captain, but otherwise it's too bad to throw men away. Let's wait five minutes."

Saburov agreed and sent one of the soldiers back to Remizov to report that everything would be in order here in a little while. For several minutes he lay by the sergeant's side and waited. All around him night fighting was going on. Like all night fighting, it was an equation with many unknown factors.

"What's happening now on Protsenko's side?" Saburov wondered. Judging by the rumble of the artillery, the distant explosion of grenades, and the frequent networks of tracer bullets over the spot where Protsenko had been expected to attack, some kind of fighting was going on there, too. Our shells from the left bank kept on carrying overhead, but they were exploding now deep in the German rear. The explosions roared almost without interruption, one every second or two, and Saburov for a moment tried to picture to himself what it would be like around him if a cannonade like this were falling right now not on the Germans, but on him and on his men. In reality, the fire was terrifying, and like all Russian infantry officers he blessed the artillery from the bottom of his heart.

When a deafening explosion sounded in front of him, just about where the German machine-gun had been hidden, Saburov stood up, and firing from his rifle as he ran, led his Red Army men into an attack.

Twice during the night Saburov was splattered with clods of earth from shells that landed near him. The sleeve of his jacket was ripped by a rifle bullet which lightly seared his left arm. Many of those who plunged forward with him no longer answered the voices of their comrades. Many had been wounded, and nurses and orderlies were dragging them from the battlefield. In the darkness and in the fever of fighting, Saburov could not see whether or not Anya was among the orderlies.

In general the fighting worked out more easily than could have been expected. The four assault groups on the right, which Saburov himself was commanding, seized fairly quickly that portion of the trenches falling to their lot. When after several hours of fighting Saburov was mopping up the trenches leading to his left, he ran into soldiers walking towards him. These were men from one of the assault groups on the left flank. So it seemed that the entire sector had been captured. The Germans had been killed or had fled, with some of them, perhaps, still hiding in the dugouts, but this could only be cleared up the next morning, with daylight.

"How is it there, still further to the left?" Saburov asked. "Have they joined forces yet?"

"Something like it, Comrade Captain," said the soldier to whom he had spoken. "They gave it to the Fritzes hot over there."

The night's assignment had probably been carried out and the division again united, Saburov thought, but there could be

319

no doubt that the chief peril would come to this small and open area in the morning. Even the fact that the Germans had been relatively easily driven from it during the night did not augur well for the morning. The Germans were unlikely to be resigned to failure. In general they did not like night action, and they had not thrown strong forces into the fighting during the night only because they had decided to save them for the morning.

In the darkness Saburov checked the men left among the living, arranged machine-gun positions with the sergeant, and ordered the trenches made deeper in places, and the embrasures repaired in dugouts which had been damaged by grenades. Then he sent two messengers with notes—one to Remizov, the other to the chief of staff—with a warning that a German counterattack must be expected at dawn; that he himself would stay where he was, and that his only request was for mortars and antitank rifles to be moved forward quickly. "And if possible," he added at the end of both notes, "at least two or three antitank guns."

The messenger to Remizov never came back; either he had been killed on the road, or Remizov could not help him anyway. From Annenski, five or ten minutes later, when it was just beginning to get light, two 45 mm. cannon with rubber wheels were drawn up, and five armor specialists came with their long "degtyarevkas" * and about a dozen riflemen. In the note which the messenger brought back, Annenski had written: "I scraped up everything I could. Hang on."

---

* Major General Georgi Degtyarev's name has been given to several types of weapons he invented during the war, one of which was an automatic rifle similar to the American Garand rifle. Here the reference is to an antitank gun.

TWENTY

FROM eight in the morning, when the first German attack began with the coming of daylight, until seven in the evening, when darkness finally stopped the fighting, eleven oppressive hours followed each other, and in any one of them it would have been hard to find five minutes of even relative quiet.

While the division was being pressed back to the shore of the river on this sector during the past week, Protsenko had tried to dig in here with special care. The entire area was covered with trenches and communications ditches; under what was left of foundation walls a great number of fox-holes and dugouts had been dug; in front there was a narrow but fairly deep ravine across which the Germans would have to throw themselves in order to reach our positions.

If it had been possible to draw a graph of the fluctuation of sound on the field of battle during that day, it would have looked like the temperature chart of a malaria patient. Three times it would have moved sharply up, and then three times receded. During the morning the Germans began to pound the position with regimental artillery. Then they added heavy mortar fire, and a little later divisional artillery; finally they began to use heavy assault cannon and severe bombardment

321

from the air. When the noise had risen to its ultimate degree, it would stop suddenly, and under the rattle of machine-gun fire the Germans would proceed to attack. At this moment everyone who had sat it out, hanging on patiently in our trenches, jumped to machine-guns, tommy-guns, and carbines. The ravine had first been christened "Death Ravine" * a week before, in the days of the first German attacks; now it won the name for itself a second time.

It took only minutes for its slopes to be covered with the bodies of dead and dying. Each last wave of attackers stopped short of our trenches by twenty, fifteen, sometimes ten meters. Each time it seemed that in one more second, or half a second, they would cover this final bit of distance. But they did not cover it. In the last second the terror of death gripped those who had almost covered it and forced them to turn back. Had it not been for this terror of death, they would have run all the way to the trenches. But they turned back, and those who had not been killed when they were running forward were killed on the way back.

When the first attack had failed, everything started again from the beginning. But while the first time the hell lasted for two hours, the second time it went on for five hours and a half. The Germans had decided not to leave one place along the shore where a man could live. The entire bank of the river was covered with shell holes to such a degree that if all the shells had exploded at the same time, then in all truth not a single man would have remained among the living. But the shells exploded at different times. Wherever a shell had just gone off, men were already lying and shooting in its crater. Where the

---

* "Death Ravine," called by the Russians "Bathhouse Ravine" before the war, cuts its way through the bluff to the Volga River between the Red October Factory, one of Stalingrad's largest industrial units before the siege of the city, and the Mamai Kurgan. The Germans held parts of Mamai Kurgan throughout the siege. Beyond it, to the south, was the former business center of the city.

next one went off, the spot was usually empty. This deadly game of hide-and-seek continued for five and a half hours and ended when, towards the end of the sixth hour, the Germans launched their second attempt to storm the sector. Again the Red Army soldiers stood up in their trenches, deaf, half-covered with dirt, numb with fatigue, and fiercely, savagely, fired at everything moving in front of them. Again they managed to beat off the attack.

Almost immediately the graph of noise climbed up again. Airplanes came over in groups of five, ten, twenty, and thirty, and dove so low that the blast of their own bombs bounced them in the air. Paying no attention to antiaircraft fire, they dove sometimes to within twenty meters of the ground. Fountains of dirt and dust went up all over the area and came down like rain.

There were concussion and fragmentation bombs, big ones and little ones, bombs which carved out craters five meters deep, and bombs which exploded on impact with the ground, their fragments flying so low that they would have mowed the grass if there had been any grass. There were bombs exploding at a two-hundred-meter height and disintegrating into tens of little bombs which also exploded in the air and fell to the ground as shrapnel. All of this went on overhead for almost three hours. But when, exactly at seven o'clock in the evening, the Germans launched their third assault, they only filled Death Ravine again with their own corpses.

Saburov had never before seen so many dead soldiers on such a small plot of ground. There were places where the machine-guns had done such a deadly job that the bodies lay one on top of another. In the morning when Saburov had counted his men after the arrival of reinforcements—he remembered the number clearly—he had had eighty-three soldiers. Now, by seven in the evening, he had only thirty-five left in action, and of these two-thirds were slightly wounded. It was clear that the situation was the same both to his left and to his right.

The trenches were ploughed up and communications lines broken in dozens of places by direct bomb and shell hits. Many of the dugouts had been smashed. Saburov, who had suffered a slight concussion three days earlier, could hear practically nothing by now. When the fighting finally came to an end there was still in his ears an almost uninterrupted roar. If he had been asked at some later time to describe what had gone on during this day, he could have told it in very few words: the Germans fired, we crouched in the trenches; then they ceased firing, we stood up and fired at them; then they retreated and began to fire, we hid ourselves in the trenches, and when they stopped firing and began to advance, we fired on them.

This was, in reality, all that he and those who were with him had done all day. But, as a matter of fact, never before in his life had he felt such a stubborn desire to remain alive. It was not any terror of death that he felt, nor any specific fear that life, with all its happinesses and sorrows, would be cut short; nor was it any thought that tomorrow would come and he, Saburov, would no longer be here in the world. No, the entire day he was sustained by the simple desire to sit it out—to wait through to that minute when quiet would come, when the Germans would rise to attack, and when he himself could stand up and shoot at them. He and all the men around him waited for that moment three times during the course of the day. None of them knew what would come afterward, but each one of them wanted each time to survive until that minute at absolutely any cost. And when the last—the third—attack had been beaten off at seven o'clock in the evening, there was a short hush, and men for the first time that day said some words other than commands and the terrifying, inhuman, hoarse obscenities which they had yelled while firing at the Germans.

These words they said in surprisingly low voices, and you could feel a kind of celebration in the air, as if something exraordinarily important, even sacred, had just taken place. Saburov felt that they had beaten the Germans today. He felt as if they had not only done what would later be described in the communique: "Such-and-such a regiment destroyed up to seven hundred or eight hundred Hitlerites," but that they had beaten the Germans today in a more general sense—they had proved themselves stronger.

At half-past seven, when it was already dark, Annenski came into the trench where Saburov was. Saburov was sitting on his folded overcoat, leaning against the wall of the trench, and listlessly poking with a fork in a tin of canned meat, trying to convince himself that he was hungry and that he must eat, although he had not the slightest desire for food.

"Well, we drove them off," Annenski said.

His face was just as black and tired as those of all the men around. Obviously, what had happened here today had also happened where Annenski had been.

"We drove them off," Saburov said. "How is it with the others?"

"We drove them off along the entire sector," Annenski said. "I came with a lieutenant who will take your place. The general has summoned you."

"How are things there?" Saburov asked.

"We beat them off there, too. You'd better get going; he wanted you immediately."

"And where is Remizov?"

"They carried him back to the dugout."

"What do you mean? Is he wounded?"

"No," Annenski said, "he wasn't wounded. But the old man fell down in a swoon about half an hour ago, when it was all over. You know, that wound of his was not only funny, it was also bad. Right now they're fixing him up. Now go on, get going to the general, or he'll be sore."

"Good luck to you." Saburov pressed Annenski's hand.

325

"Yes. By the way," Annenski said, "his command post is no longer where it was. He ordered it moved."

"Where?"

"About three hundred meters from here, right in the ravine. You'll probably find him there."

Saburov walked back along the communications trench. Two or three times he had to climb over the bodies of his own soldiers which had not yet been carried away. After walking for about three hundred paces, Saburov almost collided with Protsenko, who was standing near the edge of the ravine. He was in the same jacket he always wore, but he had on a general's cap with a red band which had just been sent to him from the rear. Some distance beyond him, two soldiers were building a dugout.

"Saburov!" Protsenko shouted. "Saburov, is it you?"

"I, Comrade General," Saburov said.

Protsenko walked up to him, stopped, drew himself very erect, and said in an official tone of voice he seldom used: "Comrade Saburov, I thank you in the name of the High Command."

Saburov also drew himself up, and standing at attention, stammered out some confused reply.

"I have recommended you for decoration, for the Order of Lenin," Protsenko said. "You have earned it, and I wanted you to know about it."

"Thanks. Thanks a lot," Saburov said without thinking what he was saying, and he smiled.

Protsenko also smiled. Looking at each other they both understood that something very great and solemn had taken place today, both for them and for all those around them. Whether Saburov had been recommended for decoration or not, and whether he received it or not, did not matter in comparison with what had taken place. For today had been a victory; they both understood this. Today had been a victory over the Germans, who according to all the military rules should have taken the shore back again and had not taken it.

"Well, how are you—still alive, and all right?" Protsenko asked, embracing Saburov and patting him on the shoulder. "Still alive?"

Saburov did not answer. What could he say?

"Someday you and I, Alexei Ivanovich, are going to remember this day," Protsenko said. "Mark my words, we're going to remember today. Maybe others will remember other days, but we'll remember this one. A kind of extraordinary feeling today, no?"

Saburov silently nodded.

"I've changed my command post," Protsenko said. "The battalion headquarters used to be here, and I ordered it made bigger for me. Tomorrow they are certain to direct their heaviest blow right here. But we're not giving this place back. Everybody felt that today. I know it; you and I and everybody felt it. I want to strengthen this feeling in everybody. So I'm moving up here with my staff, so that they'll not only feel, but know, we're not giving it back. Do you understand?"

"I understand," Saburov said. "But it was more convenient for you where you were."

"It was more convenient there, but I'll fix everything up here nice and tight. Do you know, courage is courage, but just the same every commander of a division ought to have four layers of protection over his head. By the way, I have bad news for you. Popov was killed." There was a pause. "Have you got acquainted with Remizov?" Protsenko continued.

"We've seen something of each other."

"Well, what do you think of him? A man with a heart, isn't he?"

"Yes," Saburov said.

"He will be in command of your regiment now, instead of Popov."

"And Remizov's regiment?"

"I'm thinking of leaving Annenski there. Well, that's that, first of all. Second, I weakened both regiments yesterday in order to get the assault groups together. So, they've been pushed back a little. Your battalion, too. The division is all together again; that's wonderful, but they've pushed us tighter against the shore. We gave up five buildings."

"On my sector, too?" Saburov asked with the anxious feeling of a man who has not yet been told the worst.

"Yes. They pushed yours back, too. I was there myself half the day yesterday. Maybe it was my fault—maybe I took too many of your men—but if I hadn't taken them, we wouldn't have joined up with Remizov. I sat half the day at your place. That spot where you put your command post is now practically the front line."

"So," Saburov said.

"Of your three buildings the Germans took back one, the one built like a right angle. You remember it?"

"I know it."

Protsenko was talking in a deliberately quiet tone of voice, but from the way he spoke it could be seen he felt some kind of personal guilt before Saburov, because he had taken men away from his battalion and had taken Saburov himself. Saburov could complain now that if he had been there himself, this would not have happened, although both men knew that it might have happened just as well with him there.

"The way it's worked out, go on back to your battalion and dig in there, where it has stopped. That's the chief thing. Don't be angry, don't be angry," Protsenko slapped the stubbornly silent Saburov on the shoulder. "The most important thing is that the division is all together; that's worth more than your building. Yes. By the way, we've served together a long time, but I never knew before what a secretive person you are."

"Why secretive?" Saburov asked in surprise.

328

"Of course, secretive. I've already told you that I passed half a day at your battalion. They told me everything there."

"What did they tell you?" Saburov asked, still not understanding.

"You've got married, they say."

"Ah, so it's that . . ." Saburov realized what Protsenko meant. At first it had not even occurred to him, so far away had his thoughts been.

"Yes, I've got married," he said.

"They told me you even wanted to arrange a wedding. So you were going to have a wedding and not invite me, were you?"

"I wouldn't have done that," Saburov said. "It was just talk. We would have liked to have a wedding, but we wouldn't have done it."

"Why not? It's entirely possible. I know the girl. I even gave her a decoration. She's a good girl."

"Very," Saburov said.

"Is she a hospital assistant or a nurse?"

"Really a hospital assistant."

"Have you got a regular hospital assistant in your battalion?"

"No longer," Saburov said. "He was killed while I was in the hospital."

"Well then," Protsenko said, "I can appoint her hospital assistant attached to your battalion. If regulations permit it, I can."

"According to regulations, I'm entitled even to a doctor," Saburov said.

"Well, who cares what you're entitled to? Your battalion, for example, is entitled to have eight hundred soldiers, but where are they? A hospital assistant I can give you, but only on one condition . . ."

"What is that?"

329

"The condition is that you invite me to the wedding. And one more thing. Don't be offended, Alexei Ivanovich, if I talk a little bluntly. For you, she's your wife, but for the battalion she's a hospital assistant. That means she can't have anything to do with battalion affairs, except with problems of the wounded. Otherwise—you know this—sometimes it happens that women begin to give advice, not with any malice but with a good heart, and . . . well, that just doesn't work in war."

"I agree," Saburov said. "At the same time, if you have any doubts, she can stay where she is now."

"No, I have no doubts," Protsenko said. "I simply was thinking of it in general and so I said it. That's all. Well," he added, suddenly remembering, "get on back quickly. Your Maslennikov has been waiting for you too long. Is he in love with you, or what?"

"I'm not a girl."

"But he loves you, just the same; he loves you a lot. He looked at me as if I'd eaten you up. I had to tell him: 'Your Saburov is coming back. He'll come back—don't get excited.' "

"Just who was it told you, Comrade General?"

"Who told me? Vanin told me. I have a feeling that you're angry at him. Are you?"

"No. Why?" Saburov asked.

"Well, just so; you've never told me about him. And if you are angry with him, it's foolish. He's a good man and he respects you. Well, go on, go on," and Protsenko stretched out his hand to Saburov. "I think the Germans will repeat the whole business tomorrow. But if it didn't work for them today, there's even less chance of its working tomorrow. I have a hunch about this. But," and Protsenko raised one finger, "even good hunches are still hunches, and if the Volga doesn't freeze for another two days, then we'll be out of shells. Hoard them. And hoard your food. Good-by."

"Good-by, Comrade General."

TWENTY-ONE

IT was a dark night. First to the right, then to the left, a few shells exploded several hundred meters away, and just because they were few and unexpected, they made Saburov jump. When he reached his battalion, he met a soldier who recognized him. "How do you do, Comrade Captain?"

"How do you do?" Saburov said. "Show me the command post. Where is it now, do you know?"

"Right where it was. It's still there," said the soldier.

When Saburov had walked up to the dugout he saw Petya's familiar figure in the trench next to it, and something turned over in his heart. He felt as if he were coming home.

"Comrade Captain!" Petya said happily. "We've been waiting for you."

"You should have waited less, and fought better. I must say you fixed up quite a present for my return," Saburov said, trying to hide his pleasure at seeing Petya. "You gave away a building."

"That's true," Petya said. "They ganged up on us, or we wouldn't have lost it. We just didn't have the strength. After all, the general took forty men away from our battalion."

"He didn't take them only from you, he took them from others too."

"And they were pushed back, too," Petya said, offended. "It just wasn't humanly possible. The commissar and Maslennikov have been waiting and waiting for you."

"Where are they?"

"Comrade Vanin is here."

"And Maslennikov?"

"As soon as it started to get dark, he went over to the other building. You can't get there now in the daytime."

"How far is it from here to the Germans now?"

"On the left, just as far as it was, but on this side," Petya nodded to the right, "it wouldn't be sixty meters. You can hear everything."

"Were many killed?" Saburov asked.

"Eleven killed, thirty-two wounded," said Petya, who loved exact answers. "And they killed Maria Ivanovna."

"And her children?"

"The children, too. All together. A bomb landed straight on her cellar. It left just one crater, and not a thing to be seen around it."

"When was this?"

"Yesterday."

Saburov remembered how this woman had said to him, an endlessly long time ago, it seemed—a whole eternity—in her indifferent voice: "If a bomb comes, let it come. It will be one end for me and the children together." Her prediction had been fulfilled.

"Yes, you've told me a lot of news," Saburov said. "Too much," and raising the curtain, he walked into the dugout.

Vanin was dozing at the table. He had been writing his political report of the day and had fallen asleep with his head on the paper in front of him, and his arms stretched out on the table. "There were no negative instances of moral or political behavior," was the last sentence he had managed to finish before he dozed off.

"Vanin," Saburov said standing over him. "Vanin."

The sleepy man started up.

"Vanin," Saburov repeated, "here I am."

Vanin shook his hand for a long time, looking at him as at someone from another world.

"We were getting worried about you," he said.

"It looks as if you didn't have much time to worry about anything."

"No, I'm telling you, we found the time. The devil knows why, but you've got something that makes it lonesome here without you. Maybe it's that you're so big. Without you it's as if they'd taken the stove out of the room."

"Thanks for the comparison," said Saburov.

"The comparison, maybe, is not flattering, but there's something in it. And by the way, it's getting colder. You have no right to be offended; the stove is now the most essential thing we have."

"Yes, I see you've set one up." In the dugout stood a round iron stove.

"And why not? It burns wonderfully. Don't you want to get warm?"

Instead of answering, Saburov sat down on the cot, pulled off his boots, one after the other, and stretched his legs toward the fire.

"Good," he said. "Very good indeed. So you complained about me to the general."

Vanin laughed. "Yes, I complained. I'm the commissar here. It's my business to know what's going on inside people. So, you see, I noticed that something had happened to your heart, and I reported it."

"It's your own heart that's out of kilter," said Saburov. "And until the war is over it won't be right again . . . What happened to Maslennikov—has he gone over to the other building?"

"Yes, he's very restless."

"Will he return before morning?"

"He ought to. If he doesn't get back by morning, he won't until tomorrow night. In daylight you can't go there or come back. From both sides they can shoot the path up crosswise with machine-guns."

"Who stayed there?"

"Fifteen men. Konyukov is in charge. Because Potapov was killed."

"What?"

"Yes, killed. So I made Konyukov a company commander at the critical moment on my own authority. There wasn't anyone else. When they drove us back, he stayed in the building with what was left of the company."

"Is fifteen men really all that's left of Company Two?"

"No," Vanin said, "there are ten more men. They left the building, but he stayed in it. There are twenty-five men left in Company Two."

"How about the other companies?"

"The others have a few more. Here they are—look." On a piece of paper Vanin had written down with the precision which was his habit the roster of men in all companies.

"Yes," said Saburov. "We've lost a lot. Well, and where does the front line run now?"

"Here it is—look." Vanin fumbled in a briefcase and pulled out a little map. "Maslennikov made it for your return."

The map showed the dispositions of the battalion. It no longer jutted out forward, as it had earlier, but stood on the same line with the other battalions along one side of a shattered street, and only one building, marked on the map by dotted lines, stretched out in front like a tongue.

"Accurately speaking, that building is surrounded," Vanin said. "The Germans don't let us get there in daylight. We crawl through at night."

334

"Yes, and when it comes time to take the whole street back again, it will be a good outpost for moving forward," Saburov said. "We must reinforce it."

"When the time comes to take it back . . ." Vanin repeated slowly. "I'm afraid that's a long way off."

"Why?"

"For the time being, may God help us to hold out where we are now!"

"Of course," Saburov said, "that's what I'm talking about, that we'll hold out here, God willing. We'll hold here, and then we'll take the whole street back."

"You've come back cheerful. More optimistic than usual," Vanin said.

"Yes, I'm much more optimistic than usual," Saburov said. "It doesn't mean a thing that we gave up one building. That is, it's bad, of course, but still it's nothing. The fact that we held today on the shore and didn't leave them on the Volga— that's the most important. And we'll not let them come any farther."

"Are you convinced?" Vanin asked.

"Convinced," Saburov said.

"Why are you so certain?"

"How can I tell you? I could give you a few logical reasons, but that's not it. I've got a feeling that it will be so. We held today what we could never have held before. We've broken something in them. You know, it's like a toy that winds up. You wind it and wind it, then something cracks and you can't wind it any more."

"Well," Vanin said, "I'm glad to believe it. But we have been so disappointed here about that building that I guess we've just had no feelings at all, yesterday or today, except a bitter regret." Vanin stood up and walked limping across the dugout.

"What are you limping for?"

"Wounded. Never mind, I'll live till my own wedding, as they say. Until mine, that is, and not yours, because yours, I hear, is not far off."

"Who says that?"

"Protsenko."

"Well," Saburov said, "the banquet hall is ready." He looked around the dugout. "There will be music. We'll even have foreign musicians taking part. The bridegroom's here. We've only got to wait for the bride to come to the church door with her bridesmaids."

"And today, as soon as Maslennikov gets back, we'll organize a bachelor's dinner," Vanin said. "Don't think for a minute you can get out of it. Without a bachelor's dinner, we won't let you get married."

"Except that Petya is probably a little weak on supplies. How about it, Petya?"

"I can manage somehow, Comrade Captain," Petya said. "After all, you know what I'm good at." He opened a flask and poured vodka into the cups standing before Vanin and Saburov, but they had not even begun to drink when the curtains parted and Maslennikov appeared on the threshold of the dugout, happy, noisy, and disheveled.

"Hold on," he raised his hand. "What are you doing? Without me?"

He threw himself on Saburov, embraced him, picked him up in his arms, kissed him, grabbed him by the shoulders, held him away, looked at him, pulled him back, kissed him and pushed him back on his stool—all of this in less than a minute. Then he plumped himself down on the third stool by the table and cried out in his deep bass voice: "Petya, some vodka for me."

Petya poured him a drink.

"To Saburov!" Maslennikov said. "To his becoming a general, and soon!"

Vanin lifted his cup, smiled his familiar, sad smile, and

added: "To Saburov! To his becoming a teacher of history, and soon!"

Vanin and Maslennikov were both looking at Saburov.

"In other words, a teacher of history or a general?" Saburov said. "I'm ready to be a street cleaner, if that would make this war end one day sooner. Of course, end with the victory we want. So, let's drink to her."

"To what?" Vanin asked. At this moment Maslennikov bumped his knee under the table trying to make him understand the question was tactless.* "Oh, of course, to Anya."

"To what I was talking about—to victory," Saburov explained, and he downed his drink. "And as for teaching," he said, recovering his breath, "after the war we'll all be teachers of history a little bit, one way or another."

"Well, how's everything in the other building?" he turned to Maslennikov.

"Konyukov is running things there like a tsar," Maslennikov said. He was so tired that one drink of vodka had put him in that festive but solemn mood which makes people talk in sentences so long, and sometimes so complicated, that they never reach an end. "Konyukov has made himself chief of the garrison, and he is behaving with the dignity of a lieutenant general, besides which he has put on his old St. George's Cross † which, or so they say at any rate, he's wearing now in anticipation of the day when Captain Saburov will give him the Order of the Red Star to which he is legally entitled, according to an order of the Commander-in-Chief of the Army."

"Petya, what are you doing?" Maslennikov cried out. "Our cups are empty."

Saburov looked curiously at Maslennikov. Deciding that he was ready to fall down with fatigue anyway and so needed

* Nouns in Russian have gender, and "victory" is a feminine noun, referred to by a personal pronoun as if it were a woman.
† A medal given for bravery to soldiers in the Russian Army before 1917.

sleep one way or another, he made no protest. Petya poured them each another drink.

"It's interesting," Vanin said, "that Petya never makes a mistake; he always pours out exactly one hundred grams."

"Exactly, Comrade Senior Political Instructor."

"I know it's exact. And even when the cups are different, or when one of us has a cup, and another a little glass, and a third some kind of mug, still he always pours it exactly. Can you explain the secret?"

"I don't pour by eye, Comrade Senior Political Instructor, but by ear and by count. I hold the flask at a definite angle and then with the sound I count: one, two, three, four, five—finished—one, two, three, four, five—finished."

"What a man!" Maslennikov said. "After the war you'll be working in a drugstore."

"Never, Comrade Lieutenant," Petya said. "Never."

"What are you going to do after the war, Petya?" Saburov asked.

"I'm going back to work as a supply agent," Petya said. "I'm going to do amazing things with supplies."

"I have an idea you've had a drink or two, Petya," Saburov said.

"Yes, Comrade Captain, when you were drinking to victory, I was drinking, too. Yes, I've had a little to drink," Petya said, and then he paused. He did not add that the vodka had had an effect on him it seldom had because the food reserves were nearing their end and Petya, saving them for the officers, had eaten only two rye biscuits the entire day. "After the war I'm going to work on supplies the way I used to before the war. And if anyone thinks that won't be interesting work after this war, he's making a big mistake. I want to see the time come when what I did in 1933 would seem simply funny to people. I was a king simply because I could scrounge fifty sacks of potatoes or three sacks of onions. But sometime, when this war is over, they're going to tell me: 'Petya, rustle up for the workers' dining room some oysters, and some Chablis.' I'll tell them: 'If you please, my friends.' And for dinner there'll be oysters and Chablis."

"Have you ever eaten oysters in your life?" Saburov asked. "They must be pretty terrible."

"No, I've never eaten them," Petya said. "I just said oysters as an example. I wanted to say whatever would be the last thing in your minds right now. May I pour you another drink?"

"No," Saburov said, "we've had enough." He leaned his head on his arms and thought. Petya had been talking just now from his heart; these had been his dreams. And dreams are never ridiculous.

Closing his eyes, Saburov thought how many dreams, how many thoughts about the future—belated regrets, and unfulfilled desires—had been buried deep in the Russian ground during the last year and a half, and how many people, dreaming, desiring, thinking, eager people had been buried in the same soil, never to accomplish now whatever it was they had dreamed about. It seemed to him that all that had been feasible but not fulfilled, all that had been thought of but not done, by those who were dead, lay now with all its weight on the shoulders of the living, and therefore on his shoulders. He thought about what life would be like after the war, and he could not even imagine it to himself, just as before the war he would have been unable to imagine what was happening to him now.

"What's made you so unhappy?" Vanin said to him. "Has the general been talking to you?"

Saburov raised his head: "I'm not unhappy, I'm simply thinking." He laughed a little. "Why is it with us that when someone grows thoughtful people always think he's unhappy? Petya!"

"Yes?"

"Give me my automatic rifle. I'm going out with you."

"Where?" asked Maslennikov.

"I'm going to look over the position."

"Go to sleep instead, Alexei Ivanovich. The morning is wiser than the night."

"No, to look it over in the morning . . . my life's too valuable for that," Saburov laughed. "I'm going now."

"I'll go with you," Maslennikov said.

"No, I'll go alone," and Saburov placed his hand on Maslennikov's shoulder. "That's all there is to it, Mishenka. Sit down and remember that when an officer returns to his own unit, he is received like a guest for the first half hour, and then he is the boss again. Understand? Lie down and sleep. When I come back I'll wake you up and we'll talk about plans for tomorrow. You should also get some sleep," Saburov said to Vanin as he stood up.

"I've already slept," Vanin said with a smile. "I just can't finish my political report. I've tried three times."

"But you write them so boringly," Saburov said, "so boringly that you go to sleep over them yourself. Imagine how sleepy others must feel when they read them."

They both laughed.

"Get yourself a rest now," Saburov said, "and then write something interesting, so people will read it—something like Conan Doyle. Well, good-by and good luck."

Saburov and Petya went out of the dugout. Maslennikov stretched out on the cot and immediately, burying his nose like a child, fell fast asleep. Vanin sat down at the table, and drawing before him the unfinished page of his political report, began to think. Then he went over and drew from under his cot a little suitcase with a battered cover and took from it a thick student's notebook. On its first page was written: Diary. It was here that he wrote down in his infrequent free moments

340

the different events and circumstances which really interested him.

He placed the diary next to his daily political report and wondered if what he wrote in this personal notebook were not really what he should write in his political reports. Conversations, ideas, feelings, events showing people in an unexpected light—all this that he wrote down because it interested him was perhaps interesting in general, while what he wrote every day in his official reports—"Positive manifestations" and "Negative manifestations"—was not especially interesting for him and perhaps equally uninteresting for those who had to read it. At this moment, pushing the curtain aside, Anya walked into the dugout.

"How do you do, Comrade Senior Political Instructor," Anya said.

Vanin stood up to greet her and held out his hand.

"Where is Captain Saburov?" she asked.

"He has gone out to the companies; he will be back soon."

"Permit me to report myself to you," Anya said.

"If you please."

"Hospital Assistant Klimenko, appointed to your battalion as military hospital assistant, has arrived at her appointed post," Anya said, saluting. Then, letting her arm fall, she asked: "Will Alexei really be back soon?"

"Very soon."

"I'd like to see him as soon as I can."

"I know how you feel," said Vanin. "He should be right back."

They sat down and were silent for a moment.

"Don't look at me like that," Anya said. "I didn't ask for the appointment.

"I know."

"And he didn't ask for it either," she said with conviction.

"I know. It was I who asked for it."

"You?"

"I."

Vanin thought of his own family which he had lost, and he felt a conviction that his own happiness would never come back, and a kind of goodhearted jealousy came over him.

"It's wonderful that you're here. You can't understand how wonderful it is."

Anya was silent, waiting for him to go on.

"You should understand," Vanin continued. "I was glad to help you be together. Alexei Ivanovich and I quarrel here pretty often. We're very different sorts of people. But, you see, what it's all about . . . how can I explain it to you? Wait a minute—you've known me for a long time, after all," he suddenly interrupted himself.

"Of course, Comrade Vanin," Anya said. "What Stalingrad Komsomol didn't know you?"

"You know, when I first met Saburov here, we had an argument about planting parks. Do you remember how excited we all were once about planting green trees here? He tried to prove to me that since we knew a war was coming we should have bothered less about the trees and much more about other things. And in general I even agreed with him. But don't you remember what fun it was to make the parks, how wonderful it was? Don't you remember?"

"I remember," Anya said.

"That was such happiness then," Vanin said with conviction, "such real happiness. I've always wanted everybody to be happy, and everything I used to do I did for that. Sometimes I carried out unnecessary projects just for that. I started some pretty useless plans, just to make people happy. At least, that's the way I always thought of it."

Although Vanin was talking confusedly and falteringly, Anya realized he was talking about something which had been worrying him for a long time.

342

"And now look," Vanin continued, "although it always used to seem to me that I was doing good things, so that people would be happy, now I have a feeling that Saburov is probably right. Maybe we should have had fewer green parks, fewer calisthenics and physical culture parades, fewer handsome words and speeches. Maybe we should have had more marching around with rifles and learning how to shoot."

Vanin brushed back a lock of hair which had fallen over his forehead. Anya remembered suddenly a Komsomol meeting a long time ago at which Vanin had stood up on the platform, grown warm and eloquent just as he was now, and in just the same way had brushed back a lock of hair falling over his forehead. Although not everything that Vanin was now saying pleased her, since it was obviously only a continuation of his argument with Saburov, still she suddenly thought that the man in front of her was probably a very good and a very honest man.

"Yes . . ." Vanin suddenly interrupted himself. "So I tell you: I'm especially glad you will be with Alexei Ivanovich, when all around so much is going on that's terrifying. Or not terrifying—the devil knows what—but in general tough for any man. It's good, when you're together. How did you come, straight here with all your things?"

Anya smiled. "Here are my things." She pointed to her big first-aid kit, crammed to the top.

"And what else?"

"Nothing else; this is all I have," Anya said. She took off her coat and sat down at the table.

"Anyway, we'll rebuild our green parks here again," Vanin said. "As it was before, so shall it be again. And if the young people don't pitch in as eagerly as we would like, then we, as old Komsomols, will shake up our old bones and do it ourselves."

"Of course, we'll do it," Anya said, thinking in spite of herself of what Stalingrad was like today.

Maslennikov stirred under his overcoat on the cot, then sat up swiftly, groped for his boots, pulled them onto his bare legs, stood up, and walked over to greet Anya.

"Here you are," he said.

Anya felt pleased that he had said this just as if they had been expecting her for a long time.

"How would you like something to eat?"

Anya shook her head.

"Would you like to go to sleep?"

Anya again shook her head.

"I don't want anything," she said. "I'm glad to see you."

"Tomorrow, probably, will be quiet here," Maslennikov said, partly to reassure her, partly just to continue the conversation.

"She is my old Komsomol," Vanin said. "Friends meet again —wasn't there a movie with that name?"

"There was," Anya said.

"I haven't seen a movie in a long time. We got a copy of *Pravda* somehow, and I was looking at a list of the pictures being shown in Moscow. They're even playing 'The Three Musketeers.'"

"I saw 'The Three Musketeers,'" Anya said, "when I was still a little girl."

"Wasn't that with Douglas Fairbanks?" Maslennikov asked.

"Yes."

"No, they say now some other actor is playing in it. Douglas Fairbanks died."

"Did he really?" Anya asked in surprise.

"He died; he's been dead a long time. And Mary Pickford died."

"Mary Pickford, really?" Anya said with real dismay, as if

this were the saddest of all the sad things that had taken place in Stalingrad during the last month.

"Yes, she died," Maslennikov said sternly.

To tell the truth, he had not the slightest idea whether Mary Pickford was alive or dead, but once he had started on this subject he wanted to impress his listeners with how well informed he was.

"How about Buster Keaton?" Anya asked anxiously.

"He's dead," Maslennikov said confidently.

Vanin laughed.

"What are you laughing at?"

"You're talking about them just as if you were listing the losses in some company or other during the last few days," and Vanin laughed still more loudly.

"He was a very good actor," Anya said. She felt genuinely sorry to hear that Buster Keaton had died. She remembered his long, sad, never-smiling face, and she felt real grief that he had had to die.

"He hasn't died," Vanin said looking at Anya.

"Yes, he's dead all right," Maslennikov asserted hotly.

"Well, all right, let's say he's dead," Vanin agreed. The argument, here in Stalingrad, seemed a little funny to him. "I'm going out to check the guards," he added, putting on his overcoat and trying to show by this that the conversation was finished, and that in the long run it was not really important to him whether Buster Keaton was alive or dead.

"The captain is already checking them," Maslennikov said.

"Maybe he was held up at company headquarters, and I'm supposed to check them anyway. I'll be back soon." Vanin went out of the dugout.

"You should lie down," Maslennikov said. "We'll fix you up a cot tomorrow, there in the corner, but meanwhile lie down on mine."

Anya looked at him, and although she felt no desire to lie

345

down she realized that if she did not do so at once, Maslennikov would repeat his offer inside of three minutes, so she did not argue. She took off her coat, and pulling off her boots, lay down on the cot, covering herself with her coat right up to her neck.

"All right, I've obeyed you now, but I'm not sleepy," Anya said. "Tell me how you live here."

"Splendidly," Maslennikov said in an official tone of voice, as if this were not Anya in front of him but a delegation just arrived from Chita with presents. "Splendidly." Then he remembered that this was really Anya, who knew as well as he did what was going on here, and he added. "Splendidly. Today we drove off all the attacks against us." This was his way of making clear that the word "splendid" referred not to their general way of passing time but to the fact that the fighting today had been successful. "The captain looks very well. We had grown anxious about him here."

"I had, too," Anya said.

"But he came back without a bruise. The general told us as a secret that he was recommending him for the Order of Lenin because he got through to Remizov twice in one night. Well, what else? We had a few drinks, to victory, and to celebrate his return. And I, to myself, was drinking to you, too, at the same time."

"Thank you."

"I am very glad that you are here," Maslennikov said. "Do you know, when you live only with other men, somehow you grow rough in a setting like this." He felt the sentence had sounded pretentiously masculine and grown-up, and his cheeks grew red. "Maybe you'd like to smoke," he said, covering up his confusion.

"I don't smoke," Anya said.

"I didn't smoke either until the war, but in a place like this it becomes a habit; it makes time go faster. Come on, smoke."

"Well, all right," Anya said, realizing that if she smoked it would give him satisfaction.

He took out of the pocket of his blouse the single cigarette stored up there and gave it to Anya. He began to roll one for himself. Then remembering that he had not offered her a match, he jumped up, spilling tobacco out of the cigarette he was making, pulled out a match, and held it for Anya. She lit a cigarette as all people do who do not know how to smoke, barely sucking the cigarette and releasing the smoke immediately from her mouth.

Maslennikov, who was usually clever at rolling cigarettes, took a long time and a lot of work to make this one, and still turned out an enormous, awkward object at the end of which a lot of paper was twisted, so that it flared up for a second like a torch when he lit it.

"Maybe you'd like something to eat," Maslennikov asked.

"No, thanks."

"Would you like some water brought?"

"No, thanks."

Maslennikov said nothing for a little. Here, under his protection, was the wife of his superior officer and his friend, and he felt toward her the touching and sentimental awe of a small boy. He wanted to surround her with attention, to make her understand that he was her husband's most loyal friend, that she could rely on him completely, and that there was nothing he would not do for her sake.

"Misha."

"Yes."

"You are called Misha, aren't you?"

"Yes."

"You are a very nice fellow."

Hearing these words: "you are a very nice fellow," Maslennikov felt that although he and Anya were probably the same age, she was still in some way much older than he.

347

"Misha," she repeated, closing her eyes, as if trying to remember his name.

When Maslennikov next asked her something, she did not answer. She had fallen fast asleep the very second she had closed her eyes.

He sat alone at the table in a heavy silence broken only occasionally by the sound of distant firing. On the cot, two paces away from him, a woman was sleeping, the wife of his comrade, and she seemed very beautiful to him. He would have been in love with her, had she not been the wife of his comrade, or so at least he thought. Perhaps he was already in love with her, but he would never have admitted this to himself.

For some reason he suddenly remembered his brother, and the noisy summer cottage outside Moscow where his brother often used to go when he returned from Spain, and later when he returned from Mongolia. Probably because his brother had put his life in great risk and had fought hard and a great deal, he used to love to have things noisy and happy around him on his infrequent trips home. He would come to the cottage with beautiful women—first with one, then a couple of years later with another. He was always noisy and happy, and everything seemed to come to him easily, both friends and love. But Maslennikov sometimes noticed that this was a little boring to his brother. When he had come to the cottage with a lot of friends and with some woman who seemed to Maslennikov so fascinating that he ought not to go one step away from her, his brother would say suddenly: "Mishka, let's play some billiards," and together they would lock themselves in the billiard room and play for three hours. When someone would knock on the door and a woman's voice would cry "Kolya!" his brother would put his finger to his lips and say: "Shshsh, Mishka," and they would be quiet until the light footsteps had gone away from the door, and then they would go on playing again. The brother would say: "Oh, well, let God take care of them!" and Maslennikov would be amazed.

It seemed to him incomprehensible that if the woman's voice had called to him he would have been able to stay quiet and then go on playing billiards. There would stir in him a kind of small boy's envy, the feeling of a boy who did not yet know anything, even though in talking with his companions he always pretended, like them, that he knew a very great deal. When they had finished their game, his brother would return to the company and would be very tender and very attentive to the same woman whose voice he had just refused to answer. It would seem that he was ready to do anything for her. And then later he would quietly nudge Maslennikov like a conspirator, as if saying: "Happiness is not in this, my friend, happiness is not in this." But it always seemed to Maslennikov that happiness was precisely in this, because it was something unknown to him and untried and probably wonderful.

He thought of his brother and the cottage in the country and the billiard room, and he wondered where his brother was. There had been nothing about him in the papers for a long time. Suddenly he imagined that his brother had been killed, and he thought how those who used to come to the cottage in such noisy company, and the women too, would learn about the death of his brother and how they would talk about him, and probably even drink to him, and how they would remember what it had been like at the cottage with him. Beyond this, he thought, nothing at all would happen. If Saburov should be killed, what would Anya do then? She would probably become quite different somehow from what she was now; something terrible would take place inside her. Inside those who used to visit his brother, nothing terrible would take place at all, and maybe that was the reason his brother used to walk out with him to play billiards and would not answer their knocking.

He looked again at Anya, and a youthful longing for love

—not for her, but just for love—filled him. He wanted terribly to live through to the end of the war, to go back to his brother's cottage, and not alone; but he wanted it all to be different from the way it had been with his brother. He wanted not to walk out and play billiards, and he wanted his girl to be altogether remarkable. He began to think what she would be like, but when he thought about her in the abstract he endowed her with the most extraordinary qualities, and when he tried to imagine her face, somehow he always saw the face of Anya.

He dozed off, sitting on the stool by the table, and woke only when Vanin walked back in from his tour of the guards.

"Maslennikov, you're not sleeping?"

"I dozed off a little."

"Where is Saburov?"

"Still gone."

"It's already six," said Vanin. "That means he must have got through to Konyukov's building. I couldn't find him anywhere else. There's a restless soul for you."

TWENTY-TWO

I T was correct that Saburov had gone over to Konyukov's building. It was possible to go there only at night, and even then most of the distance had to be covered by crawling, with a risk of being hit by a random bullet. Saburov and Petya had followed a half-destroyed wall and then turned away from it. At this point Petya drew himself together as if preparing for a dive.

"Well, Comrade Captain, how about it? This is an open place."

"I know," said Saburov.

"How about it, shall we crawl or shall we sprint?"

"Let's make a sprint for it," said Saburov.

They jumped out from behind the wall and ran across the thirty meters separating them from the next little wall behind which they could move in relative safety right up to the building. The Germans heard them and several bursts of fire whistled behind them.

"Who goes there?" someone's voice asked quietly in the darkness.

"Friends," Petya said. "The captain."

They walked several paces farther along the little wall.

"Through here," said the same voice. "Is that you, Comrade Captain?"

"Yes," Saburov said.

"Through here. Don't hit your head."

Saburov crawled through and let himself down several steps. He groped his way around the corner and walked into a cellar. This was a part of the same big furnace room from which Lieutenant Zhuk had once pulled out some Germans in hiding. In two months' time it had changed. The spot which had once been considered dangerous had now become, in comparison with the surface of the ground, almost a comfortable habitation for this city. Half of the furnace room had been demolished by the direct hit of a five hundred kilogram bomb. The boilers in the middle of the cellar had exploded and covered part of the floor with fantastically twisted sheets of metal. The other, smaller, half of the furnace room was still intact.

In two of the walls, forming an angle towards the Germans, something like embrasures had been made, and four machine-guns were standing in them. The staircase had been smashed in two places, and some fragments of an old fire escape led up through a hole in the ceiling. A breach in the wall made by the bomb had been filled with pieces of the boilers, and at the place where an entrance had been left four sheets hung instead of curtains. It was through here that Saburov followed his escort into the furnace room.

In the furnace room everything was smoky. A homemade iron stove with pieces of board burning in it stood on the cement floor. A pipe led outside through the wall, but it had not been put together carefully, and smoke leaked from every joint. One soldier was squatting on his heels beside the stove, and five or six were sleeping in the corner on bunks made out of spring mattresses and leather seats taken from wrecked automobiles.

When Saburov came in, the man sitting by the fire jumped

up, saluted him, and asked: "Shall I wake up Konyukov, Comrade Captain?"

"Wake him up," Saburov said.

"Comrade Sergeant, Comrade Sergeant," the soldier began to shake Konyukov. Konyukov stood up, and tightening his belt, ran up to Saburov.

"Permit me to report," he bawled out, stopping three paces away. "The garrison at No. 7 Tartar Street is ready for action. We have no sick. We have two wounded. Unusual occurrences—none. Sergeant Konyukov reporting."

"How are you, Konyukov?"

"I wish you health," Konyukov said. And, stepping back a pace, he stood erect and at attention.

In spite of all this discipline, there was something new in Konyukov's appearance, something almost guerrilla-like that appears in men who have been besieged a long time, steadily risking their lives, cut off from the rest of the world. Konyukov's belt was pulled so tight, as always, that you could not put two fingers behind it, but his cap was tilted jauntily; at his belt hung a German revolver in a triangular black holster, and on his feet he sported a pair of German flier's boots made of yellow leather and lined with fur.

From the way the soldier had asked: "Shall I wake up Konyukov?" unwilling to make the decision himself, and from the fact that although Konyukov had been sleeping, there was obviously the strictest kind of order throughout the garrison, Saburov understood that Konyukov in the last few days had become a personage of some significance here.

"It's a long time since I've been to see you, Konyukov. I came to see how you're getting along."

"We're living very well, Comrade Captain."

"Tell them to bring a bench up to the stove. I'm frozen. Sit down with me. Let's have a talk."

"Do you want me to wake up the men?" Konyukov asked.

"No, why wake them? They're tired, probably."

"That's just it, they are tired."

"Is this all the men you have?"

"By no means, this isn't all. Half are at their posts, half are sleeping. We take turns fighting, as long as there is no attack."

"And if there is an attack?"

"When there's an attack then everyone is at his post, as it is ordered. Antonov!" Konyukov called.

"Yes."

"Move a bench up to the stove for the captain," said Konyukov. "In a hurry. Put one leg here, the other there."

The little bench was not to be found, and instead of it the soldier brought two automobile cushions and placed them a little away from the stove. Then he began to fuss with the wood.

"Well, that's fine. All right, Konyukov," Saburov said. "Sit down," and he himself sat down next to the fire.

Konyukov also sat down, a little to the side of him, but even on the low automobile seat he managed somehow to keep his erect appearance.

"Well, this means you're here alone and surrounded?" Saburov said.

"Exactly," Konyukov said. "This is the third day. I stayed behind as company commander, after he was killed. Last night they sent an order making us a platoon and naming me its commanding officer."

"How many are in your platoon?"

"Fifteen men," Konyukov said, "counting myself."

"And how many were there?"

"There were seventeen. Yesterday and today we lost two . . . killed . . . by reason of their death. That means, just killed," he explained when his formal military language became incomprehensible even to himself.

"How have you arranged your men?" Saburov asked.

354

"Permit me to report. This is how it is: In the daytime four men are lying all the time at the embrasures with machine-guns. Two are sitting in trenches on the sides, so they can't get around us, and we can watch our flanks. The trenches are well dug and there's a path leading straight to them from the cellar, so they won't get hit in the head when they're crawling there. Do you see that hole over there? Two men are standing watch all the time on the first floor. They watch in front of us, so no one can come up. They're less under cover, of course, but we did build some kind of cover for them. We took the turret of a tank up there, and covered it with bricks. Yesterday Maximov was killed there. You didn't know him?"

"I think I did."

"He was a red-head. He was in my group. Well, yesterday he got it. And so, may God be good to him! Everything is arranged in good order, Comrade Captain, you can see for yourself."

"I certainly shall," Saburov said.

"While you're waiting, wouldn't you like to taste some potatoes? They're frozen, but it's made them sweeter."

"Where did you get potatoes?"

"Last night we got down to the lower cellar where the woman was with the children, who were all killed. Do you remember?"

"I remember," said Saburov.

"We sneaked down there. I stole in myself. Everything is smashed there from the explosion. I took half a sack. Don't you like frozen potatoes?"

"Why not? I certainly do," Saburov said.

"We'll have some ready right away," Konyukov said. "Turn the potatoes, Antonov. You can't cook them just on one side, you have to turn them over. Wait, I'll do it myself."

Konyukov stood up, and pulling a wide-bladed knife out of his belt, began to turn the potatoes in the frying pan.

355

"We've got quite a household here, Comrade Captain. I like everything to be in order, with a place for everything. Taste the potatoes," he said, taking the frying pan from the fire and placing it on the floor. "Look, here is a little knife. There aren't any forks; we haven't any."

Saburov took the knife and burned his mouth with several pieces of potato. They seemed especially good to him because it had been so long since he had eaten any. Konyukov had a German flask with vodka in it swinging on his belt by his side, and he wanted to ask the captain to have a drink. But discipline rose above this desire. He decided that a superior officer should know himself when to drink and when not to drink.

"Why aren't you eating?" Saburov asked.

"You go on, and we'll eat later."

Saburov ate a little more and then moved the frying pan towards Konyukov. The latter called the soldier on the guard and said to him: "Go and wake up the soldiers. Supper is ready."

Saburov stood up and said: "Fine, while they're eating let's go on up."

"Right away, Comrade Captain, this way if you please." Konyukov led Saburov to the fire escape, and hanging back a little, communicated to the soldier on guard by a kind of violent sign language that by the time he came back everyone should be looking spruced up and military so as not to let him down.

They climbed up the fire escape. Once it had served as a passage from the sixth or seventh floor on to the roof, but now its remaining fragment rose only seven or eight rungs. They found themselves under the sky when they were at about the level of the first floor, hardly higher than the ground itself.

The night was dark and full of frost.

"Keep down, Comrade Captain, behind the parapet," Kon-
356

yukov said in a whisper. "In places it's shot away and it wobbles badly, too."

Having gone about ten paces, they found the first of the sentinels behind a corner of the wall. He was lying behind a pile of debris on top of which, sideways, two iron rails had been placed, and above them some sacks filled with either sand or cement. On both sides he was protected by similar sacks.

"Sidorov," Konyukov called in a whisper.

"Here I am."

"What do you see?"

"I can't see anything."

"A little chilly?"

"I'm frozen," Sidorov said. "The cold has gone right through me."

"Be patient, the new shift is coming soon. Then you can cook some potatoes. Today you are chef."

"Just let me get to a stove," Sidorov said, "and I'll cook you anything you want. I'm cold."

"Well, keep on watching," Konyukov said. "Have you any orders, Comrade Captain?"

"None," Saburov said.

In the same fashion they crept along to the second observation post, made of the empty turret of a tank set up on a wall running between piles of scattered masonry. The upper hatch of the turret was open and a soldier was standing in it so that only his head could be seen.

"It's a strong turret, and like ice. It's cold inside it," said Konyukov. "It must be fierce to work in tanks in wintertime."

"Yes, it's cold," Saburov agreed.

"We put a mattress inside it," Konyukov said, "and spread out some blankets so it's possible to sit down. But what'll it be like in winter, in January or February? It'll be terrible if it gets really cold. How can anyone sit here? We'll have to give the man on duty here at least a double ration of vodka."

Konyukov talked about this tank turret as if it were a permanent fixture, and as if there were no doubt that he and his sentinels would be sitting right here in this turret in January or February. "When spring comes, and the sun warms it up a little, then it will be better," Konyukov continued. "What can you see, Gavrilenko?"

"There was a little rustling out there," Gavrilenko said in a whisper, "but now it's quiet."

"Well, keep on watching. Have you any commands, Comrade Captain?" Konyukov asked Saburov again, and the latter, as before, replied that he had none. Then they inspected the two observation posts set up on the sides of the building and returned to the cellar.

Here they found the result of Konyukov's fierce gestures: everyone in the cellar had tightened his belt and put on a more or less valiant appearance, even if they were a little ragged-looking, as everyone was now in Stalingrad.

Konyukov walked in with Saburov and made a motion as if he were looking for someone with his eyes. One of the soldiers sprang forward, stopped short in front of Saburov, and reported heartily: "Comrade Captain, the platoon is being fed."

"Go on and eat," Saburov said. "Eat your food. I suppose they're going to change the sentinels now?" he turned to Konyukov.

"Exactly."

They both walked over to the mattresses which were now vacant, sat down on them, and began to talk about different things which interested Saburov. These were professional questions: how many bullets Konyukov still had and where they were being stored, in different places or all together; how long his provisions would last if it should be impossible to send him any more at night for several days. Suddenly, above them, one after the other, they heard three shots.

"To your places," Konyukov yelled out, leaping up.

"That's Sidorov giving a warning," he turned to Saburov. "How about it, Comrade Captain, will you go up with me or stay here?"

"I'll go up," Saburov said.

They climbed up again and lay down beside the soldiers on the parapet, made of piles of brick and bags of cement. The night attack continued about an hour. The Germans were trying from different directions to get up to the building in groups of three, five, and ten men. They rained a curtain of automatic rifle fire against the remains of the walls. Now here, then there, sometimes very close, bullets whistled past their ears. A dozen grenades fell right beside the wall, riddling it with splinters. But, at the end, after they had lost a few killed, the Germans withdrew, as shy as ever in night fighting. Everything grew quiet again.

Saburov descended again to the cellar and gave Konyukov several instructions for the future. It was already beginning to grow light. Determined to get back to the battalion if he could, Saburov started out with Petya. Hardly had they passed the end of the little wall and begun to crawl across the open space, when heavy machine-gun fire began to rattle over them and in front of them, pinning them to the ground. There was nothing to do but go back behind the wall.

"I guess you'll have to spend the day with me, Comrade Captain," Konyukov said when he came out to meet them. "Once they've noticed you, now they'll pour it on there until nighttime. You'd better stay with me. That's the way your luck works out today."

Saburov made no strong objection. Considering the matter soberly, he realized that Konyukov was right, and he decided to remain here until night. During the day he inspected Konyukov's situation in detail and gave instructions for one of the machine-guns to be moved to a better place. Everything else was already in perfect order. Several times he climbed up to the first floor, which Konyukov called his "watchtower," to observe the Germans. On this particular day they were relatively quiet, at least in front of Konyukov's building. Only at the end of the day, towards four o'clock, they began to hammer away with about a dozen heavy mortars against the building itself, and even more, through it towards the sector where the other companies were located.

After this, the Germans took up the offensive in three groups against the command post and the company on the right flank, and the advantages of having Konyukov's building became immediately clear. From this point, and particularly from the observation post on the first floor, could be seen if not everything, then in any case a very great deal. When the Germans, no longer hiding themselves in communications trenches, jumped out in the fever of their attack onto the area hidden from the battalion but clearly visible to him, Konyukov was already lying behind the machine-gun at his higher observation post, and he fired it at them furiously. The black figures jumping from ruin to ruin in front of him fell into the snow. Forgetting his usual respect for his superiors, Konyukov turned a flushed face to Saburov, winked, and made little boastful, clucking noises with his tongue.

It was at exactly four o'clock—Saburov remembered the time precisely because he happened to look at his watch—that the Germans, judging only by sound, since they were not visible behind the debris, broke into the battalion headquarters. After a minute of threatening silence, five or six grenade explosions could be heard there all at once, then two more, and then five or six. At this moment Saburov had a feeling of pressure which he tried his best to shake off. It was anxiety mixed with some ill-defined anticipation of disaster. For the first time during all his stay at Stalingrad, Saburov at this moment thought his nerves were probably not in good shape. When this same anxious feeling came back to him again, at the sound of more grenades going off, he began to feel really worried. He shoved Konyukov over, lay down himself behind the machine-gun, and waiting cold-bloodedly for the right moment, began to fire burst after burst at the retreating Germans.

This brought him back a little to himself, but the feeling of anxiety did not leave him. He wanted to be back at the battalion even though, judging by the fact that the sound of grenades had ceased and that the Germans were now crawling back, it was clear that even if an attack had been made on battalion headquarters, it had been beaten off.

A half hour later everything had become quiet again, except for a few shells flying over the building and exploding with a slapping noise behind it. At six o'clock Saburov looked through the curtains at the doorway and saw that the dark blue of evening was beginning.

"It's time," he said.

"Permit me to report, Comrade Captain," Konyukov said. "Have patience. Wait ten minutes more. When it gets really dark, then set off."

"Well, all right," Saburov said, "I'll wait ten minutes . . . Yes," he remembered suddenly, "that Order of the Red Star they awarded you—I'll bring it the next time I come. I'll send for it especially from division headquarters."

"And many thanks," said Konyukov. "I will be very grateful to you."

"Why, are you happy to have the Order?" Saburov asked.

"Who wouldn't be happy to have it?" said Konyukov. "Only a stupid man wouldn't be happy. And I have my own pride. Alexei Ivanovich," for the first time he called Saburov this, "after the war, perhaps, we may meet somewhere. You'll see me, and you'll say: There goes Konyukov. And you know, maybe I'll get married. I'm a widower now. Maybe you'd like to smoke, Alexei Ivanovich?" he said, fishing out a little tin box. It was clear that he was treating Saburov so freely now because for the first time they were talking to each other about what would happen after the war, when he would be a civilian again and would speak to Saburov in this way, as Alexei Ivanovich, if he should meet him.

At the very moment when Saburov had heard behind him, at battalion headquarters, the distant explosion of grenades, and when his heart had been gripped by the squeezing feeling which he had tried to throw off but could not—at exactly this moment, by some strange combination of circumstances, there had taken place the greatest misfortune he could possibly have feared.

This was the day when the Germans had become tired of their unsuccessful attacks against both companies and had determined to seize the bull by the horns. Unexpectedly, after a very short mortar barrage, they had filtered through the ruins, running, without hiding, between the stones and piles of brick, and had thrown themselves directly at the command post of the battalion. This was the minute of suspicious silence which Saburov had noticed.

While they were running up, at the command post there was only Maslennikov, who had come in to telephone to regiment headquarters, two machine gunners located behind their weapon at the entrance to the dugout, and three or four communications men sitting in their own dugout. At this moment Anya happened to be bandaging the injured arm of one of them. When the Germans appeared, the machine gunners paused for a second. Their cartridge belt had run out and several Germans managed to cross the space in which the machine-gun, a few seconds later, nailed down the others. Those who had got across threw themselves onto the ground right next to the dugout and hurled several grenades into the trench and the communications path beyond it.

At first Anya understood nothing. She only heard the explosions and saw how the lanky soldier standing in front of her, whose arm she was bandaging, suddenly turned from her. Pulling the bandage from her hand, and trailing it after him, he fell full length on his back, killed instantly by a splinter from a grenade.

Anya bent down, and at this moment the second communications soldier shoved her hard, so that she fell to the bottom of the trench. When she opened her eyes, she saw that the soldier had grabbed his tommy-gun and had raised himself above the trench, firing as fast as he could. When she fell, Anya had hit her face against something hard. It was the rifle of the killed soldier lying on the bottom of the trench. She picked it up, put it on the parapet of the trench, and raising herself like the other soldier, began to fire without seeing what she was shooting at.

Then she saw Maslennikov jump out of the dugout to her left, run forward, and like a little boy begin to take small grenades from his belt and throw them one after the other in front of him. Then a machine-gun clattered again, someone yelled out in an unknown language, something flew at them from in front, the soldier dove back into the trench, she did the same, and above them all at once could be heard three or four heavy explosions.

The communications soldier stood up again and began to fire. Anya realized that she could not shoot any more because the first time she had exhausted the clip of bullets in her gun. She began to look around to see whether another clip might be lying somewhere in the trench. There was one, two paces away from her, in a linen case hanging from the belt of the killed soldier. She quickly moved across the trench, bent over, and unfastened the clip. Looking around again, she noticed that Maslennikov had jumped out of the trench and was again throwing grenades, yelling something. She thought to herself how brave he was, and picking up the bullets, went back to where her automatic rifle was lying.

When she bent down again to pick up the rifle, something arched over her head and fell into the trench. She noticed, between her and the soldier who was still firing, a German grenade—she had seen them many times before—looking like ours except for its long wooden handle. She suddenly thought how like a top it was. The soldier dropped his rifle and fell to the bottom of the trench. Anya, without thinking at all about herself, was really frightened. Now the grenade would kill the soldier, and she remembered she had read somewhere or someone had told her that in cases like this you had to pick up the grenade and throw it back. She quickly took the three steps separating her from the grenade, seized it by its handle, which was still turning, felt how long and thin the handle was, and in the very last second thought she could probably throw the grenade a long way because its handle was so long. At this moment the grenade exploded in her hand and Anya, no longer thinking about anything, fell unconscious to the bottom of the trench.

In the fever of fighting, Maslennikov had not noticed at once all that was going on. He had been throwing grenades furiously at the Germans. They had been all ready for him, piled in the lee of the trench right at the entrance to the dugout. He must have thrown at least fifteen, one after the other, before some automatic riflemen from Company Two, hearing the sound of fighting but not guessing that things were going badly at the command post itself, came up to a good position from the flank, and with relative ease and speed cut down some of the Germans who had broken through and forced the others to retreat.

When Maslennikov jumped back into the trench, he saw Anya lying between the two dead soldiers. The second soldier who had thrown himself flat when the grenade fell was also dead. Anya was lying motionless, her cheek pressed awkwardly against the side of the trench. Clutched in her hand was a piece of the wooden handle which had not been dropped even after the grenade had gone off. Maslennikov bent over her, then knelt on his knees and wiped the blood from her face with a handkerchief from his pocket. The blood was coming from a small cut in her forehead, right next to her hair. Maslennikov repeated her name several times but she made no answer, although she was still breathing weakly. Her tunic was ripped in several places and torn completely away at the shoulder and over one breast.

By pure coincidence almost the entire grenade had exploded in the same direction, towards the soldier who had thrown himself down, and he was literally riddled with splinters. Only a few splinters had hit Anya—the little one in her forehead and two in her breast and shoulder.

A light snow was falling into the trench on Anya's face, on her overcoat, on the bare head of Maslennikov, who had snatched off his cap when he first leaned over her. He was still kneeling, and repeatedly, almost soundlessly, saying her name over and over again. In his heart there was an indescribable sadness. He may have stayed there a minute, or perhaps five, and then, still without knowing what he was doing, but fulfilling some instinctive demand within him, he put his arms under Anya's body and lifted her. At this, her head rolled helplessly around, and its uncontrolled movement frightened him. He carried her along the trench, then climbed up on its parapet, took several steps along its top, and descended again into the communications path along which, still holding her in his arms, he went to the dugout.

He placed Anya on his own cot, the same one where she had slept the night before when she had been so tired. For the first time he noticed that her enormous first-aid kit was still hanging across her shoulder. It was the bag which had made Vanin ask her yesterday whether this was really all she had, and Anya had said yes, this was all.

He lifted her head, took off the bag, and laid it under the bed. Then he walked backwards, still looking at Anya, picked up the telephone, and called the chief of staff of the regiment. He told him he had both killed and wounded, that the hospital assistant herself was severely wounded, and that he needed a doctor or another hospital assistant, if this was in any way possible. This was promised him. He hung up the telephone and went out of the dugout to give orders in case the attack should be repeated. But the Germans meanwhile were quiet.

Maslennikov returned to the dugout and sat on the cot beside Anya. Looking at her he noticed that the trickle of blood from the wound on her forehead was again running across her cheek and over her entire face. He took out his handkerchief and wiped away the blood. Then he just sat there, thinking about nothing; he was waiting for a doctor or a nurse to come.

Anya's face was very white and quiet. If it had not been for the wound on her forehead and the dark spots on her tunic, one might have thought that she was sleeping. This calm and the smallness of the wounds frightened Maslennikov, who had often seen ugly, heavily-bleeding wounds which men survived; he knew that an inconspicuous wound, on the other hand, more often killed a man.

He sat there, and as if this could be of help, he wiped the little drops of blood running down her forehead. He thought about how Saburov would come back, and what he would say to him. Then he remembered a present from the People's Commissariat of Defense, sent to him for the November 7 celebration and still lying in his bag. In it there were several bars of chocolate, some biscuits, some powdered milk, and a few other things. He had never touched this because he had planned to make it his present when Saburov and Anya should get married. Then he again thought desperately what he would say to Saburov. The thought came to him: "Maybe all this will pass over, everything will be all right." He listened again to

Anya's breathing. It was faint; she hardly breathed at all. Then he realized that she would probably die—that she would certainly die—and maybe very quickly, even before the doctor's arrival.

Being quiet beside her like this was such a burden for him that he thought for a second about the Germans, and caught himself wishing they would attack again, so he could forget all this, scramble out of here with his gun in his hands, and start shooting. The Germans, as if on purpose, were behaving very quietly. "They always do everything the wrong way," he thought. And the fact that they were not attacking now, when he wanted them to, he added to his score against the Germans. It made him hate them more. The blood still ran in fresh drops across Anya's forehead and he kept on drying them until he noticed that his handkerchief was soaked through. He threw it away, reached into his bag under the cot, and fumbling in it, found a clean handkerchief. Getting up from his knees, he saw the doctor walk into the dugout.

"Where are your wounded?" asked the doctor.

"There," Maslennikov pointed.

"Ah, Klimenko," and the doctor pushed back his sleeve over his watch and took Anya's hand, feeling her pulse, with motions which surprised Maslennikov by their professional calm. Then he unfastened Anya's belt and cut the tunic away from the shoulder so he could examine her wounds. The wound on her breast made him frown. He quickly bandaged her, and looking at Maslennikov's shortsighted, frowning eyes, said: "She needs to be taken away immediately."

"What?" said Maslennikov. "How is she?"

"We'll be able to know definitely only on the operating table," the doctor said. He considered the conversation finished and shouted through the door: "Stretcher-bearers."

Some stretcher-bearers came in.

"Haven't you any other wounded?" he asked Maslennikov.

"No."

"How about yourself?"

"What do you mean, me?"

"You're wounded, too."

"Where?"

"There, on your head."

Maslennikov rubbed his head, and when he took his hand away his palm was red and sticky.

"Well, that's nothing," he said, not because he was brave but because he could feel no pain at all.

"Come on, come on," said the doctor. He walked over to him, took out of his pocket a little bottle of alcohol, wet some cotton, and wiped Maslennikov's forehead and temple.

"Yes, you're right, it's nothing," said the doctor. "Have you a hygiene instructor in the battalion?"

"There should be one somewhere."

"Let him bandage you, or it will get dirty."

During this time the orderlies had placed Anya on a stretcher, and waiting for the doctor, laid it on the floor. Somehow this seemed rude and insulting to Maslennikov, although he had seen wounded placed on the floor or sometimes on the ground dozens of times before. He did not like to see her lying at their feet, on the ground, and so he said to the doctor, who was dawdling a little:

"That's all, then."

"Yes, everything," said the doctor. "Let's go."

When the stretcher-bearers picked up the stretcher, one of Anya's arms dangled helplessly from it. One of them fixed it, lifting it back onto the stretcher.

Maslennikov walked out behind the doctor. The stretcher-bearers had already turned a corner of the trench, and he could see only the back of one of them. For several minutes he continued to stand there in a kind of stupefaction, watching them walk away. Then, suddenly and quite close, he heard rifle fire.

He thought with relief that something was starting again and he would no longer have to think about anything, but only run, command, and shoot. With this thought he jumped out of his trench, ran to the next one, and threw himself beside the machine gunners who were already firing on the attacking Germans.

TWENTY-THREE

SABUROV returned to the dugout immediately after darkness had set in. Maslennikov was there alone, sitting at the table and writing a report. His head was carelessly tied with a bandage which in one spot was soaking wet.

"What's this, are you wounded?" Saburov inquired.

"Just scratched," Maslennikov answered.

"Where is Vanin?" Saburov asked.

"He went to regiment headquarters, to introduce himself to our new commander."

"Ah, yes, we have Remizov there now," Saburov remembered.

"Yes," Maslennikov said. "So he went over to introduce himself." He repeated this, but he did not add that Vanin had been glad of the chance to go, so he could find out at the same time where Anya had been sent.

Behind the curtain Petya was rattling his pots and pans. Saburov and Maslennikov sat across from each other at the table. Neither wanted to talk, neither could talk about what filled his thoughts. Saburov would have liked to tell Maslennikov about the feeling of disaster he had had at four o'clock that day, but he was ashamed of it and did not want to mention it. Maslennikov, who knew that Saburov had not yet been told about Anya's wound or even that she had been here today, was hesitating over whether to tell him or not, and was wondering what would happen if he should say nothing at all.

While they were sitting across from each other, neither making up his mind to speak out, the eyes of both men happened at exactly the same moment to fall on the same object, the bulky first-aid kit lying half under the bed. They looked at it, then at each other, then at it again, and Saburov looked back at Maslennikov.

"Anya's?" he asked. Both his tone and the expression on his face showed Maslennikov that he knew beyond any doubt that the bag belonged to Anya.

"Yes," he said.

"Where is Anya?"

When Maslennikov hesitated a little with his answer, Saburov's heart grew cold. Everything inside him seemed to fall in and leave a kind of emptiness. He realized that this had some direct relation with the feeling he had had earlier in the day, and that now he would learn all about it.

"She was here," Maslennikov said. "She came yesterday, just after you left . . . She was wounded today . . . and taken away." For some reason he repeated the doctor's cold phrase.

"When?"

"At four o'clock."

Saburov was silent, continuing to look at the bag. He did not ask where Anya had been wounded, or whether it was severe or slight. When Maslennikov had said "at four o'clock," he knew that a disaster had happened. He did not want to ask any more.

"She's badly wounded, but the splinters are small," Maslennikov said. It seemed to him that Saburov ought to find it important that she had not been disfigured, but wounded only by small splinters. "In the breast, the shoulder, and here, too. But that one is like mine, only a scratch."

Saburov remained silent and kept on looking at the bag.

"Vanin has gone over to see the colonel. He will probably find out something," Maslennikov continued.

"Good," Saburov said indifferently. "Good. Have you checked the guards?"

"No, I haven't checked them."

"Be sure to do it."

"I'll go at once," Maslennikov said in a hurry, thinking that Saburov wanted to be alone.

"No, why at once?" Saburov said. "You can do it later when you've finished the report."

"No, I'll go now."

"Well, just as you like," said Saburov.

Maslennikov went out and Saburov continued to sit in silence. He realized clearly that, regardless of what Vanin might say when he came back, an enormous misfortune had occurred in his life. After sitting for several minutes, he went over to Maslennikov's bed and sat on it. He noticed a blood stain on the blanket and thought they had probably put Anya down here. Then he turned to the bag, lifted it, and placed it on the bed. He did all this without hurrying. He felt that now this great disaster had taken place there was no reason to hurry, he would have time for everything. He slowly opened the bag and looked for several minutes at what was in it. Then, just as slowly, he began to take everything out, one thing after another. The bag was crammed to the top. In one section were a neatly folded garrison cap, a toothbrush and soap, two towels, one handkerchief, a broken mirror. In another section were surgical supplies. These he did not touch. Then he took out two new, green shoulder straps with enamel cubes sewed on them to show Anya's rank, and a little round wooden box which he opened. It held needles and thread. He closed it again.

Next to this box lay another, also round, made of metal. In it there was lipstick. He wondered why it was there, for Anya had never used lipstick. The last things he took from the bag were two soldiers' shirts, big ones, not her size. One of them had its sleeves sewed back just as her overcoat had been that time when he had met her in the trench, and kissed her wrists where they had been rubbed sore. It occurred to him that this had been the last time he had seen her, and that now he would never see her again. He fell face down on all the things he had strewn across the cot and cried, no longer aware of anything around him.

When Vanin ran into the dugout from Remizov's, about a half hour later, Saburov was sitting at the table in his usual pose, leaning his back against the wall and stretching out his legs. On his face there was no expression of sadness or suffering. He greeted Vanin with a serious and attentive look. It was the look of a man who has lost something without which he could not imagine living, but who still had decided to go on living.

Vanin went up to the table and sat down across from Saburov. Neither spoke for a moment.

"Well, what did you find out?" Saburov asked. Vanin understood that he did not expect a good answer.

"The wound is severe. They only bandaged it here and sent her across to the other side."

"Do you mean the Volga has finally frozen?" Saburov said.

"Yes, it's frozen. Today they are sending across the first wounded."

"I see," Saburov said. "Well, that's that," and he was silent again.

Then Vanin, all at once, suddenly, and in spite of himself, began to pour out all the phrases that are usually said in such situations. Angry at himself for doing so but in no condition to control himself, he made all the unnecessary comments: that it was nothing, that it would all pass, that the wounds, of course, were serious, but not dangerous; let a month go by and they would see Anya again, yes, yes—here he clapped Saburov cheerfully on the shoulder—everything was in order and here —at this point he banged his hand on the table—here they would celebrate the wedding.

From the expression on Saburov's face, he might have been expected several times to interrupt Vanin. But he said nothing. He listened and was silent. When Vanin finally dried up under this glance and stopped talking, Saburov's expression did not change, so little difference did it make to him whether he was being talked to or not, or whether he was being consoled or not. When Vanin had finally stopped, Saburov only repeated again: "Well, that's that."

Then he took off his boots, lay down on the cot, and without pretending that he was sleeping stayed there quietly, making no move. He lay with his eyes open and recalled the entire day, remorselessly and in every detail, this day during which—who knows—perhaps nothing would have happened if he had been here the whole time and not a hundred meters away.

It was at about this time that two orderlies were carrying Anya on a stretcher across the Volga. Beyond an island, which broke the current of the river, the ice was thicker, and they had already set up a sledge road, but across the first part of the river to the island, almost a kilometer, they were carrying all the wounded on stretchers today over ice which was not yet quite solid. The Volga had stopped running only the day before. The Germans did not think that anything could yet be moved or carried across it, and over the river stood a strange silence. Everything around was white and motionless and only the snow, which was still falling, squeaked a little under the boots of the stretcher-bearers.

They had to carry her a long way. The bearers put the

stretcher down carefully on the ice several times and stood for a little while clapping their frozen hands, then thrust them back in their mittens and picked up the stretcher again. From the other shore toward the file of wounded moved a line of people sent from the rear of the division to mark the route for a sledge road for tomorrow, and to find where the ice was hardest. They walked along, stamping their feet, and testing the ice under their heels. One of them, a tall soldier, no longer young, came up close to the stretcher on which Anya was lying, and stopped.

"What is this, one of the nurses wounded?" he asked the orderlies. Turning around, he walked several steps with them.

"Yes," said an orderly.

"Did they get her badly?"

"Badly," the orderly said. "You wouldn't have something to smoke?"

"Yes," the soldier said.

The orderlies put down the stretcher and the soldier handed them each a pinch of tobacco with frozen, unbending fingers. They began to roll themselves cigarettes.

"What did you put her down for? Won't she freeze?"

"Never mind, we'll thaw her out in a minute," said the orderly. "Why do you ask, do you know her?"

"She crossed with us once, before the river froze," the soldier said. "She was a good nurse, only still very young."

"She's very young," the orderly agreed.

Covering their cigarettes with their hands, each of them took a light from the soldier's cigarette, also cupped in his hand.

"How I wanted to smoke!" the orderly said. Then both of them, after they had inhaled deeply several times, carefully put out their cigarettes, tucked them in the folds of their caps, and picked up the stretcher again.

"She's hurt badly then?" the soldier said.

"Pretty badly," the orderly said.

"She's just a young one, too," the soldier said, and turning around, walked toward the Stalingrad shore.

The stretcher-bearers carried Anya farther. When they had almost reached the island where the sledge road began, Anya suddenly recovered consciousness, perhaps from the cold, perhaps from the light squeaking and the swaying motion. She opened her eyes and saw the black sky above her, and around her; out of the sides of her eyes she saw that everything was white, nothing but white. In the first second she realized that the Volga had frozen and that she was being carried across it. But then her thoughts began to grow confused and it seemed to her it was not she who was being carried but that she was carrying someone and saying, as she always said: "Gently, brother, we'll be there right away."

In actual fact it was not she who was saying this but the orderlies who had just heard the droning of a German airplane. They were saying: "We'll be there right away," trying to reassure each other, but it seemed to her that she was saying it, and in her thoughts she tried to carry the stretcher more carefully so that it wouldn't bounce so much. Then it seemed to her that it was Saburov who was lying on the stretcher and that it was to him she was saying: "Brother," but that she did not yet know him and that he did not know who she was. Then she wanted to explain to him and she said something, but he was not listening. So she said something more. At this point her thoughts became completely confused and she lost consciousness again.

"My, how she's groaning, the poor girl," the orderly said.

Meanwhile the airplane had circled several times over the river and dropped a flare rocket which made everything suddenly white and clear. After the rocket came the bombs. They fell to the right and to the left of the people carrying stretchers. The rocket had not yet gone out; on the ice there could be seen enormous black holes, and the water, welling up through them, covered more and more of the ice around them. When the bombs first landed, the orderlies had dropped the stretcher on the ice and thrown themselves flat on the ground; then when some more bombs exploded and the airplane began to drone again in new circles over them, they stood up without a word, picked up the stretcher, and strode on, between the holes, with the heavy steps of men who are hurrying.

When they had come almost to the island, someone shouted out in front of them: "This way with the stretchers." Behind a snowdrift, at the place where the first sledge road began, could be heard the squeaking of wooden runners on the snow and the neighing of horses.

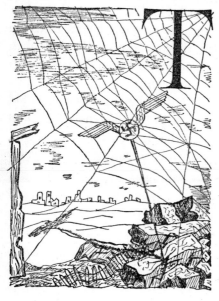

TWENTY-FOUR

HICK November darkness stood over the steppes beyond the Volga. From five o'clock, when it grew dark, it was impossible to tell what time it was—evening, midnight, or five o'clock in the morning—because the night, lasting almost fourteen hours, stayed dark and impenetrable the entire time. The cold wind sang across the steppe, and as if making up for the long time that the fields had been bare, snow fell at first thinly, then grew steadily deeper. Almost without interruption the wheels of trucks and the steel treads of half-tracks squeaked on the rolled and frozen crust on top of the snow, and at every crossroads military traffic police swung their flashlights silently.

It was all the same and unbroken; hour was like hour and day like day. Only someone standing on one of these roads, leading to Stalingrad from Saratov, from Eltonskaya, from Kamyshin, for an entire day or for two days, could have understood the scale of this monotony, and the ominous calm and quiet of what was going on during these days along the roads behind the front. It was like what had happened a year before, in November, 1941, when endless echelons of artillery, tanks, and infantry had moved up to Moscow, and as if at the stroke of a magician's wand, had disappeared into the forests around Moscow before reaching the blood-drenched front. It was just like this here. From the last days of October, night after night, at first through mud and then through snow, across dirt, through snowstorms, on the slippery ice, troops were on the move. Great covered trucks were rolling up, gigantic cannon from the reserve of the High Command, shrouded in canvas, squat T-34 tanks and little antitank guns, bumping along on trailers behind the trucks.

Sometimes a flare was dropped from a German airplane, blasting out of the darkness of the night a round white spot in which the trucks scattered to the sides of the road, men ran and threw themselves to the ground, and bombs roared down with a tremendous racket into the mud and snow. Then everything would become black again and traffic on the road would be held up for a few minutes until pieces of shattered truck had been cleared away and the dead pulled to one side. Then the crawling, rolling, and moving would begin again in the same direction. One part of all this was going from Kamyshin and Saratov, across the Volga, into the steppes and wooded valleys north of Stalingrad. This was going where the soldiers stood, facing southward some twenty kilometers from Stalingrad, holding the Germans from moving north along the Volga. Another part of the weapons, men, and tanks were moving from Eltonskaya straight to the Volga and hiding themselves somewhere in the windings of the Middle, Lower, and Upper Akhtuba Rivers, filtering out from there to the south into the steppes beyond the Volga.

In this enormous movement of people, machines, and guns, in the way they all moved together, and in the fact that they all stopped dead before they got to Stalingrad, could be felt the will and the fortitude which had already been shown a year before near Moscow.

When at critical moments the commander of the Stalingrad

army and Matveyev, member of its military council, asked several times for reinforcements from those in charge of the entire front, they were refused each time, and refused absolutely. The divisions fighting in Stalingrad were supported from the left bank of the Volga only by generous artillery fire, and by the mortar regiments which were being concentrated there in constantly greater numbers. Only twice in the very grimmest days of fighting did the staff of the front, with the permission of the High Command, release a division of troops. These divisions were thrown into Stalingrad straight from their march towards the front.

On the same night when Saburov was lying quietly in his dugout, and when two orderlies were carrying Anya across the Volga over the thin ice, Matveyev was making a wide detour on foot along the Volga to reach Protsenko's dugout, to have a long conversation with him behind closed doors, or at least behind two tightly-drawn dugout curtains.

That same evening Matveyev had returned from front headquarters on the other shore, and Protsenko was the second divisional commander he was to visit during the night. When Matveyev had been summoned to the staff headquarters of the entire front the day before, he had gone there determined to describe the full hopelessness of his situation and to request reinforcements once more. He had gone to front headquarters firmly determined to ask for a division, and to ask for it as something absolutely essential. Although he anticipated the usual refusal, at least at first, he believed that this time his own arguments would prove to be unanswerable.

Everything had worked out quite differently. The commander of the front and the member of his military council had listened quietly at first to his report and then to his request, and contrary to their usual custom, they did not immediately say either yes or no. After a long pause they had looked at each other, and the member of the military council of the front had hitched his chair nearer to the table on which an open map of the front was lying. He had placed both hands on it, as if directing Matveyev's attention to it, and then he had said:

"We don't want to turn you down, Comrade Matveyev, for what you're asking, because you're asking for something you're entitled to. But we would like very much to have you withdraw your request yourself. In order to do that, you'll have to—not understand, because perhaps this can't be understood yet in its entirety—but feel, at any rate, even feel just a little bit, what lies ahead of us."

He had looked closely at Matveyev, and on his severe but at the same time good and open face there was the smile of a man who knew something that was making him unbelievably happy.

"If we should tell you, Comrade Matveyev, that we haven't got a division to give you, or even two divisions, we wouldn't be telling the truth. We have them."

Matveyev had thought this was the usual prelude to what was always said in such situations, the prelude to telling him that there were divisions, of course, but that they had to be held in reserve; that besides Stalingrad, and despite all its importance, there was still an enormous front from the Black Sea to the White Sea, and that all this front could be defended only if free divisions were always available.

But the member of the military council of the front had not said any of this to Matveyev, but only moved his two hands on the map in such a way that Matveyev had to pay attention to their movement. He stopped one hand to the south, and the other to the north of Stalingrad, then he moved them both forward and far beyond Stalingrad, to where on the map Serafimovich, Kalach, and other cities stood on the Don—and then with a decisive gesture he brought his hands together.

"Look," he had said, and in his voice at this minute there had been something very solemn. "Look," he had repeated.

Matveyev remembered this word and this movement of his

hands across the map so clearly and so precisely that he often thought about them later, when he was talking to other people and when he was alone, and especially when everything finally happened that this word and this movement of two hands had told him.

"Do you think so?" he had asked with emotion.

"Yes, I think so," the member of the military council had said. "That's all I can tell you now," he had added after a pause, "to make you feel this yourself, and in the bad days which remain, to help you make your people feel not our plans, of course, but—well—just the words 'there will be a parade on our street, too.'* Maybe those words don't refer to any distant future. Well . . . now let's get back to your request for a division. You're telling us, I take it, that in order to hold on you've absolutely got to have a division?"

"No, we are not putting the question that way," Matveyev had said.

"Well, all right, but you still need it?"

"No, we are not asking for it," Matveyev had said.

It was with this feeling which had made him refuse a division without even consulting the commander of his army that Matveyev had come back to army headquarters, spoken to the commanding general, and then set out to visit the divisions. He took on himself the difficult job of getting in a single night to both the divisions which were cut off from the main forces. He was already tired and frozen by the time he had visited the first and gone on to Protsenko.

Protsenko was very glad to see him come. For the last week he had been able to get in touch with the commander of the

---

* From the Order of the Day of the People's Commissar of Defense, Joseph V. Stalin, No. 375, Moscow, November 7, 1942. Stalin used a Russian idiom which in the Soviet Information Bureau text of the order reads: "It will be our turn to rejoice." As with many idioms for which there is no equivalent in English, an important part of the meaning is sacrificed in this official translation, and therefore the literal meaning of the phrase is used here.

army by telephone only a few times and with difficulty, and now when he reported in detail to Matveyev about everything that had gone on recently in his division he felt that he was shifting a part of the burden from his own shoulders to those of Matveyev.

Matveyev listened carefully to everything Protsenko told him, and he asked several questions which all led up to one: how many days could Protsenko hold out with the forces he already had? Protsenko understood. They would not give him one man more. Then Matveyev moved his arm as if to sweep to one side everything they had been talking about until now, and asked Protsenko how he had understood Stalin's phrase that there would be a parade on our street, too.

At this unexpected question Protsenko looked straight at Matveyev and suddenly caught in his shining, black eyes that quickening excitement which comes to people in war when they cannot tell others, but know themselves, that something is impending, very good and very important.

"I understand those words like this," Protsenko said, talking in his excitement with an even heavier Ukrainian accent than usual. "I figure it this way: the fact that Comrade Stalin said it on November 7 means that it should happen soon. In any case, before February."

"Why before February?" Matveyev asked.

"Because if it were going to be after February he would have said it on Red Army Day, on February 23, and if it were going to be after May then he would have said it on May Day. Words like those you don't say ahead of time."

He looked expectantly at Matveyev and realized from the look that answered his that Matveyev had the same opinion on this score.

"Well, how about it? Am I right or not?" Protsenko said.

"Right, in my opinion," Matveyev answered. "We've only got to hang on."

"Hang on?" Protsenko asked as if these words carried some insult. "I, Comrade Member of the Military Council, do not expect to see the moment when a German will be here where you and I are sitting. I do not expect to see that moment because while I'm still alive it just won't happen."

Matveyev's frown was hardly noticeable; Protsenko's words seemed to him a little too eloquent, as if they had been prepared beforehand.

"And even if you think," Protsenko said, guessing the other's thoughts, "even if you think that what I'm saying sounds too eloquent, still I can't say it any other way. It just is so. And not one of my officers could say anything else."

Protsenko understood what Matveyev had tried to tell him, without going into any details. On his own initiative he turned the conversation to technical subjects. He forgot about the reinforcements which he was waiting for and about the two battalions of antitank guns which he had decided in advance, a week before, to ask for from army headquarters. The technical questions were the supply of ammunition—and Matveyev promised this; more night flights by U-2 airplanes—and Matveyev promised this also; and finally his need for a few more officers—and Matveyev refused this flatly and decisively.

Matveyev was pleased that the stubborn and cunning Protsenko had shown himself tonight cunning enough to understand at once why Matveyev had come to him, but not so stubborn as to cross-examine him on details. For this reason, although it was already time for him to start back, Matveyev gladly agreed to stay a little and to drink two big mugs of strong, almost black tea. Protsenko, who was fond of talking big, told him for some reason that it was Ceylon tea, made from the flower, not the leaf.

"Well, I don't mind if it's made from the flowers," Matveyev said cheerfully. "The chief thing is that it's hot."

Then Protsenko accompanied Matveyev a little way along the shore, and after he had returned ordered Vostrikov to give him the map. Vostrikov handed him the chart drawn by the division staff. This chart showed the five city blocks in which the division had been stationed recently.

"The map, not the chart," Protsenko said with irritation.

Then Vostrikov brought him a printed map of Stalingrad on which the sixty-five kilometer length of the city was outlined, with its suburbs and outskirts stretched thin along the arc of the Volga.

This time Protsenko laughed out loud: "No, not this map. The big map. Haven't you still got it?"

"What big one?"

"The big one, the map of the whole front."

"Ah . . . that one."

Vostrikov rummaged for several minutes, searching for the map, which they had not taken out for a long time. Just because Vostrikov had to look for it so diligently, Protsenko thought how tightly he had riveted all his thoughts on Stalingrad in recent weeks, and how little he had thought about all the rest. Two long months had gone by since he had even taken out the map of the entire front.

When Vostrikov spread the map before him on the table, with its old notations dating from September, Protsenko smoothed it out with his hands, bent over it, and began to think. He began to look for the cities, the rivers, and the lines of earlier positions, and a feeling grew in him that he was somehow escaping into freedom from these buildings, these city squares, from Stalingrad. Only when he saw the tremendous scale of the map did he really understand what Stalingrad meant. Even if it were only a point on this big map, all the other cities and all the people in them had lived through the last two months just because of this litle dot—Stalingrad—and partly just because of these five city squares and the dugout in which he was now sitting. He looked at the map with new interest. Both his hands moved automatically across it with the same movement as those of the member of the military council of the front, and in the same way they came together, somewhere in the west, far beyond Stalingrad.

There was in this movement, obviously, not only coincidence but a kind of logic, because in war the great decisions and the huge strategic plans are always logical necessities in their essence, understandable to everyone and as clear as daylight in the simplicity which is born in them of the iron logic of facts correctly understood.

At five o'clock in the morning, not long before dawn, Protsenko summoned all his regiment and battalion commanders. He timed his summons so that they could get back to their jobs while it was still dark. During the night, at last, sleds had been dragged across the ice on the Volga with provisions and vodka. In Protsenko's snug dugout the big table where the maps usually lay was covered with newspapers on which stood flasks of vodka, and instead of glasses, neatly trimmed American tin cans. On two platters were thick slices of sausage and warmed-up canned meat and potatoes. In the center stood a plate on which Protsenko's cook, determined to excel himself, had fashioned an elaborate structure out of butter with little curls and rosebuds.

Protsenko was sitting in his usual place, in the corner. It was hot in the dugout. The general was wearing a clean dress uniform pulled out of his bag; the tunic was unbuttoned and under it could be seen a fresh white silk shirt. All night long they had been boiling water for Protsenko, and an hour before the arrival of his guests he had taken a bath here in the dugout in a child's zinc bathtub in which he had bathed more than once before, without ever admitting it to anyone except Vostrikov. Protsenko sat there literally steaming with good humor, feeling the pleasant freshness of the clean silk cloth against his skin.

The whole setting, the crowded, neat dugout, its long table, and the host sitting with his tunic unbuttoned—all this made Remizov think of the sea and the wardroom of a little ship.

386

When he came in, he greeted Protsenko and said: "Comrade General, this is just like being at sea."

"Why at sea?"

"It's as snug here as in a cabin."

They all arrived at almost the same time. Remizov got there at six sharp, with the punctuality of an old soldier; the others came a couple of minutes early or a few a little late. Saburov arrived last, five minutes late; in the communications trench he had stumbled, hurting his knee, and he had had to limp the rest of the way.

"Ah, Alexei Ivanovich," Protsenko said.

"Forgive me for being late, Comrade General," Saburov excused himself.

"Never mind," Protsenko said. "Your penalty will be an extra drink."

"Sit down here," Remizov said, moving over on his stool, "take half of this with me."

When Saburov sat down, Remizov put his left arm around him to make him more comfortable and added: "That's the way people get along, when they're close together."

"Well, comrades, pour yourselves a drink, please," Protsenko said.

When vodka had been poured for each of them, there was a little pause. Then Protsenko said:

"I haven't brought you here for a conference, but simply to meet with each other, and to look each other in the eye. Maybe we won't all live through to the happy hour" (the words "happy hour" sounded unexpectedly solemn); "perhaps we won't all live through to the happy hour," he repeated, "so I wanted us all to gather here to look at each other and to feel sure that every one of us will stand to the end. Even if not every man of us, still the division will live through until the happy hour. Our first drink tonight," he said, standing up, and all the others stood up with him, "we will drink to there being, and soon, a parade on our street, too." In this phrase, which had been quoted by many people in the last few weeks, and in the way he said it, there was something especially solemn.

After the first toast there was a little silence. They all ate like wolves, for during the last few days the provisions situation had been bad and the only reason people had not noticed they were hungry was because they were too tired. Then the second toast was proposed, which was traditional in every division with self-respect, the toast to the day when it might be made a Guards Division.* After this, they all drank as they liked, each making separate toasts with his neighbors.

Protsenko joked a good deal, and was warm and cordial to everyone. Although he wanted several times to turn first to one, then to another officer with some concrete question which suddenly occurred to him, he restrained himelf. He did not want to break the general atmosphere of solemnity and friendly hospitality.

Saburov sat next to Remizov, directly across from Protsenko, and was able to watch the general all evening. He had known Protsenko a long time and very well, and he could see something in the general's eyes which was perhaps not so noticeable to the others. From the way Protsenko talked and carried himself, everyone felt his belief in the future and in the fact that everything would turn out well for them in the long run. But besides this Saburov saw in Protsenko's eyes, in some of his movements, in an expression on his face, that Protsenko not only knew everything would be all right, but had also guessed how this would happen. Several times Saburov noticed that Protsenko would begin a sentence, as if he wanted to say something important, and then stop in the middle and change the conversation to another subject. It seemed to Saburov that

---

* In the first year of the war, the Russians revived the term "Guards" for units which distinguished themselves in battle. The term was originally introduced by Peter the Great, and abandoned in 1917. Soldiers in Guards units receive double pay, new unit flags, and tremendous public acclaim; they are the shock troops of the Red Army.

Protsenko badly wanted to say something he alone knew, and that he was controlling himself with difficulty.

When the time came to leave, Protsenko again looked around the officers sitting at the table. "There sits Remizov," he thought. "Before him his regiment was commanded by Popov, and he's dead. Before Popov, it was Babchenko, and he's dead, too. There sits Annenski; he may be a little weak to command a regiment, but just the same he's gone through the whole school of siege and his regiment has gone through it, too, and he knows how to command. There sits Saburov, not knowing what I know about him: that if, may God prevent it, they kill Remizov, or wound him, or Annenski, or Ogurtsov, then I, if I myself am still alive by then, will without any question make Saburov commander of a regiment. And none of these men sitting here know what fate will befall them in this war, whom they will command, where they will be fighting, under the walls of what cities they will find their death, if they have to find it."

There was something magnificent and deeply moving to Protsenko in this picture. He was feeling it for the first time after months of being burdened with big and little affairs, orders, reports, lists, and all the daily complications of war. He felt it as he looked at his officers gathered around the table, tired men already grown gray with experience and misfortune. It was a feeling that made his back grow cold and put a lump in his throat. This is something, he thought, that men will later write about in history books; it is a feeling to be envied by generations to come who will not have experienced it in their own lives.

He wanted to say in farewell some special and impressive words but, as often happens with Russian people, he could not find these words to save himself at this minute, just as he had never been able to find them at the other decisive and, perhaps, most beautiful moments of his life. So he simply stood up and said: "Well, that's that, my friends. It's time. There'll be fighting to do in the morning."

389

They all stood up. He shook each man's hand as they went out. He held back only Saburov.

"Sit down a minute, Alexei Ivanovich," he said. "You can go in a minute."

Protsenko wanted to find out whether the officers had understood what he had tried to tell them, and so he asked Saburov: "Did you understand me, Alexei Ivanovich? Did you understand me?"

"I understood, Comrade General," said Saburov. "I am eager to live until that moment."

"That's it exactly, that's it exactly," said Protsenko. "I, too, want terribly to live until then. From tomorrow on, I'm going to duck my head more often when I walk along a trench. That's how much I want to go on living now. And I advise you to do the same."

For a moment both were silent.

"Would you like to smoke?" Protsenko asked, offering Saburov a cigarette.

"Thanks."

They both began to smoke. "Remizov told me," Protsenko said, "about your bad luck. I sent a man to the rear today and I ordered him to find out on the way what hospital she's in and how she is. So that you don't lose track of her."

"Thank you, Comrade General," Saburov said in a voice that sounded almost indifferent. The general's solicitude touched him deeply. He was not worried over finding Anya, because he knew that if she were alive he would find her sooner or later, beyond any doubt. But was she alive? Compared with this terrifying and unanswered question, what Protsenko had been talking about did not worry him at all.

"Thank you very much, Comrade General," he repeated. Then he broke the rules by standing up first. He shook Protsenko's hand firmly, and forgetting even to say the traditional phrase: "May I go?" he turned and walked quickly out of the dugout.

TWENTY-FIVE

LTHOUGH it is often said that grief and suffering make time go slowly, the first three days after Anya's injury went by as furiously for Saburov as all days in Stalingrad. When he tried later to remember how he had felt during those days, he could sometimes remember only the fighting and sometimes, on the contrary, it seemed to him his heart had been filled only with a sense of what he had lost. Actually both were true, but the feeling of loss was so constant in those days, never leaving him, that its very monotony made him forget at moments that it was there at all.

Saburov returned from the meeting at Protsenko's to his battalion with a feeling that it was urgent to do something big in the next few days, something he would remember all his life. What they had already done and what they had still to do did not seem heroic. The men defending Stalingrad had developed an unfailing and stubborn resistant strength which grew out of many different reasons: because the longer they fought the more impossible it became to retreat; because to retreat now meant to die uselessly while you were retreating; because the nearness of the enemy and the unceasing danger gave some of them an actual taste for danger and others a feeling that it was inescapable; and finally because all of them, crowded on this little piece of ground, had grown to know each other, with all their vices and their virtues, better than anywhere else on the front. All these circumstances together gradually created that stubborn force which came to be called "the men of Stalingrad." The heroic strength of this phrase was understood throughout the country, all around them, much earlier than it was in Stalingrad itself.

No man in his own heart can ever believe in the endlessness of anything. Everything must come to an end some time. Saburov was like all those who were then in Stalingrad: he did not know concretely and could not even guess when this siege would end, but he never imagined that it would go on forever. From that night at Protsenko's, when he sensed rather than understood that something big was going to happen not in months, but in weeks or perhaps even in days, this feeling that the end might come soon, and with victory, gave him new strength.

Saburov described his supper at Protsenko's to Vanin and Maslennikov and then at dawn he left them at the command post and went out himself to the companies. The number of men in his battalion was no longer large and he made a point of trying to talk to every soldier, to infect them all with some of the feeling of approaching victory which he had himself.

Fighting went on all day. It was as if the Germans had agreed by their behavior on this day to confirm the hunch Saburov felt within himself. They bombed and fired with a kind of special planlessness, they attacked often and in a hurry, as if afraid that what they did not seize today they would not be able to seize tomorrow. It seemed to Saburov like the last convulsions of a seriously wounded beast.

But today and the days that followed seemed on the surface as they had before: the fighting continued with unabated fury, the Germans seized the area four times between Konyukov's building and the positions of Company Two, and four times were driven back from it. Saburov behaved with his usual caution; he lay down when shells went off, he hid behind stones when an enemy sniper's bullets began to fly around him, and he sat out bombings under cover. His grief did not make him go out and take unnecessary risks. This had always been alien to him, and it was alien now. He wanted to live, most of all because he expected victory, impatiently and with conviction. He expected victory in the most exact and definite sense of the word. He was waiting for the moment when he could take back from the Germans that nearest piece of ground, that building they had given up a week before, and the ruins just beyond it which people still called a street out of old habit, and then the next block, and then another street—in a word, everything within his field of vision.

And when they added up the results of the day and talked about how two more soldiers had been killed and seven, or eleven, wounded; or about how they needed to move two machine-guns on the left flank from the ruined transformer building into the cellar of the garage; or about whether it would be good, perhaps, to appoint Sergeant Buslayev to take the place of Lieutenant Fedin who had been killed; or about how the battalion, as a result of its losses, was receiving twice as much vodka as it was entitled to and how this was a good thing—let them drink, because it's cold; or about how the watchmaker Mazin had broken his arm yesterday so that if Saburov's undamaged watch, now the last one in the battalion, should stop there would be no one to fix it; or about how fed up they were with eating porridge every day—it would be wonderful if they could only bring something else across the Volga, even frozen potatoes; or about how they should recommend this soldier or that one for a medal while he was still alive and fighting, and not later, when it might be too late; in other words, when they talked every day about the things they had always talked about it was still true. The feeling that great and surprising events hung over them did not disappear for Saburov nor did it grow less strong.

Did he think about Anya during these days? No, he did not think of her, but he felt a pain in his heart which did not go away. Whatever he did, this pain continued all the time somewhere inside him. He felt convinced that if she had died, and he was almost sure she had died, there would never again be any kind of love in his life.

Saburov began to watch himself, something he had never thought of doing before. Just because sorrow was heavy in him, he often looked himself over and asked himself whether he was doing everything as he had done it before, and if there were not something in his behavior to which his sorrow had driven him, something that had changed him. He tried to overcome his suffering, and to carry himself just as he always had.

On the fourth night, Saburov had received from regiment headquarters Konyukov's Order and several medals for men in his garrisons, and he crept through again to Konyukov's building to award these decorations. As happened rarely in Stalingrad, every man destined to receive one was alive and well. Konyukov asked Saburov to pin on his Order for him because his left hand hung limp as a whip. His wrist had been cut by a grenade splinter. When Saburov had cut a little hole in Konyukov's tunic, soldier-fashion with a pocket knife, and had begun to fasten on the Order, Konyukov said, standing at attention:

"I think, Comrade Captain, that when we attack them, the best way to go would be straight through my building. They've got me here in siege, but from here we could jump them hard. How does that seem to you as a plan, Comrade Captain?"

"Wait a while," Saburov said, "the time will come, and we'll do it."

394

"But is the plan all right, Comrade Captain?" asked Konyukov. "What do you think?"

"It sounds all right to me," Saburov said, thinking to himself that if an attack should come off, Konyukov's simple plan might actually prove to be the most correct.

"Straight through my building and jump them," Konyukov repeated. "With complete surprise."

He used the words "my building" often and with great satisfaction. It was obvious that the soldiers' grapevine had brought him rumors that this building was now officially called on staff maps "Konyukov's building," and he was immensely proud of this.

"The Germans are still trying to kick us out," Konyukov said as Saburov prepared to go. "Things have come to a sorry pass: they beat up a landlord in his own house," and he laughed as he pointed to his wounded hand. "It was such a little splinter, but it went right across the bone. The fingers don't move at all . . . So you report to the top command, Comrade Captain, that when an attack comes off they should make it through my building." Konyukov repeated this again as he said good-by to Saburov. This certainty of an offensive in the future, as real in Konyukov's mind as in Protsenko's, strengthened to an even greater degree Saburov's own feeling that this was what would happen.

When Saburov came back from Konyukov, it was almost morning. Vanin was out with the companies and Maslennikov was sitting at the table although he had no work to do and could have gone to sleep. The last few days he had tried to go everywhere with Saburov. That night he had told Saburov that he would go with him to see Konyukov. Saburov had turned him down flatly and he had to stay behind. So Maslennikov sat and worried. Although it was as clear as daylight that he could not defend Saburov, nor protect him from a splinter or a bullet, still it had become almost an emotional necessity for Maslennikov to be near him during these days.

Saburov walked in silently, nodded to Maslennikov, and just as quietly pulled off his boots and his blouse and lay down on the cot.

"Do you want to smoke?" Maslennikov asked.

"I'd like to."

Maslennikov handed him a cigarette case with tobacco. Saburov rolled himself a cigarette and lit it. He had noticed and he was grateful for the sensitive and tactful silence which Maslennikov observed, a rare gift which comes only from sincere friends at times of unhappiness. Maslennikov asked him about nothing and never tried to comfort him, at the same time reminding him all the time by his quiet presence that he was not alone in his sorrow.

Saburov suddenly felt a surge of tenderness towards this man sitting beside him. For the first time during these last days he thought with pleasure about something after the war, when they would meet somewhere far from here. It would be in some quite different building, they would be dressed entirely differently, and they would recall everything that had happened in this hole in the ground under five layers of cover, in these cold trenches, under the snow. These tin cans would suddenly become memories to be cherished, and these Stalingrad "Katyusha" lamps, and all the discomforts of trench life, and even the dangers which would be behind them. He sat on the cot, stretched out his hand to Maslennikov, and grasping him firmly by the shoulder pulled him toward himself.

"Mishenka."

"What?" said Maslennikov.

"Nothing," said Saburov. "Nothing. We'll see each other again sometime, you know, and we'll have something to remember, no?"

"Of course, we'll remember," Maslennikov said after a short

396

silence, "that here we sat on the 18th of November around an iron stove in Stalingrad and smoked this foul makhorka."

"November 18th?" Saburov said in surprise. "Is today really the 18th of November?"

"Yes."

"That's strange, I quite forgot."

"What did you forget?"

"If today is the 18th of November, it means I'm thirty years old."

"Are you really thirty?" Maslennikov asked. It seemed to him that thirty years was very old indeed.

"Thirty, Mishenka, thirty," Saburov repeated.

"Well, how shall we celebrate your birthday?" Maslennikov asked.

"How?" said Saburov. "Here's how: we'll sit here and keep quiet."

He went on sitting on the cot, rocking back and forth and blowing rings of smoke one after another. He was thirty years old and here they were in their dugout, and after all that had gone on around him now for seventy days he had still survived to be thirty, and Anya was not here, and he did not even know whether she was alive. He sat for a long time and said nothing. Then he lay down on the cot and suddenly, almost at once, fell fast asleep with his hand hanging from the cot, still holding the cigarette which had gone out.

He slept perhaps an hour, perhaps an hour and a half. When the telephone woke him it was quite dark, and through the pipe which ran through the wall of the dugout to serve as window not a single ray of daylight came. Saburov stumbled in his bare feet across the dirt floor to the telephone:

"Captain Saburov speaking."

"This is Protsenko. What are you doing, sleeping?"

"Yes, I was asleep."

"Well, get up as fast as you can and put on your boots." In Protsenko's voice excitement could be heard. "Go outside and listen."

"What's happened, Comrade General?"

"Never mind, call me back later. Report to me, whether you heard it or not. And wake up your men. Let them listen."

Saburov looked at his watch: It was six o'clock in the morning. He hurriedly drew on his boots and without putting on his tunic, and in his shirt, he ran out into the open.

From six to seven in the morning at Stalingrad was usually the hour which came closest to being quiet. Sometimes for fifteen or twenty minutes there would not be a single volley of artillery from either side, with only occasional rifle shots to be heard or the dull thump in the distance of a random shell.

When Saburov ran out of the dugout, snow was falling, dropping a heavy white shroud over everything beyond a few paces from him. It occurred to him that he must strengthen the guards. Protsenko's unexpected telephone call had made him anticipate something extraordinary but at first he could hear nothing. It was cold, and the snow fell inside the unbuttoned collar of his shirt. He stood there for a minute or two until he heard, very far in the distance, a kind of unbroken rumbling. The rumbling seemed to come from his right, from the north. There was shooting far away, perhaps thirty or forty kilometers from here, but the sound carried all the way, and in spite of the distance it seemed to shake the earth with little tremors. It produced a feeling that wherever the noise was coming from something monstrous was going on, unheard of in its size, a kind of hell of firing that no one had ever seen or heard before. By this time Saburov no longer felt the cold and he stood there listening, sometimes brushing off with his hand the snowflakes dropping on his eyelashes.

"Is this really it?" he thought, and he turned to the soldier standing next to him. "Do you hear anything?"

"Why, what do you mean, Comrade Captain? Of course I hear it. It's ours."

"What makes you think it's ours?"

"You can tell by its voice."

"Has it been going on long?"

"For about an hour," the soldier said. "And it never lets up."

Saburov walked quickly back into the dugout and woke up Maslennikov, then Vanin who had come back from the companies a short time before and was sleeping in his boots and overcoat.

"Get up, get up," Saburov said in the same excited voice that Protsenko had used five minutes before.

"What is it? What's happened?" asked Maslennikov pulling on his boots.

"What's happened?" Saburov said. "An awful lot's happened. Go outside and listen."

"Listen to what?"

"Just listen. Let's talk later."

Vanin, who was already dressed, ran out with Maslennikov, half-dressed, stumbling after him. When they had left, Saburov asked the telephone operator to get him Protsenko.

"Hello," he heard Protsenko's voice over the telephone.

"Comrade General, I am reporting: I heard it," Saburov said.

"Ah . . . everyone's heard it. I woke them all up. It's started, old man, it's started. I shall see again the Ukraine where I was born, I'll stand on Vladimir Hill in Kiev. Can you believe it?"

"I believe it," Saburov said.

As long as Saburov had known Protsenko, the latter had never once mentioned the Ukraine he loved so tenderly, or Kiev, neither when they had fought together on the western front nor around Voronezh nor here. And he had not liked it when others had talked about them in his presence. It was his sore spot. Now he was talking about Kiev himself.

"This is the fourth night I couldn't sleep," Protsenko said. "I kept on going out, listening . . . hasn't it started? Our side always likes to start just before dawn. So I couldn't sleep, I kept on going out and listening. I went out today and the concert had already started . . . Can you hear it well, Saburov?"

"Very well, Comrade General."

"I still haven't got any official communication from army headquarters," Protsenko said. "Wait before you announce it to the men. But, I don't know, what is there to announce? They can hear it themselves. They'll guess. But, anyway, don't announce it officially. I'll find out right away from the commander, then I'll let you know."

Protsenko hung up the telephone, and Saburov did, too. He did not know exactly how or where anything was happening, but without the slightest doubt he knew that it had started. Although it had begun only an hour ago, it had already become impossible to imagine what life would be like without this magnificent distant rumbling of an artillery offensive. It went on in his mind regardless of whether or not it could be heard at any particular moment.

"Has it really started?" Saburov asked himself again, almost frightened of the question, and he answered it himself with deep conviction: "Yes, yes, of course, it's started."

He was sitting then in a mousetrap almost on top of the Volga River. Only eight hundred meters separated the Germans from the Volga, and about sixty meters stood between them and Saburov's dugout. In spite of this he was feeling for the second time in his life, just as he had the December before below Moscow, the incomparable happiness of a great attack.

"Well, how about it? Did you hear it?" he asked Vanin and Maslennikov solemnly as they came in.

400

For fifteen minutes they sat there without moving, occasionally exchanging disconnected sentences, dazed by this feeling of happiness.

"Is there no chance of its stopping?" Vanin asked.

"Don't worry," Saburov said. "Don't worry. Maybe a month ago it could have, but now that we've sat here this last month for its sake, it can't stop. It can't dare to stop."

"Oh, how I wish I were there right now!" Maslennikov said. "How I wish I were there!" he repeated excitedly.

"What do you mean—there?" Saburov asked.

"There, where they're attacking."

"One might think, Misha, that you were sitting now somewhere in Tashkent."

"No, I'd like to be right there where we are attacking."

"We're going to attack here, too," said Saburov.

"Yes, but that will be when . . ."

"It will be today."

Saburov, without meaning to, said this especially loudly and solemnly.

"Today?" Maslennikov asked. He waited for Saburov to go on, but the latter said nothing. A plan had suddenly come to him and he didn't want to talk about it ahead of time.

"Well, it's wonderful, if that's so," Maslennikov said after a minute. "Maybe we could have a drink to the attack, no?"

"The first thing in the morning?" Saburov said in surprise.

"If we want to we can pretend it's evening. It isn't light yet," Vanin threw in.

"Petya," Saburov shouted. But Petya did not answer. "Petya!" he shouted again.

Petya was standing outside just as they had been standing a few minutes before, listening. He had heard Saburov call him the first time, but he had paid no attention to it, he wanted so badly to hear the sound of the cannonade. Saburov had to go out himself into the communications trench.

"Petya!" he shouted again.

Petya, as if he had just heard, ran up to Saburov.

"Well, did you hear it?" Saburov asked him.

"I heard it," Petya answered smiling.

"Come on, pour us a drink," Saburov said.

Petya rattled the tins and flasks for a half a minute and then brought into the dugout a tray with three tin cups and an open can of meat from the top of which three forks stuck out fanwise.

"Pour one for yourself," Saburov said, breaking his usual custom. Petya pushed aside the curtain, walked out, and came back with his own cup, which judging by his speed had already been poured.

Clinking their cups together, they drank in silence. Everything was clear and there was no need to say anything. They were drinking to the offensive.

A half hour later Protsenko telephoned, and in a voice which had grown a little calmer but was still excited said he had received from headquarters an official confirmation that our troops had gone over to the offensive to the north of Stalingrad at five o'clock in the morning after a powerful artillery preparation.

"We'll cut them off, we'll cut them off," Maslennikov cried out happily when Saburov had hung up the telephone and told them what Protsenko had reported.

"Get going," Saburov said. "You, Vanin, to Company One, and you to Company Two. Tell the men."

"Are you going to stay here?" Vanin asked.

"Yes. I want to talk to Remizov."

Saburov sharpened a pencil and took out of the folder of staff documents a piece of paper on which was outlined the disposition of the units of his battalion and the buildings in front of them. He began to think. Then on the outline he made several rapid notes, one after the other. Yes, they should attack today. This was clear to him. He knew of course that the most important events were taking place far to his north, and perhaps to his south, and his own lot was still to sit where he was for a long time. But nevertheless, now that this great affair which they had awaited with such anxiety had finally started, an irresistible hunger for activity grew in him. Everything that had piled up in his own heart and in those of his men had to find an outlet now, today. He telephoned Remizov:

"Comrade Colonel?"

"Yes."

"Comrade Colonel, permit me to come over to see you. I have a plan for a small operation."

"Operation?" Remizov said, and his smile could almost be heard over the telephone. "Are you jealous of the laurels of the attacking armies?"

"I guess I am," Saburov said.

"Well, so you are. Maybe it's a good thing," Remizov said. "But don't come over here, I'll come to see you."

"When will you be here?"

"Right away."

Remizov arrived only a half hour later. Until he had unbuttoned his short trench coat and taken off his fur hat, his face, reddened by the cold wind, and its gray moustaches, made him look like a kind of jovial Santa Claus. He took off his things and sat down next to Saburov. He started to drink the hot tea Petya brought him.

"To a certain degree I experienced a similar feeling during the days of the Brusilov offensive after a long wait in Galicia.* It was an excellent feeling, especially during the first days. But now it's bigger."

---

* In the summer of 1916, the Russian armies under General Brusilov drove the Austrians back along the front stretching from the Pinsk marshes to the Romanian frontier. They took 350,000 prisoners and 400 cannon, at enormous cost. It was the last great offensive of the tsarist armies.

"What's bigger?" Saburov asked.

"Everything's bigger, both the attack and the feeling."

"Do you think this is a very big attack?" Saburov asked.

"I'm convinced of it," Remizov said. "Either it's enormous, something gigantic, or it would be an unforgivable mistake. And I no longer believe in the possibility of mistakes. We've had enough—it's the second year of war—there won't be any more mistakes, there mustn't be. Well, what's your plan?" he said, pushing his mug to one side.

"The plan is simple—to capture that building I used to hold beyond Konyukov's."

"When?"

"Tonight."

"And how?"

Saburov tersely laid out before Remizov the plan Konyukov had talked to him about the night before, not suspecting that its execution might be so close.

"The chief thing is not to attack where they are expecting us but straight ahead of Konyukov and out of the besieged building, where the Germans don't expect anything except passive defense."

Remizov pinched his gray moustache.

"And men? The plan's all right. But men?"

"That bothered me, too, earlier," Saburov said. "At first I thought the attack might be possible only if they gave us more men but today, after this," he nodded toward the entrance where from beyond the door the rumble in the distance could still be heard, "after this, I think that . . ."

"That we can do it anyway?" Remizov interrupted him.

"Yes, exactly. And besides," Saburov said, smiling, "just to celebrate, you'll give me a few, won't you?"

"I'll give," Remizov said, smiling in his turn.

"And the general, when you report to him, maybe he'll give us a few."

404

"Beyond any doubt, he'll give," Remizov said. "I don't know yet whether I'll give you any or not, but the general will give."

"But you will give me a few?"

"Surely I will. I was just joking. And the first man I'll give you will be myself. Oh, Lord, how bored I am with sitting on the defense! You know what?" He looked at Saburov with a frown on his face. "We will certainly take that building. With an accompaniment like this from the north, it would be simply shameful not to do it. That building . . . what's a building after all?" He smiled, but then at once became serious again. "As a matter of fact that building is an awful lot. It's almost everything. It's Russia." He leaned his stool back against the wall and repeated in a slow drawl: "Russia . . . you can't even imagine the feeling we'll have when by dawn tomorrow we've got that building. What is the building? Four walls, and not even walls—four ruins. But your heart tells you: look, just like that building, we'll take all Russia back again. You understand, Saburov? What's important is to begin. To begin, with that building if we have to, but to feel at the same time that we'll keep going. And we will keep going, until it's all finished. All."

"Now, just how do you propose to get your men up to Konyukov?" he asked in a businesslike tone of voice.

Saburov explained how he planned to send soldiers up to Konyukov during the night, moving them quietly, and how they could carry mortars up in their arms and perhaps even take a few small cannon in their arms. In a half hour they had finished their preparatory plans and they telephoned Protsenko.

"Comrade General, I am at Saburov's right now," Remizov said. "We have worked out a plan for an offensive operation with his battalion."

Hearing the words "offensive operation," Protsenko said

405

quickly: "Yes, yes, both of you come to see me at once, both you and Saburov. At once."

They set off for Protsenko's headquarters along the communications trench. It had already begun to grow light. But the white curtain of the snowstorm still covered the entire horizon on all sides of them. The distant roar of cannon fire had grown no weaker with the dawn. It seemed it could be heard even more clearly.

Protsenko was in an expansive mood. He was walking up and down his dugout with his hands behind his back. He was dressed in the same dress uniform in which he had entertained his officers, but today it was cold in the dugout and the general had put on his old padded jacket on top of his dress tunic.

"It's cold! It's cold!" he greeted Saburov and Remizov. "Vostrikov, the son of a bitch, didn't rustle up any firewood. This stove is almost dead." He waved his hand at the iron stove which was barely warm. "Vostrikov."

"Yes, Comrade General."

"When will that firewood be here?"

"In an hour."

"Well, be on the watch for it. It's terribly cold," Protsenko repeated. "Well, what kind of offensive operation are you talking about?" Impatience was in his voice. "Report, Colonel."

"With your permission," Remizov said, "let Captain Saburov report. It's his plan."

"Well, all right, if it's his, let him. The chief thing is that there should be an offensive operation. Who reports is not so important. Well, go on, report."

For the second time that morning Saburov tersely outlined his plan for capturing the building.

"In one night can you manage to get your men together in Konyukov's building so you can attack before dawn?" Protsenko asked.

"I'll manage," Saburov said.

406

"How many of your men can you send?"

"Thirty," Saburov said.

"And how many more can you give him?"

"Twenty more," Remizov said after thinking a moment.

"That means you can manage to assemble and to prepare fifty men?" Protsenko asked Saburov.

"Yes. I can manage."

"And if I give you thirty more, and that makes eighty men, could you still manage?"

"I could manage all the better, Comrade General," Saburov said with a happy feeling.

"Well, that's that. Good, good," Protsenko said. "We'll begin our attack with this operation. But don't forget," he turned to Saburov, "I won't give you any men to waste. We'll take the building—I don't doubt it for a minute—but here in Stalingrad it's still we who are besieged, and not the Germans, no matter how well things are going up north. Do you understand?"

"I understand," Saburov said.

"Comrade General," Remizov said.

"Yes."

"Give me your permission to take part in the operation personally."

"Yourself?" Protsenko frowned. "What does that mean? That you will be at Saburov's command post? Well, of course, that's how it should be, you're commander of the regiment. Or maybe you want to crawl up to Konyukov's building? Did you mean that? You want to go up there?"

Remizov was silent.

"Are you going up there?"

"I'm going, Comrade General."

"Well, that's also permissible. But in front of that, into the other building, I do not give you permission to go. Let Saburov go on up there. Do you understand?"

"I do, Comrade General," Remizov said.

"He'll go all the way, you only up to Konyukov's building, and maybe I, myself, will come up as far as the command post. Let's decide it that way. Well, on your way. I'll give orders immediately to round up thirty men for you. But take care of them. They're the last. Keep that in mind."

"May I go?" Saburov asked.

"Yes. Telephone me how your preparations are going. Report in detail. I'll be interested," he said suddenly and very simply, almost like a child. "Yes, one thing more. In the name of the general tell your soldiers and officers: the first man into the building gets an Order, the second man a medal. And whoever gets a prisoner also gets a medal. Pass that on. Konyukov, you say, made this proposal first?" Protsenko turned to Saburov.

"It was Konyukov."

"Then a medal for him. I gave him an Order just a little while ago, didn't I?"

"Yes," Saburov said.

"Well, that's fine. Now he gets a medal. Let him wear it. You tell him. He gets a medal from me. Well, that's all. You may go."

TWENTY-SIX

THE whole day was spent in preparation for the night attack. Everything moved quickly, without delays and with surprising efficiency. It seemed as if some feverish thirst for activity had seized every officer in the division, beginning with Saburov and ending with Protsenko. In two hours the chief of staff of the division had telephoned Saburov to tell him that thirty men had been assembled from the division's reserve. Artillerymen from different units had fixed up three cannon to be moved up to the building that night immediately after its capture. In a corner of the dugout Petya was fussing with the tommy-guns—his own, Saburov's, and Maslennikov's—cleaning them and oiling them as carefully as if the entire fate of the operation depended on it. He even pulled out of a corner Saburov's torn cloth bag for hand grenades and mended it neatly.

For once, the strict secrecy demanded by military regulations during preparations for an operation was not observed in the battalion. On the contrary, everyone knew that the capture of the building was planned for that night and everyone was glad at heart about it although many of them, perhaps, stood to lose their lives before the night was over. The distant

409

cannon fire, never stopping, was evidence that the main attack was still going on, and this unexpected idea of capturing a building after standing still for so long kept everyone from thinking about death, or at least made them think about it less than usual.

Towards evening, Remizov appeared at battalion headquarters. He said his men and those from Protsenko were ready and waiting. The four of them, Vanin, Maslennikov, Saburov and Remizov, ate together quickly and not too well, because Petya had been preoccupied with cleaning the guns, and for once had slipped up as cook. Then they talked over the division of responsibilities. Vanin was to stay at battalion headquarters. He had just come back from the companies. All day long the usual firing had gone on against their positions, and the Germans had twice set up small attacks. In a word, everything had proceeded as if no miracle had happened in the north, as if there were no rumble of artillery confusing everything in people's minds.

It was up to Vanin to be on duty all night at battalion headquarters. Someone would have to stay there. He agreed without quarreling, although Saburov could see on his face that he was unhappy about it and was controlling himself only with difficulty. Maslennikov was in a fine mood. He was to go forward with Saburov and Remizov to Konyukov's building.

The moment it grew dark Saburov with Maslennikov and the first group of soldiers pushed up successfully to Konyukov's building.

"Comrade Captain, may I ask you a question?" Konyukov greeted Saburov.

"Well?"

"Does this cannon fire mean we are encircling the Germans?"

"Yes, that's what it must mean," Saburov said.

"That's the way I explained it," Konyukov said. "They

410

kept on asking me: 'Comrade Lieutenant—they all call me Lieutenant since I'm head of a garrison—Comrade Lieutenant, is that our side attacking?' and I told them: 'Beyond any doubt, we're attacking.' "

"Beyond any doubt we're attacking, Konyukov. Beyond any doubt," Saburov said. "And tonight we're going to attack here, too."

Then he told Konyukov that Protsenko had decorated him with a medal. At this Konyukov drew himself up and said: "Glad to do my best."

Konyukov's men and those who had just arrived began quietly to clean out an opening through which the storm units could burst out of the building. They moved the bricks one by one, in their hands. Dynamite and grenades were gradually moved up along the communications trench; then several anti-tank rifles and two of the battalion's mortars were dragged up.

Saburov left Maslennikov to handle this and went back to his command post where he found a young lieutenant, a battery commander, who reported to him that he had three cannon already there. The lieutenant asked instructions on how to move them farther.

"In places you can pull them," Saburov said, "but in other places you'll have to carry them by hand."

"We'll carry them by hand," the lieutenant said with the special eagerness which everyone was showing today. "We can carry them by hand the whole way if we have to."

"No, the whole way is not necessary," Saburov said. "But if you make any noise, and if the Germans don't kill you on account of it, then I will. That's all. Carry out the order."

"We won't make any noise, Comrade Captain," said the lieutenant. Saburov turned him over to Petya as an escort, since the latter had already gone up to Konyukov's three times.

It was midnight before Saburov had assembled in the building his own men and Remizov's and the unit of thirty men who had come up from Protsenko. He divided them into small groups and began to send them up to Konyukov's building. Last of all, he went up himself with Remizov.

In the cellar, on concrete slabs, the soldiers had fixed up a place to smoke. They were taking their turn, squatting close together on their heels like hens on a roost. When the tobacco ran out, three or four of them took turns on the same cigarette. Saburov took his tobacco pouch out of his pocket and poured it out into the soldiers' hands, down to the last fine dust. He did not want to smoke himself. He felt almost no excitement, but all the time he was trying desperately to remember whether something had not been forgotten and whether everything had been done.

Communications soldiers had stretched a telephone wire from Konyukov's building to Saburov's command post. In the daytime the Germans would have seen it and broken it but at night it could do its job. On this line Saburov talked to Protsenko.

"Where are you talking from?" Protsenko asked.

"From Konyukov's building."

"Good fellow," Protsenko said. "I wanted to suggest that you run a wire there. Well, how is everything?"

"The last preparations have been made, Comrade General."

"Fine! Can you begin in half an hour?"

"We can," Saburov said.

"That means, at 00:30. That's fine."

They did not begin at 00:30, but forty-five minutes later, at a quarter past one. It had proved impossible to drag the antitank cannon through the breach in the wall and they had had to take the whole wall down, brick by brick.

At last, when all fifty men who were going to make the first attack were divided into four assault groups, when the sappers were finally ready with their bundles of dynamite and their grenades, and the tommy gunners who were to go along with them; when the muzzles of the cannon were pointed through the breaches in the wall at the other little walls which could be seen not far away and where the German machine-guns were located, at a quarter past one the command to begin the attack was given in a whisper.

The mortars roared out deafeningly, and their echoes bounced from wall to wall and roared through the ruins. The cannon began to fire point-blank in front of them, and two of the assault groups led by Saburov and Maslennikov moved forward. The Germans were ready for an attack from anywhere at all except from this besieged building which had seemed to them completely blockaded. They began to fire desperately, but in disorder, and it was clear that they were badly confused.

Like all night fighting, this attack was full of the unexpected. The shooting was blind, grenades exploded directly under foot, there was everything that makes not numbers but strength of nerve decisive in night fighting. Several times Saburov had to throw grenades; once he fired point blank with his tommy-gun; several times he collided with masonry in the darkness and fell flat. Finally, having run through all the ruins in the cellar of the building, he came out on its western side, and breathing hard with fatigue, ordered one of the soldiers next to him to pass on word that the cannon should be dragged up as quickly as possible.

For the Germans everything had taken place so unexpectedly that many of them were killed and the others were forced to run from the building before they had even realized what was going on. But news that the Russians had seized the building apparently so excited the nearest German commanders that they assembled all the men immediately available, and without counting the cost, against their usual habit, sent them into a counterattack without waiting for the dawn. The first counterattack was driven back. Then a half hour later, after strewing shells over the building, the Germans attacked a second time. In his heart Saburov thanked Protsenko again for having given him extra men. There was not one intact wall left in the building; everywhere were holes, breaches, and craters through which the Germans could crawl, and it was necessary to defend each of them in impenetrable darkness.

In the heat of the second German counterattack, Maslennikov crawled up to Saburov and asked him if he had any grenades.

"I have," Saburov said, unfastening a grenade from his belt and handing it to him. "What's the matter, have you used all yours?"

"I've thrown quite a few," Maslennikov said.

"Tell them to bring some mortars up here, if only a couple. We don't need them now, but they ought to be here by morning. You know, Misha, you and I will fix up a command post here and we'll never leave it. Understand?"

"I understand," said Maslennikov.

"Well, go on, tell the mortars."

"Right away," Maslennikov said. He was still in the full excitement of the fighting, and he did not want to go away.

"Alexei Ivanovich," he said quietly.

"Well?" Saburov turned away from his tommy-gun.

"Alexei Ivanovich, is the big offensive going all right? What do you think?"

"It's going well," Saburov said and he turned back to his tommy-gun; it seemed to him something was moving in front of him.

All at once several Germans jumped through a breach in the wall to their left; they had somehow found an undefended place in the wall of the building. Saburov fired a long burst, then his ammunition ran out. He moved his hand to his belt where a grenade should have been hanging, but it was not there. He had just given it to Maslennikov. By this time the

414

Germans were almost on top of them. From behind Saburov's shoulder Maslennikov threw the grenade, but for some reason it failed to explode. Then Saburov took his tommy-gun by the barrel and swung its butt end with all his might at a black shape moving past him. There was a crunching sound, and a groan. He had swung with such power that he could not keep his balance, and dropping the tommy-gun he fell flat. This proved to be what saved his life. A long burst of tracer bullets flashed over him.

Maslennikov, who had fired several times with his revolver in the darkness, saw a German waving his gun over Saburov's prostrate figure. Throwing away his empty revolver, Maslennikov jumped from the side on top of the German, grabbed him with both hands around the throat, and they both swayed and then fell onto the stone floor. They rolled over several times, each man trying to pin the other's arms. Then Maslennikov's left arm slipped down between two stones; he could hear it break, and then he could no longer move it. With his other hand he continued to clutch the German's throat, and the two men kept on rolling over, first one on top, then the other. The last thing Maslennikov was aware of was something hard and cold pressed against his chest. The German had succeeded in pulling his revolver out from his belt, pressing it with his free hand against Maslennikov's body and squeezing the trigger several times in succession.

After he had fallen, Saburov had jumped up again and seen the black tangle rolling on the ground. Then he had heard shots, the knot untied itself, and a large unfamiliar form began to stand up from the ground. Saburov had nothing in his hand; he snatched the ammunition clip from his belt, and just as it was, in its case, he swung it with both hands on the German's head—once, twice, and a third time—with all the strength he had.

By this time soldiers had run in from the next section of the cellar and they were already lying behind the wall and firing. The counterattack was beaten off.

"Misha," Saburov cried out. "Misha."

Maslennikov was silent.

Saburov knelt on the ground and pushed away the dead German. He fumbled over Maslennikov with both hands. He felt his insignia, the Order of the Red Star on his tunic, then he touched Maslennikov's face and again he said: "Misha." Maslennikov was silent. Saburov fumbled over him again. On the left, over the heart, the wet blouse stuck to his fingers. Saburov tried to lift Maslennikov. The strange idea came to him that if he could lift him now so he could stand, this would be very important, and probably he would live. But Maslennikov's body hung limp and helpless in his arms. Saburov lifted him as Maslennikov had lifted Anya four days before and carried him, stepping carefully across the stones.

"Have you dragged up the cannon?" he asked when he heard the voice of the artillery lieutenant giving a command.

"Yes."

"Where have you put them?" Saburov asked again, standing there as if he had forgotten that Maslennikov was lying in his arms.

"One here, aimed straight in front, and two on the flanks."

"That's right," Saburov said.

He walked through to a part of the cellar where a piece of the concrete ceiling had been left and where it was possible to light a match. He sat down on the floor, still holding Maslennikov's body in his arms.

"Misha," he said again. Then he lit a match and cupped it quickly in his hands. In the flickering light before him he could see for a moment Maslennikov's white face, with his curly hair thrown back, and one lock, wet and limp, hanging over his forehead. Saburov straightened it.

Although only a few minutes had gone by since their last

416

conversation, it seemed to Saburov that an endless time had passed. He shuddered, and still holding Maslennikov in his arms, he began to cry bitterly, for the second time in these five days.

An hour later, when the last German counterattack had ended, and when it had become clear that the Germans had decided to postpone their next attack until the morning, Saburov summoned the commander of a sapper platoon which had taken part in storming the building and ordered him to dig a grave for Maslennikov.

"Here?" the sapper asked in surprise, knowing that whenever it was at all possible the bodies of officers who had been killed were taken somewhere to the rear, out of the fighting.

"Yes," said Saburov.

"Maybe it would be better on our own territory?"

"No, here," Saburov said. "This is now our territory. Carry out the order."

The sappers tried the ground for a long time, trying to find some less frozen spot next to the foundations, but the frozen earth did not yield to picks or shovels.

"What are you messing about there for?" Saburov asked roughly. "I'll show you where to dig."

He led the sappers to the very center of the building where pieces of the superstructure still loomed above like a black cross.

"Here," he said, striking his boot with a hollow noise against the concrete floor. "Drill a hole here, put in some dynamite, explode it, and then bury him."

His voice was unusually rough. The sappers quickly made a little hole, put in several kilograms of dynamite, and then hid behind the neighboring wall and lit the fuse. There was a short explosion, hardly to be distinguished from the dozens of shell explosions which could still be heard around them.

A pit a little more than a meter deep appeared in the broken floor. They scraped the pieces of brick and cement out of it and lowered Maslennikov's body into the hole. Saburov jumped down and stood beside the body. He took off Maslennikov's coat, slipping the sleeves with difficulty from the already stiffening arms, and covered the body with the coat so that only the face could be seen. The dawn was just barely breaking and when Saburov leaned over he could see Maslennikov's face. Saburov took all the papers he found in Maslennikov's pockets and unfastened his Order.

"Who has a rifle?" he asked as he got out of the grave.

"We all have."

"Well then, a volley into the air, and then cover the grave. I'll give the command. Ready! Fire!" He had reloaded his own revolver and he fired with the others. The little volley sounded dry and quiet in the cold air.

"Now cover it up," Saburov said, and he turned away from the grave, not wanting to watch the pieces of cement and stone fall on the body of the man whom an hour before he could not possibly have imagined dead. He did not turn around, but he felt in his back how the cold pieces of rock fell into the grave, how they piled higher and higher with the sound growing less as the grave was filled. Finally he heard the scrape of a sapper's shovel evening it out with the level of the floor.

Saburov squatted on his heels, took a notebook out of his pocket, tore out a sheet of paper, and scrawled across it several lines. "Maslennikov has been killed," he wrote. "I am staying here. If you agree, I think it would be wise for Vanin and the staff to move, too, nearer to me, up to Konyukov's building. Saburov."

He called a soldier and ordered him to carry the note to Remizov.

"Well, now we shall fight," Saburov said in the same rough

voice. "Now we shall fight," he repeated, not speaking to anyone in particular. "Is the company commander here?" he called.

"Here."

"Let's go. Over there, in the right wing of the building, I think we must dig a machine-gun post under the foundations. Have you got a machine-gun on the first floor?"

"Yes."

"They'll smash it. We'll have to put it under the foundation."

They walked several steps, stamping on the cement floor. Saburov stopped suddenly.

"Wait a minute."

There was a moment of silence during which neither we nor the Germans were firing. Through the ruins blew an icy wind from the west, and carried by the wind there could be heard the clear sound of distant cannon fire.

On the Middle Akhtuba, fifty kilometers from Stalingrad, in a place to which the distant cannon fire did not carry and where the first rumors of an offensive had only just begun to come, it was early morning. In a peasant hut being used as an operating room, Anya was lying on a stretcher. She had already gone through one operation, but they had not managed to remove one deep splinter. During these days she would recover consciousness and then lose it. Right now she was lying motionless, the blood drained from her face. Everything was ready and they were waiting for the chief surgeon who had agreed to make a second operation on which all hope depended now. The doctors were talking to each other.

"What do you think, Alexander Petrovich, will she live?" a young woman doctor asked a much older surgeon, wearing a white cap pulled down almost to his eyebrows.

"In theory, no, but I think he can pull her through," the

surgeon said. He rolled a cigarette and then added: "It depends on how her heart holds out. She may pull out of it."

The door opened and from the other half of the hut, bringing with him a blast of cold wind, a short, stubby man walked in with quick steps, holding his hands in front of him. Their thick red fingers, obviously, had just been washed with alcohol. Under his heavy grayish-brown moustache a cigarette was hanging in the corner of his mouth.

"On the table," he said looking to one side where Anya was lying on the stretcher. "Somebody light my cigarette."

They brought him a match and he leaned his cigarette into the flame, still holding his hands in front of him.

"They say," he said, walking up to the operating table, "our troops have gone over to a general offensive. They have captured Kalach and they are encircling the Germans beyond Stalingrad. That's all. That's all." He made a decisive gesture with his hands. "Details later, after the operation. Somebody take my cigarette. Give me light."

This was on the second day of the general offensive. Along the great curve of the Don, between that river and the Volga, in the black darkness of November night, mechanized army corps were crawling forward. Trucks were moving slowly, sinking in the snow. Bridges were being blown up or broken. Whole villages were burning, and the flashes of heavy gunfire blended against the horizon with the glare of the burning towns. Along the roads, in the middle of fields, corpses lay like black spots, stiff and frozen in the night.

Scrambling through the snowdrifts, stamping their feet and clasping their arms against the wind, the infantry marched over the white fields. In their arms they carried their artillery through the snowdrifts. They knocked down barns and sheds for the beams and planks with which they fashioned sleazy bridges across ravines.

Two armies were moving on this winter morning, like two hands coming together on a map, coming closer and closer to each other, ready to meet in the Don steppes, far to the west of Stalingrad.

In the area they encircled, inside their rough embrace, there were still hundreds of thousands of German soldiers. There were an Army corps and divisions with staffs, generals, discipline, cannon, tanks, landing fields and airplanes. There were hundreds of thousands of men who, it seemed, might still have thought themselves with some justice to represent a military force, but who were at the same time nothing but tomorrow's dead.

In newspapers that night men were printing on linotypes the usual restrained communique of the Soviet Information Bureau, written carefully not to anticipate events. Before they went to bed, people listened to the last news broadcasts on the radio and were still anxious in their hearts for Stalingrad, knowing nothing yet of the great fortune of war, won in battle, which was beginning during these hours for Russia.

About the Author

POSSIBLY THE *most remarkable thing about Konstantine Simonov is his versatility: he has written reportage, short stories, a novel, plays and lyrical poetry so intimate that when a volume of his wartime "Lyrical Notebook" appeared, Stalin is reported to have said: "This volume should have been printed in two copies only—one for himself and the other for his wife." Simonov's play called "Russian People" won the Stalin prize in 1942. His works are now read in 21 languages in the USSR and have sold several million copies.*

He is one of Russia's outstanding war correspondents. He was born in Leningrad in 1915. He worked as a turner from 1930 to 1935. He wrote poetry which appeared on the wall-paper of his factory and in 1934 entered the Literary Institute of the Writer's Union. He became a professional litterateur in 1936 and was graduated from the Institute in 1937. Two years later he went to the Far East to cover the battle of Khalkhin Gol in Outer Mongolia.

On June 24, 1941, he left for the front, and during the course of the war covered practically every front from the Berents to the Black Sea and from Stalingrad to Berlin. His experiences in Stalingrad form the basis of the background for Days and Nights.

He has been awarded the Order of the Red Banner and medals for Khalkhin Gol, Stalingrad, Odessa and Moscow.